# The Decision Science Process

# The Decision Science Process

INTEGRATING THE QUANTITATIVE AND BEHAVIORAL

**THAD B. GREEN**
*Mississippi State University*

**SANG M. LEE**
*The University of Nebraska–Lincoln*

**WALTER B. NEWSOM**
*Mississippi State University*

editors

a petrocelli
book
new york  princeton

**Library of Congress Cataloging in Publication Data**

Main entry under title:

The Decision science process.


1. Decision-making—Mathematical models—Addresses,
essays, lectures. 2. Operations research—Addresses,
essays, lectures. I. Green, Thad B. II. Lee, Sang, M.,
1939-     III. Newsom, Walter B.
HD30.23.D39      658.4'03      78-24021
ISBN 0-89433-060-8

*to our wives—*

*Joyce*
*Laura*
*Ellen*

# Contents

## B. Bridging the Gap

## Part II: Premodeling

### A. Understanding the Client

### B. Interpersonal Relationships with the Client

### C. Intraorganizational Relationships with the Client

### D. Communication and Premodeling

## Part III: Modeling

### A. Modeling for Managers

### B. The Modeling Function

## Part IV: Implementation

### A. The Implementation Partnership

### B. Communication and Implementation

### C. Organizational and Behavioral Factors

*Part V: Conclusion*

_____

# *Preface*

One of the primary reasons for man to pursue knowledge is the basic human and environmental problem of satisfying unlimited human desire with limited resources. Most human organizations, whether they are business enterprises, governmental agencies, or nonprofit social institutions, have all evolved in such a way to effectively narrow the gap between desires (objectives) and resources (constraints).

Man's desire to take the most effective action has led to a continuous struggle to comprehend the norms and conditions under which the environment functions. The increase in man's body of knowledge has led to new discoveries, inventions, and innovations, and these in turn have resulted in greater benefits, comforts, and fulfillment for man. Thus, the progress of a society has been basically determined by the production and rate of increase in knowledge. Inasmuch as knowledge is sought for more effective action, this pursuit is the basis for a cognitive system that we shall call "science."

Through scientific analysis, man has recognized many of the relationships of his environmental systems. This new knowledge has provided man with the opportunity to manipulate environmental conditions to produce desired consequences. Man has thus acquired much control over nature, providing new horizons of civilization and growth. However, this is also the genesis of the problem of decision analysis, since different decisions may result in different consequences. Man attempts to select the course of action, from a set of alternative courses of action, that will best achieve his objectives. Decision analysis is a process of increasing man's understanding and control over environmental conditions.

Traditional economic theory postulates that rational decision making is an optimization process where the decision maker objectively selects a course of action which will achieve his desires to the greatest possible extent. This thesis has been the foundation for the development and application of various quantitative techniques to decision making. Quantitative analysis (management science, operations research, or decision sciences) has greatly improved the decision maker's understanding of the problem in question and generally resulted in better outcomes of the decision. However, decision analysis is not synonymous with quantitative analysis.

Decision analysis involves more than quantitative analysis. It includes exogenous and indogenous factors that describe the environment in which the problem exists. Also, it involves people who actually make the decision, provide information to the decision maker, and those who are affected by it. Decision analysis is not a totally isolated, impersonal, and objective process. Thus, it is impossible to have a rational decision analysis process without a consideration of the decision environment and behavioral implications. There is an abundance of evidence that suggests that the practice of decision analysis is affected by the nonquantifiable environmental factors and the epistemological assumptions of the decision maker. Indeed, the practice of scientific methodology and rational choice are not always directly applicable to decision analysis.

This book is intended to underscore the need to integrate quantitative and behavioral objectives in order to make the decision analysis process effective and productive. It includes a set of articles written by some of the most distinguished researchers in the broad field of decision science. This book is structured as either a primary text in an upper-level undergraduate or graduate decision analysis course or as a supplementary reader for an advanced decision science course. It is also intended to enlighten the perspective of practicing decision scientists and managers.

This book is a result of our long-term interests and frustration in attempting to make our lectures more relevant. Many friends and colleagues provided us with suggestions, encouragements, and even discouragements. We are especially grateful to Mr. O. R. Petrocelli, who recognized the potential contribution of this volume and decided to publish it without financial considerations. We are also indebted to talented ladies who helped us to put this book together: Rita Christopher at Mississippi State University and Joyce Anderson and Sharon Blecha at the University of Nebraska. A special word of appreciation goes to Dr. Dennis F. Ray, Chairman of the Management Department at Mississippi State University for his support throughout this research endeavor.

Thad B. Green
Sang M. Lee
Walter B. Newsom

# Part I: Introduction

# A. The State of the Art: Overview

## 1. INTEGRATING THE QUANTITATIVE AND BEHAVIORAL

*Thad B. Green, Walter B. Newsom*
*and Sang M. Lee*

---

What is all of this business about integrating the quantitative and behavioral? What does it mean? Why do we need it? How do we achieve it?

Decision scientists are beginning to give careful consideration to these questions—and for good reason. The destiny of the decision science area may in large part be embodied in the answers. The future of the discipline does not look as promising as it once did. The utilization of quantitative techniques has not been as pervasive and successful as previously predicted.

Editors' Note: Original article written especially for this book.

One possible solution to these concerns may well be found in the integration of the quantitative and behavioral.

## The Meaning of Integration

Integrating the quantitative and behavioral is the bringing together of two separate disciplines. From the point of view of the decision scientist, it means developing behavioral insights and skills and applying these simultaneously with efforts to solve problems through the application of decision science techniques. Behavioral insights such as cognitive style, role ambiguity, power and politics, to name a few, are a major influence in quantitative strategies and decisions. Communication and interpersonal relations skills, for example, are major vehicles for quantitative success. Additional behavioral skills such as conflict resolution, nominal grouping and contingency management are as integral to success as the decision science techniques per se. Using all of these insights and skills, and many more, in applying decision science techniques is what we mean by the integration of the quantitative and behavioral.

## The Need for Integration

Why do we need to integrate the quantitative and behavioral? It's a long story that begins on a positive note, but then moves to the negative. However, it is the negative which truly answers the question because the problems point to the need for change. But first, the positive side.

Decision scientists have a lot going for them. Theoretical developments in the quantitative area have advanced rapidly and with few exceptions the state of the art is viewed favorably. Furthermore, when theory is transferred to reality, the applicability of the techniques receives reasonably high marks. Not only is the technical wherewithal standing on a positive note, the training of the decision scientists is well above standard. University programs have come on strong in recent years and consequently there are many graduates possessing the necessary theoretical credentials and capabilities for developing technically sound models.

Yet, the weight of the negative dimension seems to be tipping the scales. The negative side focuses first on the potential use of the models. Specifically, and as noted many times elsewhere in the literature, the potential user often does not understand decision science techniques generally, and specific models in particular. More often, the user does not understand the model output—what it means, or how to use it. Even with this understanding, he may not have an appreciation for the value of the techniques or information provided. In the absence of either understanding or appreciation, it is unrealistic to expect users to enthusiastically support efforts to utilize decision science techniques. User deficiencies, however, represent only one part of the negative dimension. Deficiencies of an equally important magnitude reside on the other side of the coin. The problems represented by this other side are manifest in the extent to which decision science techniques are utilized and the degree of success which has been achieved. The best evidence available on measurements of the extent of use reveals an alarmingly low utilization and success rate compared to the extent predicted for the 1970s. Empirical studies by Green, Newsom and Jones [14] and others [4,7,8,11,16,22,23,31,33,34,35] point this out rather clearly, as do firsthand reports by capable persons in prominent positions, such as Grayson [12]. In summation, there is substantial evidence for an intensified if not a new concern about the future of the decision science area.

But the utilization and success rates are only symptoms of the problem. Although comprehensively stating the problem is elusive, there are at least three major dimensions. One dimension focuses on the decision scientist. In some cases they have theoretical deficiencies. In others, there is the difficulty of translating their theoretical expertise into the development of effective models. But even in the best of circumstances, the theoretical and applications capabilities are necessary but insufficient conditions. Decision scientists also must have other capabilities. In combination with theoretical and applications orientations, the decision scientist must possess a proficiency in the nonquantitative elements, i.e., the behavioral dimensions. Herein lies a major deficiency area—perhaps the largest of the three.

The behavioral dimensions come into play in the beginning when the decision scientist needs to gain credibility, acceptance, cooperation, and support. Ineffectiveness at this point creates resistance and information problems which make it difficult to develop effective models. The importance of the behavioral dimensions continues throughout the model-building process, and then beyond to their implementation. Throughout the entire process, the success of the decision scientist is inescapably dependent upon many people for information and cooperation. Successful interaction with a wide variety of people is essential to quantitative success. Decision scientists cannot succeed on their modeling skills alone. Herein lies the justification of, indeed the necessity for, a new and unparalleled emphasis on integrating the quantitative and behavioral.

### Achieving Integration

The deficiencies of both the decision scientist and potential users are explainable since neither typically receives formal education in other disciplines; thus it leaves us with a double-edged sword—one that needs sharpening on both sides. This essentially is the solution approach recommended by Churchman and Schainblatt [6] in 1965. They advocated a "mutual understanding" between the decision scientist and the user as the ideal solution.

*Figure 1: The decision science process*

More than a decade has passed, however, and there is little evidence of progress toward mutual understanding. This is explainable due to the very nature of the situation. Managers who do not see the value in using decision science models are reluctant to use them. Yet, until managers use the models, they likely will not perceive them as having much value. Thus, we are in a vicious cycle. Breaking out of it is a slow and difficult process for the manager. Consequently, mutual understanding is a lengthy proposition at best. Without abandoning this avenue for long-range success, it seems that we must turn from the ideal to the interim strategy for short-run gains.

Rather than focusing on both the user and the decision scientist, perhaps the burden should be placed temporarily on the shoulders of the decision scientist. This simplifies the solution since potential users greatly outnumber decision scientists. In another way, too, this approach seems reasonable because decision scientists may be better able to learn the few necessary behavioral insights and skills than potential users are to learn all they need to know to truly reach a state of mutual understanding. Furthermore, the success and future of the decision scientist is more dependent upon his learning the behavioral dimensions than the success and future of the manager is upon learning the quantitative side; that is, the decision scientist has more to gain. For these, and perhaps other reasons, it appears that decision scientists as a group should be willing to show the responsibility for integrating the quantitative and behavioral.

## The Quantitative Side of Achieving Integration

In order to achieve integration, the decision scientist must not only give a new focus to the behavioral dimensions, he must at the same time begin viewing the quantitative side in a behavioral context. That is, he must truly integrate the quantitative and behavioral. One way of doing this is to give prime attention to implementation while viewing it as one of three functions in the decision science process. Implementation receives a special focus because without successful implementation, all other quantitative efforts will have been in vain. Implementation, however, is preceded in the process by the premodeling and modeling functions as illustrated in Figure 1.

The three functions of premodeling, modeling, and implementation represent only the basic process, i.e., the framework, for achieving integration. It is necessary to take a major step forward and view each of the three functions specifically in a behavioral context. That is, the behavioral dimensions must be superimposed onto the decision science process. In doing so, the premodeling function focuses on understanding the user, developing a good working relationship with him, recognizing the relationships between the various units within the organization, and achieving effective channels of communication. All of this is necessary in order for the decision scientist to gain acceptance, elicit cooperation, develop reliable information sources, and to overcome resistance to change in order to facilitate model building and the implementation of results. The modeling function focuses on the user as a vital element in the model-building process and stresses behavioral dimensions to be considered when building the model. The principal thrust of the implementation function is on the user-modeler partnership, communication, and the behavioral/organizational relationships of the variety of persons involved with implementation. Figure 2 summarizes the recommended steps within each of these three major functions, and in total represents a quantitative approach for integrating the quantitative and behavioral.

## The Behavioral Side of Achieving Integration

The behavioral emphasis in this quantitative approach is directed toward various behavioral insights and skills. There must be an emphasis on behavioral insights in order for the decision scientist to better understand himself and the user, and to recognize how their worlds differ. This kind of understanding is a necessary condition for successful usage of decision science techniques. Likewise, a variety of behavioral skills are necessary when the

*Figure 2: The decision science process—*
*with subfunctions*

THE PREMODELING FUNCTION

    Understanding the User
    Interpersonal Relationship with the User
    Interorganizational Relationships
    Communication and Premodeling

THE MODELING FUNCTION

    Modeling for Managers
    Model Building

THE IMPLEMENTATION FUNCTION

    The Implementation Partnership
    Communication and Implementation
    Organizational and Behavioral Factors

decision scientist is working with users and other nonquantitative people in order to enhance the probability of successful implementation. These skills are readily acknowledged and used in the behavioral side of management, and are invaluable to decision science success. Included in these skills are numerous behavioral techniques and strategies which when appropriately used will enable the decision scientist to perform more effectively.

BEHAVIORAL INSIGHTS. We will focus on two major categories of differences in the decision scientist and the manager. One is that decision scientists as individuals are different than managers. It is important that the decision scientist recognize this. These differences are further magnified by the difference in the second major category: the environment in which each group operates. First, let us look at how managers and decision scientists differ as individuals.

*Differences in perception.* A useful starting point is to understand the differences in perceptions between the decision scientist and the manager. C. Jackson Grayson suggests that, "Managers and management scientists are operating as two separate cultures, each with its own goals, languages, and methods" [12, p.41]. Understanding the manager's perceptions of the roles of the decision scientist and the use of decision science techniques is extremely important for the decision scientist. Strange as it may sound to the decision scientist, Churchman stated:

> It is a well-known fact that managers may feel threatened by modern techniques of analysis. They have reason to believe that analysis with the help of high-speed computers, may take over their roles. In order to preserve their status, they resist the recommendations that analysis provides. [5, p.35]

Argyris further notes that management information systems are perceived by the manager as reducing space of free movement, and decreasing feelings of essentiality [3]. McKenney and Keen suggest that, "The manager scans his environment and organizes what he perceives. His efforts are as much geared to clarifying his values and intents as to dealing with predefined problems" [27, p.81]. Hammond notes that, "'Data' in the external world is filtered by the individual, a process called cognitive filtering" [19, p.7]. Based on these and many other similar observations, it can be concluded that perceptions differ.

Ackoff suggests that, "The manager needs the information he wants" [1, p.B-149]. The problem is that very often he doesn't know what he wants because he doesn't know which model to use. So, to play it "safe", he says he wants everything. This reinforces the perception of the decision scientist who believes that if in fact that manager were given more information, he would perceive the world differently [1]. McKenney and Keen note the paradox which results. The two groups of people are different, and decision scientists can't understand that managers may feel threatened by the very approaches the decision scientists are using to bring about greater acceptance of their models [27].

However, it is possible that some managers do not feel threatened by decision scientists. Therefore, they are willing to try techniques. However, problems may still occur. Little suggests that there are differences between the two groups in defining what constitutes a good model [25]. Hayes and Nolan submit that, "What is important is not that the model contains a complete, or even a correct, representation of reality, but that it matches the manager's (or company's) own understanding of the reality that exists" [21, p.109].

Ford suggests that another problem is that decision scientists create a false perception on the part of the managers by promising too much too soon. Managers who were willing to use techniques now perceive them as less than useful [10]. Hayes and Nolan propose that the large-scale, comprehensive corporate model is doomed to failure before it begins because of the expense involved in its creation and because it is impossible to use [21]. Hankin has listed an entire page of the principal factors affecting the perception of managers and thereby the acceptance of operations research results [20, p.294].

Decision scientists, therefore, should be cognizant of two aspects of perceptions: (1) many managers are already threatened by decision science techniques, and (2) some decision scientists enhance negative feelings toward the use of decision sciences by false promises.

*Personality.* Understanding the personality of individuals is important also. Churchman wrote:

> When a change is suggested to a manager, he reacts in ways that are typical to his own personality. Part of him will resist the suggestion, and often resistance is so strong that he will reject the suggestion altogether. Nevertheless, the persons responsible for making the suggestion may learn enough about the manager's personality so that they know what to say to him to break down his resistance. [5, p.35]

The decision scientist should be acutely aware of what part of the manager's personality will adjust to change and what will remain fixed. Moreover, the decision scientist should be aware that, "Managers come to prefer issues that are current, specific, and ad hoc, and that are presented in verbal form" [28, p.B-97]. Argyris expresses well how MIS will affect many managers:

> Psychological failure occurs whenever someone else defines the individual's goals, path to his goals, his level of aspiration, and criteria for success. The manager, in short, because of the MIS, will now tend to experience the frustrations that the employees have experienced in the past as a result of the industrial and quality control engineers who have designed their work and monitored their performance. [3, p.B-278]

*Cognitive style.* Since perceptions and personalities of decision scientists and managers differ, it is not unexpected that there are differences in cognitive style also. McKenney and Keen suggest that managers are often intuitive thinkers and preceptive (look at relationships) thinkers; management scientists are systematic thinkers and receptive (look at details) thinkers [27]. Hammond says that managers are heuristic and maybe analytic; management scientists are very analytic (almost always more analytic than managers) [19, p.14].

*Problem-solving style.* The differences in cognitive style lead to substantial differences in problem-solving style. Hammond notes that managers define problems in a loose, less explicitly, often broader scope than management scientists who define problems in a more explicit but narrower scope [19, p.14]. McKenney and Keen state that managers are more intuitive, and decision scientists are more systematic [27]. Little clearly states the difference in problem-solving style with the following:

> The difference (managerial) people know only two degrees of probability, zero, and one, and the similarity (scientific) people recognize every degree of probability except zero and one. The difference people tend to act before they think, if they ever think; whereas the similarity people think before they act, if they ever act. [25, p.B-469]

In addition to differences between the individuals who are managers and decision scientists, there are substantial differences in the environments in which they operate. The time horizon differs, for example. Hammond notes that the time for analysis *and* the time covered by the analysis are much shorter for the manager than for the management scientist [19, p.14]. But there are a variety of other differences also.

*The manager's job.* Mintzberg has recently described the roles that managers perform:

> Managers perform ten basic roles which fall into three groupings. The interpersonal roles describe the manager as a figurehead, external liaison, and leader; the information processing roles describe the manager as the nerve center of his organization's system; and the decision making roles suggest that the manager is at the heart of the system by which organizational resource allocation, improvement, and disturbance decisions are made. [28, p.B-97]

McKenney and Keen state that, "The manager's activities are bounded not only by formal constraints of his job, but also by the more formal traditions and expectations implicit in his role" [27, p.81]. Therefore, the decision scientist should be attuned to the fact that the job of the manager is quite different than his. Mintzberg describes the work well: "Because of the huge burden of responsibility for the operation of these systems, the manager is called upon to perform his work at an unrelenting pace, work that is characterized by variety, discontinuity and brevity [28, p.B-97].

However, the decision scientist should not categorize all managers as having the same job characteristics. Ford notes that, "The consultant often fails to tailor his approach to the unique and different circumstances of his client" [10, p.5]. Therefore, the decision scientist must note the similarities and differences between and among the jobs of the managers with whom he has contact. But most important he should be aware that there is a very high probability that the manager's job will be different than his own.

*Power and politics.* Many decision scientists do not understand the role of power and politics in the organization in which they operate. Starr makes two cogent comments in this regard: "First, management should encourage model builders to maintain a keen awareness of politics. Second, model builders should respect the importance of political error as well as scientific error" [32, p.36]. Ackoff suggests that decision scientists should make an analysis of the decision system [1]. Hayes and Nolan describe a typical decision system:

> First, decisions are made by people, often while working together in an unstructured fashion. The process by which alternatives are formulated, refined, analyzed, pruned, resolved, and finally, sold to others is a lengthy and complex one. Seldom does an important corporate decision ever emerge automatically and stand on its own merits; it must be nurtured and defended, often in a hostile environment. And it needs at least one powerful champion—someone who believes in it strongly enough to devote major effort to its acceptance. [21, p.109]

Neal and Radnor found in their empirical studies that there are significant relationships between top management orientation, knowledge, interest, and involvement in OR/MS, and group success [29]. Hammond states, "Models (should) have management support or, better yet, a champion" [18, p.114]. Radnor et al. also found in their studies that, although awareness concerning OR/MS was slight at the presidential level, interest and sponsorship of OR/MS activities had been occurring at the vice-presidential level. Moreover, they found that, "There is a strong relation between the fortunes of the sponsors and their OR/MS groups" [30, p.134]. This suggests that decision scientists should not try to acquaint everybody in the organization with the advantages of decision sciences, but should try to acquaint powerful or soon to be powerful people of the advantages.

Why is the manager so concerned about power and politics in the first place? Mintzberg lists as two of the 10 roles that managers play those of disturbance handler and resource allocator [28]. Any person who has had to play those two roles knows that power and politics influence the manager. Any manager who has not taken into account power and politics will remember Fenske's words:

> The best way to create people problems is to ignore the people. This involves concentrating on techniques, specifically the mathematics, computer programs and physical implications of the problem and ignoring the human factor entirely. [9, p.31]

Yet this is what many decision scientists would prefer to do. Hammond also suggests that although decision scientists or planners are out to change current procedures with their models, they should "stick to established company procedures at first" [18, p.116]. "If the model builder's mentality is not a political one and his solution does not include political considerations, then the model builder doesn't understand the managerial context of his problem" [32, p.35].

*Managers' goals.* All of the above suggest that the goals of the manager and the goals of the decision scientist may differ significantly. Hammond goes so far as to say that, "Part of the problem is that the manager's goals are often different from his organization's goals" [19, p.3]. McKenney and Keen note that the manager's "decision making activity is strongly influenced by his perception of his position" [27, p.81]. "The manager is more likely to gather environmental information that leads to successful (or at least comfortable) problem finding" [27, p.82]. They also state that, "Generally, theories assume that the situation has already been defined; the manager is presented with a neatly packaged problem and instructions on what he should do." Included in the behavioral theories of decision making should be "problem finding, problem recognition, and problem definition" [27, p.82].

Decision scientists should remember two aspects of managers' goals: (1) managers often not only are not systematic in problem solution, they are not systematic in problem finding or problem definition, and (2) managers will often review models and recommendations not in terms of the organization, but in terms of himself and in terms of those people who will affect him. Churchman summarizes the importance of this point:

> A coalition may arise because the members of the coalition recognize certain common economic advantages. But it is well known that coalitions also come about because of the personalities of their members; some mix of attitude, trait, and opinion creates a loyalty that is hard to dissolve. The loyalty is strengthened by opposition. . . . Thus, in the context of managerial politics, the researcher is apt to find that his recommendations are viewed from the point of view of their effect on a coalition, and not from the point of view of the whole organization. [5, p.36]

*Motivation.* Specifically, what motivates a manager? What goals does a manager have? Hammond states that managers are motivated by subunit goals not organizational goals. Managers are pragmatic and work toward ends which can be recognized by the control system: sales, profit, etc. This differs from the decision scientist who may desire a combination of professional recognition and achievement of total organization goals [19]. The decision scientist must recognize that what motivates the manager and what motivates the decision scientist seldom are the same. At the same time the decision scientist should be aware that managers may in fact not be as interested in an "optimum" solution as the decision scientist. Mintzberg describes the manager as follows:

> The manager acts as the mechanism by which organizational influencers (owners, governments, employee groups, the general public, etc., or simply the "boss") make their preferences known to the organization. It is the manager's duty to integrate these value positions. . . . [28, p.B-105]

Managers are often motivated to try to integrate these positions. They are often not "optimizers" in the view of the decision scientist. The decision scientist should try to understand the complex individual who is the manager and should try to understand the complex environment within which the manager must operate.

Green and Ray ask the questions that any decision scientist should ask about the manager. "What is in it for him? How is he benefitted? Or, how is he hurt?" [15]

BEHAVIORAL SKILLS. In the above discussion we focused on gaining insights into the manager and his environment. These insights are particularly important at the beginning of the decision science process. But the decision scientist must continue to focus on those insights as he moves with the manager through the decision science process. Yet, insight is only a beginning. The decision scientist must sharpen his skills and should also add to his repertoire of techniques and strategies which will enhance his skills.

*Communication from manager to decision scientist.* It is vital in the early stages of the decision science process that the decision scientist be able to get the manager to communicate with him. Churchman and Schainblatt describe the "communication" position in their Dialectic Implementation:

> The communicator emphasizes the need for creating more understanding on the part of the manager, i.e., for creating better lines of communication. [6, p.B-69]

What should be in this early communication? The decision scientist should be alert to the fact that often the manager himself doesn't know for sure what he wants to know. Ford indicates that a major problem is that the client fails to accurately identify the problem [10]. Consequently, communications skills such as nondirective interviewing should become part of the repertoire of the decision scientist. In addition, Green recommends the use of nominal grouping as a way of facilitating communication, especially in the premodeling or problem identification stage [13].

The decision scientist must obtain from the manager in a nonthreatening way a great deal of information necessary to make the decision science process work. Hammond suggests the following:

> Specifications must be fixed. This step consists of defining the purposes of the model exactly, its primary inputs and outputs, the main aspects of the structure, and how it would be used. [18, p.112]

Ford notes that the decision scientist must "recognize the individuality of the client's problems" [10, p.5]. And Hayes and Nolan stress that the decision scientist "must replace the concept of 'realism' with the concepts of 'adequate' and 'useful'" [21, p.109]. There are other facets the decision scientist should be alert to, however. Green and Ray note that:

> It is necessary to realize that each individual represents his own personal interest, and in doing so he often withholds information or in some cases even deliberately falsifies. [15]

In the pursuit of the real situation, however, the decision scientist should note that some individuals wish to take the decision scientist aside and pass along confidential information. Unfortunately, as others see this "confidential" communication, they may "clam up" [15].

Basically, the decision scientist should be slow and cautious early in the decision science process while he obtains the pertinent information from the manager and lays out what is to follow. The importance of communication at this stage is often overlooked.

*Communicating the results with the manager.* As we move through the decision science process, the decision scientist must communicate results to the manager. To a great extent the success of communication in that direction is a function of the success of the communication in the other direction earlier. However, there is more to it than that. The communication to the manager may be examined from three standpoints: (1) what is communicated, (2) method of communication, and (3) the role of the decision scientist in this communication.

Hammond recommends that decision scientists "express input and output in familiar formats" [18, p.116]. Hayes and Nolan state, "Simple models are best at the outset" [21, p.110]. Green and Ray warn that decision scientists should watch the "Jargon Jungle" [15]. Little states that:

> A model that is to be used by a manager should be . . . easy to communicate with. . . . easy to communicate with means that the manager can quickly and easily change inputs and obtain and understand outputs. [25, p.B-466]

Keep it within the understanding of the manager.

The results on the best method of communication are mixed. Mintzberg says, "The manager demonstrates a strong preference for the verbal media" [28, p.B-101]. But Churchman states, "We can find no evidence that the mode of communication makes any difference. . . . Of course, I am not saying that the mode of communication has no effect whatsoever. . . . What I am saying is that the formula will not do" [5, p.34]. His advice is excellent. Decision scientists should know how to communicate both verbally and in writing, and should try to understand which is more appropriate. Hammond doesn't worry about the method of communication but does encourage frequent interaction with more immediate results [19].

Hankin stresses the communication theme by pointing out that the process of communication should start at the beginning of the decision science process [20, p.300]. Moreover, he stresses factors affecting good communication, and the methods for communicating in a report with the following statement about a formal report: "It requires much imagination and skill and far too little attention is given to it by many workers" [20, p.297].

Churchman and Schainblatt address the persuasion position in their Dialectic of Implementation:

> The persuader views the implementation problem in terms of the manager's personality. Here the problem is not to provide for the manager's complete understanding of the scientist—since the former is too busy—but to ensure that the scientist understands enough about the manager so the scientist can overcome managerial resistance to change *per se*, alter specific managerial attitudes, or persuade managers to accept recommendations. [6, p.B-69 and B-70]

The persuader should adopt the following philosophy: "The users must be educated, and the model must gain acceptance. . . . The education process requires an understanding of the human and organization obstacles to acceptance, such as resistance to change, and of the actions appropriate to overcome them" [18, p. 113]. Starr even discusses the usefulness of transactional analysis [32, p.35]. But remember that it is inappropriate indeed to assume that managers need more information. Many have an overabundance already [1].

What is the role of the decision scientist in the communication process? Amspoker et al. reported on an empirical study involving groups made up of OR analysts, representatives from the user group, and representatives from the management information unit in the organization:

> The perceived group leaders in the least effective groups appeared to monopolize group communication. The perceived group leaders in the most effective groups took a more active internal communication role than did the perceived leaders in the moderately effective groups, but they did not monopolize internal communication. The most effective operations research project groups also directed a greater amount of their internal communication to representatives from the USER corporate area than did the less effective groups. [2, p.104]

Argyris perhaps states the whole communication process best when he makes a plea for openness. But note his definition of openness:

> Openness requires a particular combination of rational *and* emotional communication. Openness does not mean that each individual should express whatever is on his mind regardless of any concern for the feelings of others. The aim is to create a situation in which the MSOR Team members can express how they feel in such a manner as to help the line executives express themselves in a similar open manner. [3, p.B-290]

*Interpersonal skills.* As decision scientists and managers work together, a variety of potential interpersonal conflict situations arise. To effectively cope with these situations, Argyris says that "the competence of *both* managers and MIS professionals in dealing with emotionality and strain in interpersonal and intergroup problems must be raised" [3, p.B-290]. More specifically, Argyris makes the following suggestions:

> Behavioral science research suggests than in order to increase one's interpersonal competence the individual needs to be aware of his self and his defenses. Next, it is helpful if the individual strives to attain a minimum of psychological conflict and acceptance of his self so that he can create conditions that lead to trust, openness, risk taking, and effective confrontation of "conflict." [3, p.B-290]

Green and Ray relate this competence to attitude:

> It is advantageous to have a 'success-conducive attitude'. The assignment likely will not be successful if it is viewed primarily as an opportunity to test some theory or to experiment with a sophisticated model. Instead, success more likely comes from a 'service-oriented attitude', i.e., a mental frame of mind compatible with serving and fulfilling the client's needs." [15]

Fenske suggests that if the decision scientist wishes to ensure failure, he should "establish OR as the prima donna of the organization" [9, p.30]. Interpersonal competence is a rather nebulous concept. We could define people with high interpersonal competence as those individuals who other people perceive as having high interpersonal competence. This means that the best judges of whether an individual has high interpersonal competence are those who work with the individual. Amspoker suggests that interpersonal competence and communication skill are related in the eyes of many managers [2]. Starr relates decision scientists' ability to understand managers' problems with interpersonal competence [32]. "If the model builder's professionalism does not seem to allow him to be scientifically political in his professional judgment, then the bureaucratic manager perceives the model builder as an additional 'thing' to cope with" [32, p.36]. Amspoker reports on his four project group sets in his empirical study:

> The most effective set had the highest positive interaction qualities and the least effective set had the lowest positive interaction qualities. The positive interaction qualities are measures of the extent to which the members of a project are friendly, cooperative, share important information, and are judged competent in performing their assigned tasks. [2, p.104]

The above qualities may be good proxies for the way people perceive interpersonal competence.

*Using participative management.* The decision scientist is seldom a leader with great formal power. Argyris suggests that decision scientists should realize leadership is based more on competence than on power [3, p.B-278]. Therefore, decision scientists must be perceived as competent by managers and probably should not threaten the manager in order to be able to operate in a leadership position. Therefore, many authors who have examined the manager-decision scientist interface suggest that group problem solving with the decision scientist working *with* the manager or even *for* the manager may in fact be an appropriate way to lead [5,9,10,15,18,21,24, 26,29,30]. This is participative management. One of the primary reasons for this participation is stated by Hayes and Nolan:

> Managers are beginning to realize that the real value of a model comes not just from *using* it, but from *creating* it. Just as the person advances his understanding of a situation under the tutelage of experience, so does his understanding evolve during the modeling process. Over 50% of the value comes from 'getting there'; a model provides an opportunity to gain synthetic experience. As the model is developed and used, it will begin to challenge implicit assumptions of the user and suggest opportunities for improvement. Hence a good corporate model is not only a decision-making aid, but also a powerful educating and developing tool for management. [21, p.110]

A second reason for participative management is summarized in the Argyris study—"Individuals are incomplete without others. Again this tends to be at variance with the feeling and beliefs of MSOR Team members. They felt 'completed' by relating themselves to a world of symbols, models, and concepts" [3, p.B-291]. The implication is that with participative management, ideas, models, and plans for implementation will be better.

However, the third reason may be the most important. Through the use of participative management, the probabilities of implementation should be greater. Hammond points this out in his statement that the decision scientist must "Involve the potential users in the development process. The decision makers—the users—must be drawn into the development process right from the start" [18, p. 115]. Lonnstedt's empirical study supports this. His conclusion was that, "In the twelve firms studied there exists a positive relationship between the user's participation in defining the problem and the implementation of OR proposals" [26, p.28]. We have already noted Fenske's methods of insuring rapid termination of OR/MS departments:

> The best way to create people problems is to ignore the people. The next best step is to treat people like other inanimate factors of a project without considering the behavioral aspects. [9, p.31]

With participative management many of these problems can be avoided.

Participative management must be used throughout the decision science process. Konczal states, "While managerial input is important in all model building activities, managerial guidance is most important in (1) formulating the philosophy of model construction, (2) providing judgment that will temper the objectiveness of model methodology, (3) insuring that the model is an accurate model, and (4) providing an efficient administrative structure for model work" [24, p.12].

*Employing change strategies.* It is useful for decision scientists to remember their place in the organization and a particular work group, but in fact decision scientists represent change to the manager. How can the decision scientist effectively bring about change? We have already noted Churchman's comments:

> When a change is suggested to a manager, he reacts in ways that are typical to his own personality. Part of him will resist the suggestion, and often the resistance is so strong that he will reject the suggestion altogether. Nevertheless, the persons responsible for making the suggestion may learn enough about the manager's personality so that they know what to say to him to break down his resistance. Thus, they recognize that there is a part of the manager's personality that will adjust to change. On the other hand, there may be a part that remains invariant, no matter what the environment. [5, p.35]

Argyris stresses that the decision scientist should note that change may be perceived by the manager as requiring new requirements for conceptual thinking, decreasing feelings of essentiality, psychological failure and double bind [3]. Managers are likely to react favorably to change only when they perceive that the advantages of the potential change outweigh the probable disadvantages of the change.

*Applying the contingency theory of management.* The decision scientist should *always* focus on the kinds of behavioral concepts previously mentioned as a principal means for gaining an understanding of the manager and manager's environment. Furthermore, he should *always* concentrate on exemplifying behavioral skills, particularly interpersonal competence and communication. Likewise, he should *always* employ participative management.

However, in applying these behavioral dimensions, it is necessary to realize that the importance of the insights and skills varies from one situation to another. Politics and power may be the dominant consideration in one circumstance, while in another it may be only a minor concern. Persuasion might be appropriate in one situation while in another situation a completely different strategy may be used to bring about change. Because of this variation, the relative importance of each in any given situation varies. This same relativism holds for the extent to which the behavioral techniques should be applied in a particular situation.

The task of the decision scientist is to assess each situation in terms of the relevant issues, not to determine whether or not to direct attention to understanding personalities, politics, etc., but rather to determine *how much* emphasis is appropriate. In short, a contingency approach is called for. Both the direction and intensity of effort are contingent upon the particular circumstances of the situation.

Contingency theory stresses the points made by the following authors. "The modeler must understand the company and its industry, and what the manager who will use his model wants" [18, p.119]. "Thus the first question a planner must face is whether the climatic conditions in which he lives are favorable for computer planning models" [18, p.113]. "The degree and direction of the scientist's efforts will be very different, depending on how he perceives the manager's needs in the situation" [27, p.88]. "It is not, however, solely the relationship between user and operations researcher that determines the success of the project. Problem characteristics may also have an influence" [26, p.28].

Both Hankin and Halsbury [20 and 17] stress that in the presentation of results to managers, the decision scientist must take into account who the manager is, how the presentation should be, etc. There is no one universal answer.

Those authors who have conducted empirical studies concerning the relationship between decision scientist and manager and/or the success of implementation of decision science recommendations strongly believe in the contingency theory. They will use words such as likely, suggest, etc. [2, 26,29,30].

There isn't any universal answer to increasing the implementation of decision science recommendations. Argyris mentions that an organization could move line people into decision science groups and make decision science experts line managers for a period of time [3]. Hammond even suggests that an organization might have people serving in the role of the integrator [19]. Little suggests a matrix structure [25]. None of the authors is advocating these as universal solutions, since the managers and decision scientists are quite different and some may not be able to adapt to new roles. But these are strategies that may fit some environments.

Therefore, the purpose of this book is not to create decision scientists who think and act like managers. The purpose is not to make all decision scientists fit into a single mold either. The purpose is to add to the decision scientist's repertoire of behavioral insights and skills. Moreover, we are attempting to develop a level of behavioral sophistication on the part of the decision scientist so that the application of decision sciences may reach their potential.

### Integrating the Quantitative and the Behavioral

The following matrix presents the integration of the quantitative and the behavioral. Across the top are the articles included in this book, grouped by stage in the decision process and the major subsets in that stage. Down the side are a variety of behavioral insights and skills, which the decision scientist should become familiar with. The Xs indicate topics covered in each article. This should enable the decision scientist to see that although there are both stages in the decision science process and behavioral insights/skills to consider, there are substantial interrelationships between and among all of these aspects at all levels.

Table 1: A list of the readings and the behavioral topics included in each

Readings Which Discuss the Various Behavioral Topics
(Readings Keyed to Table of Contents)

| Behavioral Topic | Part II: Premodeling | | | | | | | | | | Part III: Modeling | | | | Part IV: Implementation | | | | | | | |
|---|---|---|---|---|---|---|---|---|---|---|---|---|---|---|---|---|---|---|---|---|---|---|
| | 1 | 2 | 3 | 4 | 5 | 6 | 7 | 8 | 9 | 10 | 1 | 2 | 3 | 4 | 1 | 2 | 3 | 4 | 5 | 6 | 7 | 8 |
| **INSIGHTS** | | | | | | | | | | | | | | | | | | | | | | |
| Perception | X | | | X | X | X | X | | | | X | | | X | X | | X | X | | | | |
| Personality | | | X | X | X | | | | | | | | | | | | X | | | | | |
| Cognitive Style | X | | | | | | | | | | X | | | | | | X | | | | | |
| Problem Solving Style | X | | | | | | | | | | | | | | | | | | | | | |
| The Manager's Job | X | | | | | | X | | | | | | | | | | | | | | | |
| Power & Politics | | | X | X | | | | X | X | | X | | | X | | | | | | | X | X |
| Manager's Goals | | | X | | | | | | | | | | | | | | X | | | | | |
| Motivation | | | | | | X | | | | | | | | | | | X | | | | | |
| **SKILLS** | | | | | | | | | | | | | | | | | | | | | | |
| Communication from Manager to Decision Scientist | | | | | X | X | X | | | | | | X | X | X | | X | | | | | |
| Communication from Decision Scientist to Manager | X | X | X | X | X | X | X | X | | X | X | | X | X | X | | X | | | X | X | |
| Interpersonal Competence | | | | X | X | | | | | | | | | | | | | | | | | |
| Participative Management | | | X | X | | | | | | | X | | X | | X | | X | | | X | | |
| Change Strategies | | | | X | | | | | | | | | | X | | | | X | | | | |
| Contingency Theories of Management | X | | | | X | | | X | X | | | | X | | X | X | X | X | X | | | |

## REFERENCES

1. Ackoff, Russell L. "Management Misinformation Systems." *Management Science*, Vol. 14, No. 4 (December 1967), pp. B-147–B-156.
2. Amspoker, Robert D.; J. Randall Brown; Robert D. Smith; and Robert H. Culhan. "Organizational Factors Related to Operations Research Project Group Effectiveness." American Institute for Decision Sciences *Proceedings* of the Fifth Annual Meeting, Boston, 1973, pp. 102–105.
3. Argyris, Chris. "Management Information Systems: The Challenge to Rationality and Emotionality." *Management Science*, Vol. 17, No. 6 (February 1971), pp. B-275–B-292.
4. Burack, Elmer and Robert Batlivala. "Operations Research: Recent Changes and Future Expectations in Business Organizations." *Business Perspectives* (Fall 1972), pp. 15–21.
5. Churchman, C. West. "Managerial Acceptance of Scientific Recommendations." *California Management Review*, Vol. VII, No. 1 (Fall 1964), pp. 31–38.
6. Churchman, C. W. and A. H. Schainblatt. "The Researcher and the Manager: A Dialectic of Implementation." *Management Science*, Vol. 11, No. 4 (February 1965), pp. B-69–B-87.
7. Ciecka, James E.; James M. Comer; and Clovis N. daSilva. "The Use of Quantitative Methods in Business Decision Making: A Survey," in Manfred W. Hopfe (ed.), *Advancing, Applying and Teaching the Decision Sciences*. Boston: The American Institute for Decision Sciences, 1973, pp. 192–195.
8. Coppinger, Richard and Stewart Epley. "The Non-Use of Advanced Mathematical Techniques." *Managerial Planning* (May/June 1972), pp. 12–16.
9. Fenske, Russell W. "Programming Counterproductive Methods to Insure the Rapid Termination of Operations Research/Management Science Departments." *Interfaces*, Vol. 3, No. 1 (November 1972), pp. 30–32.
10. Ford, Charles H. "Developing a Successful Client-Consultant Relationship." *Human Resource Management*, Vol. 13, No. 2 (Summer 1974), pp. 2–11.
11. Gaither, Norman. "The Adoption of Operations Research Techniques by Manufacturing Organizations." *Decision Sciences*, Vol. 6, No. 4 (October 1975), pp. 797–813.
12. Grayson, C. Jackson. "Management Science and Business Practice." *Harvard Business Review*, Vol. 51, No. 4 (July-August 1973), pp. 41–48.
13. Green, Thad B. "Improving Modeller-User Interaction." *Operational Research Quarterly*, Vol. 28, No. 3, 1977, pp. 527–537.
14. Green, Thad B.; Walter Newsom; and Roland Jones. "A Survey of the Application of Quantitative Techniques to Production/Operations Management in Large Corporations." *Academy of Management Journal*, Vol. 20, No. 4 (December 1977), pp. 669–676.
15. Green, Thad B. and Dennis F. Ray. "How Do Your Quantitative Specialists Stack-Up?" *Business and Economic Perspectives*, Vol. 11, No. 2 (Spring 1977), pp. 41–47.
16. Groff, Gene. "Applications of Quantitative Methods." *AACSB*, 5 (October 1968), pp. 22–31.
17. Halsbury, The Rt. Hon. The Earl of. "The Art of Exposition." *Operational Research Quarterly*, Vol. 11, Nos. 1/2 (March/June 1960), pp. 1–15.

18. Hammond, John S. "Do's and Don'ts of Computer Models for Planning." *Harvard Business Review*, Vol. 52, No. 2 (March-April 1974), pp. 110-123.

19. Hammond, John S. "The Roles of the Manager and Management Scientist in Successful Implementation." *Sloan Management Review*, Vol. 15, No. 2 (Winter 1974), pp. 1-24.

20. Hankin, B. D. "The Communication of the Results of Operational Research to the Makers of Policy." *Operational Research Quarterly*, Vol. 9, No. 4 (December 1958), pp. 293-301.

21. Hayes, Robert H. and Richard L. Nolan. "What Kind of Corporate Modeling Functions Best?" *Harvard Business Review*, Vol. 52, No. 3 (May-June 1974), pp. 102-112.

22. Hertz, David. "Industrial Operation Research in the U.S." *AMA Management Report* #10 (1958), pp. 23-39.

23. Hovey, Ronald and Harvey Wagner. "A Sample Survey of Industrial Operations Research Activities." *Operations Research*, Vol. 6 (1958), pp. 876-881.

24. Konczal, Edward F. "Models Are for Managers, Not Mathematicians." *Journal of Systems Management*, Vol. 26, No. 1 (January 1975), pp. 12-15.

25. Little, John D. C. "Models and Managers: The Concept of a Decision Calculus." *Management Science*, Vol. 16, No. 8 (April 1970), pp. B-466-B-485.

26. Lonnstedt, Lars. "Factors Related to the Implementation of Operations Research Solutions." *Interfaces*, Vol. 5, No. 2 (February 1975), pp. 23-30.

27. McKenney, James L. and Peter G. W. Keen. "How Managers' Minds Work." *Harvard Business Review*, Vol. 52, No. 3 (May-June 1974), pp. 79-90.

28. Mintzberg, Henry. "Managerial Work: Analysis from Observation." *Management Science*, Vol. 18, No. 2 (October 1971), pp. B-97-B-110.

29. Neal, Rodney D. and Michael Radnor. "The Relation Between Formal Procedures for Pursuing OR/MS Activities and OR/MS Group Success." *Operations Research*, Vol. 21, No. 2 (March-April 1973), pp. 451-474.

30. Radnor, Michael; Albert H. Rubenstein; and Alden S. Bean. "Integration and Utilization of Management Science Activities in Organizations." *Operational Research Quarterly*, Vol. 19, No. 2 (June 1968), pp. 117-141.

31. Schumacher, Charles and Barnard Smith. "A Sample Survey of Industrial Operations Research Activities II." *Operations Research*, Vol. 13, No. 6 (December 1965), pp. 1023-1027.

32. Starr, Martin K. "The Politics of Management Science." *Interfaces*, Vol. 1, No. 4 (June 1971), pp. 31-37.

33. Turban, Efriam. "A Sample Survey of Operations Research Activities at the Corporate Level." *Operations Research*, Vol. 20 (May/June 1972), pp. 708-721.

34. Vatter, William. "The Use of Operation Research in American Companies." *The Accounting Review*, Vol. XLII, No. 4 (1967), pp. 712-730.

35. Weston, Frederick C., Jr. "Operations Research Techniques Relevant to Corporate Planning Function Practices." *Academy of Management Journal*, Vol. 16, No. 3 (September 1973), pp. 507-510.

# 2. MANAGEMENT SCIENCE AND BUSINESS PRACTICE

## C. Jackson Grayson, Jr.

"What we need to do is humanize the scientist and simonize the humanist." This dictum is a popularization of C. P. Snow's view of science and the humanities as two distinct cultures, and it is all too true when applied to management. Managers and management scientists are operating as two separate cultures, each with its own goals, languages, and methods. Effective cooperation—and even communication—between the two is just about minimal. And this is a shame.

Each has much to learn from the other, and much to teach the other. Yet, despite all kinds of efforts over the years, it seems to me that the cultural and operating gap which exists between the two is not being closed. Why?

I can offer some explanations, based on my years as an academician, consultant, businessman, and, most recently, head of an organization with control over a large part of our economy—the Price Commission. I can also suggest a way to build the bridge so badly needed between the two cultures and the people who make them up. This bridge must span the gap between two quite different types:

*The management scientists.* As people, they want to help managers make decision making more explicit, more systematic, and *better* by using scientific methodology, principally mathematics and statistics. They can be found largely in universities and in staff operations of enterprises. They may belong to any of a number of professional associations, such as The Institute of Management Sciences (TIMS), Operations Research Society of America (ORSA), and the American Institute for Decision Sciences (AIDS).

*The managers.* They make and implement decisions, largely by rough rules of thumb and intuition. They are the operating executives, found principally in the line.

The lines of distinction are never so pure, but most people, I believe, understand what I mean.

What I have to offer to the management scientists is a few bouquets and then a load of bricks. First, the bouquets:

Management scientists have had *some* impact on real-world operations and managers.

Some management science tools have been successfully applied in accounting, finance, production, distribution, and weapons systems.

Managers do tend to give a little more conscious thought to their decision making than in previous years—but still precious little.

By indicating how abysmal our knowledge is about decision making, management scientists have highlighted areas for further research.

Both the faculty and the students at business schools have gained some added prestige in the business and academic communities for being more "scientific."

And now the bricks. The total impact of management science has been extremely small. Its contribution looks even smaller than it is if one compares it to the revolution promised for management offices in the early years. And the "wait-until-next-generation" theme is wearing thinner and thinner.

Let me quickly acknowledge that there are *some* management scientists who operate effectively in both cultures. But they are rare birds. Most management scientists are still thinking, writing, and operating in a world that is far removed from the real world in which most managers operate (and in which I personally have been operating). They often describe and structure nonexistent management problems, tackle relatively minor problems with overkill tools, omit real variables from messy problems, and build elegant models comprehensible to only their colleagues. And when managers seem confused or dissatisfied with the results of their activities and reject them, these scientists seem almost to take satisfaction in this confirmation of the crudity and inelegance of the managerial world.

Have I overdrawn the picture? Only very slightly.

## Why the Gulf?

I do not mean to say that management scientists have purposefully created this cultural gap. Most of them feel that much of what they are doing today is really helpful to managers. But I'm afraid it simply isn't so. Others argue that much of what they are doing is "pure research," which will be useful one day. I do not discount the value of pure research; some of it is needed. But the fact remains that only a small fraction of management science "results" are being used.

Those management scientists who do acknowledge a gap often excuse it by one of two reasons:

"The manager doesn't understand the power of the tools."

"He isn't sympathetic to systematic decision making and would rather fly by the seat of his pants because this is safer for his ego."

I myself am a counterexample to both these excuses. I have had some fairly good training in management science. I have done research in the area and written a book urging the use of more explicit decision tools in a specific in-dustry—oil well drilling.[1] I have taught various courses in the area, for ex-ample, in statistics, management control systems, and quantitative analysis.

And yet, in the most challenging assignment of my life—putting together the Price Commission—I used absolutely *none* of the management science tools explicitly. One might think that in the task of developing an organiza-tion of 600 people (mostly professionals), creating a program to control prices in a trillion dollar economy, and making decisions that involve costs, volume, prices, productivity, resource allocations, elasticities, multiple goals, trade-offs, predictions, politics, and risk values, an expert would have found ways to use his familiarity with management science to advantage. I did not.

A defender of the faith will quickly say that, although I did not use them explicitly, I probably used them *implicitly*, and that they helped to disci-pline my approach to decision making. I agree that this is probably true. But I nevertheless think it is a damning indictment that I can identify *no* in-cident of a conscious, explicit use of a single management science tool in my activities as head of the Price Commission.

Further, my conscience is clear. To my mind there are five very valid reasons for my rejecting the idea of using management science.

SHORTAGE OF TIME. Although I thought about using management science tools on many occasions, I consistently decided against it because of the shortage of time. Management scientists simply do not sufficiently under-stand the constraint of time on decision making, and particularly on deci-sions that count; and the techniques they develop reflect that fact. They may write about time as a limitation. They may admonish managers for letting time push them into a "crisis" mode. They may recognize the con-straint of time with a few words and comment on its influence. They may say that they, too, experience time constraints. But their techniques are so time consuming to use that managers pass them by.

Does this mean that all management science work ought to be thrown into shredders? No, it simply means that management scientists (a) need to get out of their relatively unpressured worlds and *experience* the impact of time on the decision-making process, and (b) need to build the time factor into models instead of leaving it as an exogenous variable.

INACCESSIBILITY OF DATA. The second reason for ignoring management sci-ence in practice is related to the time problem. A manager will ordinarily use data or a management science tool only if both are conveniently, speed-ily accessible. If he is told that the needed data are buried in another part of the organization, or that they must be compiled, or that the model must be

[1] *Decisions Under Uncertainty* (Boston, Division of Research, Harvard Business School, 1960).

created, nine times out of ten he will say, "Skip it." I did, ten times out of ten.

True, many management scientists would say that I must have developed "trade-offs" in my mind, weighing the cost of obtaining data or building a model against the probable opportunity payoff, and that my mental calculator ground out negative responses on each occasion. This is perfectly plausible. Unconsciously I probably did build a number of such informal investment-payoff models.

But where does this leave us? It leaves us with management scientists continuing to construct models that call for substantial investments in design and data collection and managers discarding them. The statement is made ad nauseam that most data are not in the forms that most models call for, or that they are not complete; yet the management scientists go right on calling for inaccessible, nonexistent, or uncompiled data to suit "theoretically correct" models. And hence managers continue to say, "Skip it."

Instead of asking a manager to lie in the Procrustean bed of the theoretically correct model, why shouldn't the management scientist design a realistic model, or a realistic part of a model, or come up with a realistic data prescription? The result might be extremely crude; it might embarrass a theoretician; it might be shot down by the purist and the theoretician. But it just might be *used*.

RESISTANCE TO CHANGE. The third reason that I did not use management science tools explicitly is that educating others in the organization who are not familiar with the tools, and who would resist using them if they were, is just too difficult a task. Management scientists typically regard this problem as outside the scope of their jobs—at most, they remark on the need to educate more people and to change organizations so they become more scientific. Or, if they *do* recognize the problem, they grossly underestimate the time and organizational effort needed to "educate and change." I suggest that management scientists do two things:

1. They should build into their models some explicit recognition of the financial and emotional cost of change of this kind and make explicit allowance for the drag of change resistance. I am quite aware that some change techniques are being used: sensitivity training, Esalen-type devices, management by objectives, quantitative analysis courses for managers, and so on. I have used them myself, and I know that they help. But the magnitude of time and energy required to install them is not generally appreciated—certainly not by management scientists—and their impact is highly overrated.
2. They should get themselves some education and direct experience in the power, politics, and change-resistance factors in the real world of management so they can better incorporate the imperfect human variables in their work.

LONG RESPONSE TIME. Fourth, few management science people are geared up to respond to significant management problems in "real time." Management science people in universities live largely by the school calendar, and if they receive a request for help, they are likely to respond in terms of next semester, next September, or after exams. And once again the manager is likely to say, "Skip it." Even most management science personnel in staff positions of live organizations operate in a time frame that is slower than that of the line managers. It is their nature to approach a problem in a methodical, thorough way, even when the required response time dictates that they come up with a "quick and dirty" solution.

INVALIDATING SIMPLIFICATIONS. Fifth, and finally, it is standard operating procedure for most management science people to strip away so much of a real problem with "simplifying assumptions" that the remaining carcass of the problem and its attendant solution bear little resemblance to the reality with which the manager must deal. The time constraints, the data-availability questions, the people problems, the power structures, and the political pressures—all the important, nasty areas that lie close to the essence of management—are simplified out of existence so that a technically beautiful, and useless, resolution may be achieved.

This is somewhat paradoxical since management science originated in wartime Britain, when many interdisciplinary talents were forced into combination to grapple with the problems of total mobilization. That situation tolerated no fooling around. But in subsequent years management science has retreated from the immediate demands for workable results. It has increased its use of the hard sciences of mathematics and statistics, hardening itself with methodological complexity, weakening its own reliance on the softer sciences of psychology, sociology, and political science, and losing the plain, hardheaded pragmatism with which it started out.

Realizing this, many managers think it pointless to turn the really important problems over to management science. Their experience has shown them the impotence of emasculated solutions.

At the risk of repeating a tired joke, let me recall the story of the man who said he had a way to destroy all the enemy submarines in the Atlantic during World War II: "Boil the ocean." Asked next how he would do this, he replied, "That's your problem." Similarly, when managers ask management scientists how to solve a problem, they too often say, in effect, "Boil the company." They leave it to the manager to worry about shortages of time, inaccessibility of data, resistance to change, slow response times, and oversimplified solutions.

# Firing the Furnace

At the Price Commission we operated, I think fairly successfully, without getting the data we "should" have had, without using any explicit decision tools, without once formally consulting a management scientist, and without building models of our decision-making processes. I am not especially proud of these facts; I am a member, and an intellectually loyal member, of ORSA, TIMS, and AIDS. I believe in the general direction in which these organizations want to go. But I also have a personal dedication to action, a sense of the urgency and immediacy of real problems, and a disbelief in the genuine responsiveness of management science models to my managerial needs.

I have asked myself the question whether we might have done better by using some management science models, and my honest answer is *no*. Using models would have slowed decision making. It would have frustrated most of our personnel. Given the fact that most models omit the factors of time, data accessibility, people, power, and politics, they simply would not have provided sufficient predictive or prescriptive payoff for the required investment of energy.

Consider the severity of the demands that were made. Establishment of the Price Commission required fulfillment of seemingly impossible tasks and directives:

Create and staff a fully competent organization.

Work out regulations worthy to bear the force of law.

Keep the program consistent with policies established in Phase I and the current state of the economy.

Work in conjunction with the Pay Board, the Internal Revenue Service, and the Cost of Living Council.

Control the prices of hundreds of millions of articles and commodities in the world's largest economy.

Do not inhibit the recovery of the economy.

Do not build a postcontrol bubble.

Do all of this with a regulatory staff of 600.

Have the entire operation functioning in 16 days.

A natural first reaction to such demands might well have been General McAuliffe's famous one-word response: "Nuts!" It would have been very easy to point out, for example, that:

Nobody could begin to do the job of price control with 600 people, even with the services of 3,000 Internal Revenue Service agents to help with enforcement. It had taken 60,000 people to handle the assignment in World War II and 17,000 in the Korean War.

To do the job right would require a thoroughgoing study of what was involved—the resources and kinds of personnel required, the most efficient way of actually controlling prices, the optimum method of working in concert with other federal agencies—as well as the accumulation of data about the economy and the testing of various models.

The 16-day period was too short. There was not enough time to get the Price Commission appointed, let alone to build, organize, and house the right kind of staff, promulgate regulations, and get it all functioning.

I might have pointed out these things and many others. I did not. I simply started bringing in staff, renting quarters, creating an organization, framing regulations, and developing a modus operandi. In 16 days the organization was accepting requests for price increases from U.S. business; the staff was at work—in some cases eight to an office, four to a telephone, and a good many spending up to 20 hours a day on the job.

I cite this record not to boast. Our achievement did not grow out of extraordinary capability. It was simply a matter of orientation and intuition —orientation and intuition toward action. But just as managers incline toward intuition and action, management scientists incline toward reflective thinking. They tend to be scholarly, less action-oriented, and averse to taking risks—even risk of criticism from their peers. They dissect and analyze, they are individualistic, and they are prone to trace ideas much as one can trace power flows in a mechanical system, from gear to belt to gear. They have not cared much about firing the furnace that makes the steam that drives the gear in the first place.

The manager offers an almost complete contrast. He integrates and synthesizes; he sees situations as mosaics; his thoughts and decision processes are like electrical circuits so complex you can never be sure how much current is flowing where. At the core of his value system are depth and breadth of experience, which he may even permit to outweigh facts where the whole picture seems to justify it.

For his part, the management scientist tends to optimize the precision of a tool at the expense of the health and performance of the whole. He has faith in some day building ultimate tools and devising ultimate measurements, and this lies at the foundation of his values and beliefs.

The problem, then, boils down to two cultures—the managers' and the management scientists'—and not enough bridges between them. Somebody has to build the bridges.

### Who Shall Build the Bridges?

Closing any gap requires that one or both cultures change. It is my strong belief that the management scientist must move first, and most. *The end product is supposed to be management, after all, not management science.*

Further, as a philosophical point, I think science has greater relevance to our world if it moves constantly toward art (in this case the management art) than the other way around. Then, instead of moving toward increased and separated specialization, both evolve toward a mature symbiosis, a working and dynamic unity of the kind found in successful marriages, détentes, and mergers.

The management scientist is not going to find it easy or comfortable to change, and yet it is he who must change most in attitude, action, and life style. He is going to have to think in terms of the *manager's* perceptions, the *manager's* needs, the *manager's* expectations, and the *manager's* pressures —that is, if he wants to have impact in the real world of the manager. If not, he will go on missing the mark.

What, concretely, can be done? Let me offer a few suggestions to the management science people and the managers they are supposed to be helping.

INSIDE OPERATING ORGANIZATIONS. First, top management should not isolate the management science people but sprinkle them throughout the organization in situations where they can really go to work. It should give them *line* responsibility for results. Their natural tendencies will cause them to flock together at night or on weekends to compare and refine tools, and that, again, is as it should be; but their prime responsibility should be to the line unit, not to a management science group. To put the matter another way: management should not think of having an operating person on a management science team—it should think of having a management scientist on an operating team.

Second, managers should demand implementation by management scientists; they should not tolerate "package" solutions that leave out the complicating factors. In that way, managers can avoid simplistic, unworkable solutions that ignore the factors of time, data accessibility, unwillingness of people to change, power, and so on.

Third, even when professional management scientists are brought into companies as consultants, they are often given the easy, old problems, for the reasons that I have named. This expectational cycle has to be broken.

AT THE UNIVERSITY. The same general approach is valid within universities.

First, both management science faculty and students have to get out of the isolated, insulated world of academe. They must go beyond structured cases and lectures and become directly involved in real-world, real-time, live projects, not as a way of applying what they know, but as a way of learning.

It is a mistake to teach the student linear programming or decision theory and then search for a problem to which the tool can be applied. That creates the classic academic situation from which managers are revolting— the tool in search of a problem. Instead, tackle the *real* problem. This will be frustrating, but the frustration of trying to reach a *workable* solution can be used to teach the management scientist or student in a way that is useful both to him and to the business or government unit. The solutions thus derived may not be so elegant as they might be, but they may be used. The student who wants to reach for higher, more sophisticated theories should be treated as a special case, not the general case.

Second, management science people should stop tackling the neat, simple problems, or refining approaches to problems already solved. These projects may be easier, but working and reworking them will not help bridge the cultural gap I am talking about. Instead, tackle the *tough* problem. The management of time pressure and the use of the persuasion and negotiation required by a real, tough problem will give both the faculty member and the student some salutary discipline in convincing others to follow a strange idea, to cooperate, and to listen.

The best example of what I am describing occurred at Case Institute in the early days of Russell L. Ackoff, E. L. Arnoff, and C. West Churchman. There, faculty and student teams worked on real problems in real time in real business settings. That example does not seem to have caught on at other universities, partly because of the difficulty of doing it, and partly because it flies against the nature of the management science personality that I have described. The process is messy, people-populated, schedule-disrupting, time-demanding, and complicated by power and politics. That is exactly as it should be.

Third, faculty members should plan to get out of the university, physically and completely, for meaningful periods of time. They should plan their careers so that they schedule at least a year, periodically, in which they get direct, real-world experience in business, nonprofit organizations, or the government.

One helpful device with which I am familiar is the Presidential Personnel Interchange Program of the federal government, now in its third year. So far this year it has brought 60 business executives into government work and 18 federal government managers into business. These numbers should be expanded tremendously, and the organizations involved should include universities. The universities could well join in a three-way interchange, or start their own program with business.

Finally, universities should bring in real managers and involve them directly in problem-solving and joint-learning sessions. Doctors expect to return to medical school as part of their normal development; so should managers. The universities can offer managers an update in science; corporate managers can offer universities an update in management.

These are some of the ways to build bridges. There are other ways to tear them down, or to maintain the gap. Jargon, for example, will drive away managers. So will intellectual snobbery toward "intuitive" decision making. Management scientists should dispense with both. Managers can maintain the gap by continuing to refer to past disillusionments and never allowing management science people to tackle executive-suite programs. Managers should recognize that. In fact, defensive behavior on the part of either group can block reconciliation and progress.

People *do* exist who effectively bridge the two cultures. Such people do not always bear an identifying brand; one cannot distinguish them by their degrees, university course credits, titles, experience, or even home base. But they do have one strong, overriding characteristic—they are *problem- and action-oriented*. They are essentially unicultural; they employ a healthy mix of science and intuition in their decision making.

## Words to the Wise

I am not suggesting that the two specializations—management science and management—be destroyed. Primary bases and modes of operation can be preserved, provided that both groups are receptive to and understanding of the other's basic orientation, and that they work together in harmony, not in dissonance. And all should remember that the problem is the thing, not the methodology; the function, not the form.

My slings and arrows have been directed mostly toward management science—rightly so, I think. But managers must assist in the bridge-building process:

> They should stop recounting tales of how "they never laid a glove on me" in encounters with management scientists. They should make it a point of future pride to use management science.
>
> They should make available the real nasty, complicated decisions to management scientists.
>
> They should not expect a lot.
>
> They should not deride small gains.
>
> They should hold any management science approach or individual accountable for producing *results*, not recommendations.

The management science people must play their part, too:

> Get out of the monasteries, whether these are universities or staff departments.
>
> Submerge the paraphernalia (journal articles, computer programs, cookbooks) and rituals ("sounds like a linear programming program to me" or "we need to get the facts first").
>
> Put people, time, power, data accessibility, and response times into models and create crude, workable solutions.
>
> Learn to live with and in the real world of managers.

Again, I submit it is the management science people who will have to change most. They should take the first step toward closing the gap between the two cultures. The consequences can only be better for managers, for management science, and for the problem itself.

# B. Bridging the Gap

## 3. BEYOND PROBLEM SOLVING

*Russell L. Ackoff*

---

A luncheon address is expected to be like an after-dinner mint: a sweet of little substance. Such sweets are not to my taste. What I am about to subject you to is more like a bitter pill. But this pill is not likely to aid your digestion even though it is intended only to upset your minds.

We are brought together by a common interest in decision making. To make a decision is to choose from among alternative courses of action or inaction in situations in which the decision maker's choice can make a difference in the value of the outcome to him. Our common interest tends

Editors' Note: Reprinted with permission from *Decision Sciences*, April 1974, pp. x–xv.

to focus on decision situations in which the decision maker is in a state of doubt about what to do. Such doubt converts the possibility of choice into a problem. One of the primary objectives of the decision sciences has been to improve the efficiency and effectiveness of problem solving. My message relates to this objective. Put briefly, it is that it is time to move on beyond this objective.

The first position that I would like to take, and whose implications I would like to explore with you, is that problems exist only as *abstract subjective constructs*, not as concrete objective states. Furthermore, I will argue that even if they were objective states *they would not have solutions*, if by "solutions" we mean actions that extinguish a problem or put it to rest. I will maintain that in dealing with problems and solutions we have been dealing with shadows rather than substance. I will *not* argue, however, that we have been wasting our time. The sleight of mind in which we have been engaged has been, and can continue to be, useful. But its usefulness is limited, and there is a bigger, more difficult, and more important job to be done. My plea, therefore, will be that we turn at least part of our effort to tasks that will be more useful to those we attempt to serve, including ourselves.

Now to elucidate.

Problems have traditionally been assumed to be *given* or *presented* to an actor much as they are to students at the end of chapters in text books. Where they come from and why they are worth solving is implicitly assumed to be irrelevant to consideration of how they should be solved or what their solutions are. Books dealing with the methodology of research and problem solving seldom give more than a polite nod to problem generation, identification, and formulation. They move impatiently to problem solving. They do this despite advice to the contrary given by two eminent American philosophers, William James and John Dewey. They sought to make us aware of the fact that problems are *taken up by*, not *given to*, decision makers. William James argued that problems are extracted from unstructured states of confusion. John Dewey referred to such states as *indeterminate* or *problematic*. I prefer to call them "messes."

What decision makers deal with, I maintain, are messes, not problems. This is hardly illuminating, however, unless I make more explicit and precise the meaning of "mess." Let me try to do so.

A mess is a system of external conditions that produces dissatisfaction. It can be conceptualized as a system of problems in the same sense in which a physical body can be conceptualized as a system of atoms. Now we do know something about what a system is. It is an entity which has four essential characteristics.

First, it has two or more parts. Hence, it is *not* an ultimate element or an indivisible part. It is a whole which has parts and may itself be part of a larger whole. Some of its parts may themselves be wholes.

Second, each part can have an effect on the behavior or properties of the whole. Therefore, the whole is dependent on each of its parts, though not necessarily equally.

Third, the effect that each part can have on the whole depends on the behavior or properties of at least one other part. Hence, no part has an independent effect on the whole, and each part depends on at least one other part.

Finally, any subgrouping of the parts yields subsets which have the same characteristics as I have just attributed to the parts: they can have an effect on the behavior or properties of the whole; they are interdependent; and if the subsets are combined into larger subsets, they also have the same properties.

Put in less precise but perhaps more revealing terms, a system, viewed structurally, is a whole that can be divided into parts. However, when its parts are separated it loses some of its essential characteristics. Therefore, from a functional point of view, *a system is an indivisible whole*. It is the antithesis of an atom or other ultimate elements.

If the reality with which decision makers deal consists of messes from which systems of problems can be abstracted, then there are a number of important implications to the decision sciences. Let me explore some of them with you briefly.

First, then, a problem is an ultimate element abstracted from a mess. In this respect it is treated by decision scientists as other scientists have treated such elements as atoms and cells. It is important to recognize that ultimate elements are necessarily abstractions which *cannot* be observed. It is not possible for us to conceive of something which can be observed but cannot be divided into parts. We cannot see geometric points; they are abstractions. What we see and call points are small areas. Therefore, what we see and call problems are small messes, mini-messes.

Problems, even as abstract mental constructs, do not exist in isolation, although we isolate them conceptually. They are elements of systems. Therefore, each affects the fate of the messes of which they are part; none has an independent effect on the fate of any of these messes; and every subgrouping of them also has these properties. This systemic property of problems has several important consequences for decision theory.

The "solution" to a mess—whatever it may be—is not the simple sum of the solutions to the problems which are or can be extracted from it. No mess can be solved by solving each of its component problems independently of the others because no mess can be decomposed into independent problems. For example, an attempt to assemble the best available automotive parts regardless of make will not yield the best possible automobile. It will not even yield an automobile, because the parts will not fit together. Even if they were made to do so, they would not work well together.

The optimal solution to a mess is not the sum of the optimal solutions to its component problems treated independently of each other.

Now I am not denying the existence of simple situations which can be improved by extracting one problem from them and solving it. After all, we can make an inoperative automobile work by replacing one defective part. But I deny that *all* problematic situations can be handled in this way or that any of the organizational, institutional, or societal messes which face us today can be so treated with any effectiveness.

Decision makers, particularly those with responsibility for others, must cope with messes. Improved methods of solving problems do not assure improved methods of coping with messes. On the other hand, decomposing messes into independent problems, even ones that are solvable optimally, does assure failure to cope with at least some messes as effectively as possible.

We need a theory and methodology for coping with systems of problems *as systems*, as wholes, as indivisible sets of interdependent elements. These are precisely what methodologists of *planning*, in contrast to methodologists of problem solving, try to provide. Planning is essentially an effort to deal with sets of interrelated problems in a way that takes all their interrelationships into account. We do not have as well developed a methodology of planning as we do of problem solving. We have a great need for one.

Hence, my first appeal to you is that you direct some of your attention to decisions that are parts of richly interactive sets of decisions, and not aim all of it at decisions that are conceptualized to enjoy the splendid isolation with which we have endowed freely falling bodies. Real bodies and real messes neither rise nor fall freely; they do not exist in a vacuum.

To put my plea in other words: please turn some of your attention to what might well be called "mess management."

Now let us move from the fore to the aft of problem solving, from the problem to its so-called solution. Clearly, if problems are abstractions that have no objective reality, then the same must be true for their solutions. But this is not a particularly fruitful way of dealing with them. It is more useful to determine why, even if problems were not abstractions, solutions to them would be.

As I have already observed, a problem is the presence of choice and doubt about it in a situation in which the choice can matter to the decision maker. In such a situation the decision maker controls some variables which affect the outcome; these define the possible choices. But there are also a set of variables which the decision maker does not control but which affect the outcome. These constitute his noncontrollable environment. Using these notions we can identify two conditions that must be satisfied if a problem, once solved, is to stay solved. First, the relevant environmental variables must not change significantly after the solution is implemented. Second, the relevant values of the decision maker and the efficiencies with which he can implement possible choices must not change.

We need not argue about whether these conditions are ever satisfied. It is enough for my purposes here to obtain agreement that they are not satisfied in a significant number of cases involving problems or messes. For example, few would maintain that our economic, ecological, transportation, educational, and a number of other social problems will ever be *finally* solved. Like fashion models they keep reappearing in different costumes and different shows.

There is a further complexity. The more important a problem is, the more complex it tends to be and, hence, the longer it takes to solve. Because of the increased rate of technological and social change so effectively dramatized by Alvin Toffler in his book, *Future Shock*, we can no longer expect either decision makers or their relevant environments to remain unchanged while difficult and important problems are being solved. For example, essential aspects of the energy crisis change daily, particularly the situation in the Mid-East. Race relations are altered dramatically by an unexpected incident while we try to cope with them. In short, many of the problems we try to solve change while we are trying to do so. In such situations we often obtain solutions to problems that no longer pertain.

Because many problems do not remain solved and because many that can be solved change in significant ways while being solved, to pursue their solutions—optimal, satisficing, or any other brand—is to pursue a mirage. It may appear in the distance, but it disappears before we can reach it.

If my analysis is correct, then we need an alternative to problem solving. What alternative is there? It is the design and development of decision-making processes and systems that enable us to *learn* and *adapt* more effectively. To learn is to increase one's efficiency or effectiveness over time under constant conditions. To adapt is to maintain or increase one's efficiency or effectiveness over time under changing conditions.

We can no longer ignore the following truism: in the long run it is better to start with poor initial solutions that improve over time than with good ones that deteriorate over time. We can no longer ignore this tautology because, with accelerating rates of technological and social change, the long run is becoming shorter, and the time required to solve the important problems that face us is getting longer.

Hence, my second plea is that more attention be given to how to improve, or at least maintain, responses to messes over time under changing and unchanging conditions. In the long run, if not the short, this will be more fruitful than increasing our capabilities for finding solutions that are best, at most, at a moment of time.

There is another aspect of problem solving to which I would like to call your attention. Any satisfactory characterization of a problem requires consideration of the values that the decision maker places on the possible outcomes. His relevant values are of two types: *intrinsic* and *extrinsic*. Only extrinsic values have received adequate attention in decision theory and practice.

Something is valued extrinsically if it is sought for what consequences or outcomes it leads to. For example, a car is valued in this sense as a means of transportation and a house as a means of obtaining shelter. Money is probably the best example of something that is extrinsically valued. Ambrose Bierce defined it as "a blessing that is of no advantage to us excepting when we part with it."[1] Those things that we value extrinsically may be said to constitute our instrumental objectives.

Something is valued intrinsically if it is sought for its own sake, as an end-in-itself. For example, one may listen to a symphony, play a game, read a book, or hike through the woods only for the pleasure that doing so brings. Their value is not primarily instrumental. Intrinsically valued things are part of our *style*; they are our *aesthetic* objectives. These lie at the core of our mounting concern with the quality of life.[2]

The intrinsic values of outcomes of a decision can be dealt with in principle, if not in practice, by most of current decision theory. But what about the intrinsic value of the *process* of problem solving, in contrast to that of its product? Problem solving is not only a means to an end; to many it is also an end-in-itself. To those of us in the problem-solving business, process is valued more than the product. There is often more satisfaction derived from the pursuit of a solution than there is in obtaining it. How we go about solving problems or coping with messes, and what kinds of solutions or responses we seek, are determined by consideration of satisfactions to be derived from the pursuit of a solution, not only from catching it.

The intrinsic process-related values of the problem solver are not incorporated into models of his decision-making process. We conceive of the problem solver in mechanistic terms. This is apparent from the fact that we seek decision-making processes that a machine can be programmed to carry out. Such processes may not be suitable for people. A person or a group differs from a machine precisely because he or it considers alternative decision-making processes in terms of their intrinsic values as well as their extrinsic values. Methodology is not just a matter of logic and efficiency; it is also a matter of style.

Anyone who has worked with public administrators or private managers is aware of the fact that they often are more committed to a particular way of pursuing a solution than they are to obtaining the best solution. The route that even the common man takes from an origin to a destination may be influenced more by the scenery on the way than by considerations of time, cost, and other measures of efficiency. Moreover, in some cases each of us picks the destinations that justify the route we want to take. Ends are thus converted into means and means become ends.

---

[1] *The Devil's Dictionary* (Cleveland: The World Publishing Company, 1911).

[2] One thing, event, or state may, of course, have both extrinsic and intrinsic value.

Therefore, my third plea is for study of the aesthetics of decision making as well as its logic, economics, and ethics.

Not only do we ignore the intrinsic values of the decision-making process, but we also ignore those of at least some of the consequences of the outcomes produced by the solutions employed. Because we assume problems are given, solutions are taken to be the end of a problematic episode and hence we treat the transformation problem-to-solution as a quantum, an indivisible and independent unitary event. But a little reflection on our own experience reveals that every solution gives rise to new problems. Were this not the case, science would have long since come to an end, not to mention management. Therefore, solution-to-problem is at least as sensible a unit as problem-to-solution.

*Unsolving* problems—that is, converting solutions into problems—is a major activity of professors, consultants, critics, reviewers, bosses, and parents, to mention but a few. They examine situations that others consider to be under control, problems that are supposed to be solved, and try to find ways of opening them up to further improvement. They try to unsettle the settled. This, it should be noted, has been acknowledged since Plato to be a function of art, an aesthetic function. The eminent American philosopher, E. A. Singer, Jr.,[3] argued that it is art's function to produce dissatisfaction with states no matter how satisfying they may be, to provide visions of how they might be improved, and to give us the courage to pursue the visions it calls forth.

Unsolving problems contributes at least as much to progress as solving them does. Most of us are aware of the fact that the failures of society and its institutions derive more from their failure to face the right problems than from their failure to solve the problems they face.

Decision theory has very little, if anything, to say about unsolving problems. Hence my last plea, like that of the producer of a well-known soft drink, is for more attention to *un*.

There are other aspects of our conception of decision making and problem solving that deserve attention. But I fear that the pill I have given you is already too large to swallow.

[3] *In Search of a Way of Life* (New York: Columbia University Press, 1948), Chapter II.

# Part II: Premodeling

# A. *Understanding the Client*

## 1. How Managers' Minds Work

*James L. McKenney and Peter G. W. Keen*

A common topic in management literature over the past few years has been the difference between managers and management scientists, usually in relation to the argument that their association has not been a productive one. For example, a recent article by C. Jackson Grayson, Jr., compares the situation with C. P. Snow's famous notion of the two cultures of science and humanities:

Editors' Note: Reprinted with permission from *Harvard Business Review*, May-June 1974, pp. 79–90. Copyright © 1974 by the President and Fellows of Harvard College; all rights reserved.

> Managers and management scientists are operating as two separate cultures, each with its own goals, languages, and methods. Effective cooperation—and even communication—between the two is just about minimal.[1]

Perhaps this is an overpessimistic viewpoint, but it is one that is expressed often and by individuals who have substantial experience with the use of analytic methods in management.

Management science techniques have been very successful in such areas of business as logistics planning, resource allocation, financial forecasting, and so forth. It appears that, on the whole, these techniques have found the applications for which they are best suited, and managers make substantial and continued use of them.

However, in other areas of business they have been unable to gain any real foothold. Most obviously, they have had little impact on areas of decision making where the management problems do not lend themselves to explicit formulation, where there are ambiguous or overlapping criteria for action, and where the manager operates through intuition.

The major issue for management science as a discipline now seems to be to get managers in such situations to make use of the formal techniques that can clearly be so helpful to them but have not yet been so in practice. There seem to be two main factors affecting this problem.

One concerns the actual techniques available. Obviously, process chemists use linear programming because it suits the constraints and natures of the problems they deal with.

The primary factor, however, is the differences in approach and behavior between the two cultures. A feature under little control by either manager or scientist is that each has a distinctive style of thinking and problem solving. In its own context, each style is highly effective but not easily communicated to the other. The differences in thinking are neither "good" nor "bad"; they simply exist.

In a way, it is platitudinous to state that managers and scientists are different, but a reason for focusing explicitly on this factor is to examine the argument, maintained by management writers, that to bridge the gap between the two groups each should become a little more like the other. In this view, the differences themselves are the problem, and education is generally recommended as the solution: the manager should be trained in elementary quantitative techniques, and the scientist, in interpersonal and managerial skills.

Yet it is this very differentiation of thinking style that makes each of them successful in his chosen specialization. But the cost of differentiation is the increased difficulty it presents in integration. Therefore, the issue for both manager and scientist is complex: how to communicate with each other; how to complement each other's strengths without sacrificing too much of one's own.

[1]"Management Science and Business Practice," *HBR* (July-August 1973): p. 41.

In this article, we are explicitly concerned with these differences in thinking between the two cultures. We shall offer suggestions as to how the manager and the scientist can best work together in the development and use of analytic models and decision aids.

We suggest that such aids must be designed to amplify the user's problem-solving strategies. Thus it seems that the central factor determining whether a manager will use a model to reach a decision is the extent to which it "fits" his style of thinking. The main body of this paper largely defines what we mean by "fit."

Over the past four years, we have developed and tested a model of cognitive style, drawing on the developmental psychology that has in recent years reinvigorated the whole study of thinking and problem solving.[2] Our main aim has been to better understand the cognitive aspects of the decision-making process.

In the first section of this article, we shall provide a statement of our model in terms applicable to problem solving and decision making in general, rather than just to analytic techniques. Next, we shall discuss the experimental data we have gathered in validating the model. Finally, we shall extend our findings to the implications of cognitive style for implementing formal analytic models.

### Model of Cognitive Style

We view problem solving and decision making in terms of the processes through which individuals organize the information they perceive in their environment, bringing to bear habits and strategies of thinking. Our model is based on the dual premise that consistent modes of thought develop through training and experience and that these modes can be classified along two dimensions, information gathering and information evaluation, as shown in Exhibit I.

*Information gathering* relates to the essentially perceptual processes by which the mind organizes the diffuse verbal and visual stimuli it encounters. The resultant "information" is the outcome of a complex coding that is heavily dependent on mental set, memory capacity, and strategies—often unconscious ones—that serve to ease "cognitive strain." Of necessity, information gathering involves rejecting some of the data encountered, and summarizing and categorizing the rest.

*Preceptive individuals* bring to bear concepts to filter data; they focus on relationships between items and look for deviations from or conformities with their expectations. Their precepts act as cues for both gathering and cataloging the data they find.

---

[2]See Jerome S. Bruner, Jacqueline J. Goodnow, and George A. Austin, *A Study of Thinking* (New York: John Wiley & Sons, 1956).

```
                          Information    Preceptive
                          gathering

Information evaluation
                                         |
Systematic                               |                    Intuitive
                                         |
                                     Receptive
```

*Exhibit I: Model of cognitive style*

*Receptive thinkers* are more sensitive to the stimulus itself. They focus on detail rather than relationships and try to derive the attributes of the information from direct examination of it instead of from fitting it to their precepts.

Each mode of information gathering has its advantages in specific situations; equally, each includes risks of overlooking the potential meaning of data. The preceptive individual too easily ignores relevant detail, while the receptive thinker may fail to shape detail into a coherent whole. In management positions, the former will be most successful in many marketing or planning roles, and the latter in tasks such as auditing.

*Information evaluation* refers to processes commonly classified under problem solving. Individuals differ not only in their method of gathering data but also in their sequence of analysis of that data. These differences are most pronounced in relation to formal planning.

*Systematic individuals* tend to approach a problem by structuring it in terms of some method which, if followed through, leads to a likely solution.

*Intuitive thinkers* usually avoid committing themselves in this way. Their strategy is more one of solution testing and trial-and-error. They are much more willing to jump from one method to another, to discard information, and to be sensitive to cues that they may not be able to identify verbally.

Here again, each mode of information evaluation has advantages and risks. In tasks such as production management, the systematic thinker can develop a method of procedure that utilizes all his experience and economizes on effort. An intuitive thinker often reinvents the wheel each time he deals with a particular problem. However, the intuitive person is better able to approach ill-structured problems where the volume of data, the criteria for solution, or the nature of the problem itself do not allow the use of any predetermined method.

| Production & logistics manager Statistician Financial analyst | Preceptive | Marketing manager Psychologist Historian |
|---|---|---|
| Systematic | | Intuitive |
| Auditor Clinical diagnostician | Receptive | Architect Bond salesman |

*Receptive thinkers tend to—*

Suspend judgment and avoid preconceptions.
Be attentive to detail and to the exact attributes of data.
Insist on a complete examination of a data set before deriving conclusions.

*Preceptive thinkers tend to—*

Look for cues in a data set.
Focus on relationships.
Jump from one section of a data set to another, building a set of explanatory precepts.

Our research supports the concept that particular tasks and roles are more suited to one cognitive style than to another. Exhibit II shows careers that seem to be especially compatible with the skills and predispositions implicit in each of the cognitive modes of style.

## Experimental Results

We have carried out a range of experiments over the past four years aimed at validating the assertions made in the preceding statements.[3] The main effort in the experiments has been to identify and measure cognitive style. In the spring of 1972, a set of 12 standard reference tests for cognitive factors, developed by the Educational Testing Service, was administered

[3]These experiments are described in detail in Peter G. W. Keen, "The Implications of Cognitive Style for Individual Decision Making," unpublished doctoral dissertation, Harvard Business School, 1973.

to 107 MBA students. Each test was specifically chosen to fit one particular mode of style. The results confirmed most of the main characteristics of each style summarized earlier.

INITIAL TESTS. In our first set of experiments, 70% of the sample showed distinct differences in performance level between the systematic and the intuitive tests or between the receptive and the preceptive. This supports our basic contention that individuals tend to have a definite style.

We chose a conservative approach for our tests, classifying a subject as "intuitive," "systematic," and so on, only when the scores on tests requiring, say, an intuitive response were substantially different from those measuring capacity for the other mode of style along the same dimension. The comparisons focused on relative, not absolute, performance. The numeric scores were converted to a 1 to 7 scale, with a "1" indicating that the subject scored in the lowest seventh of the sample and a "7" corresponding to the top seventh.

From our main sample of 107 MBA students, we selected 20 whose test results indicated a distinct cognitive style for a follow-up experiment. This made use of a "cafeteria" set of 16 problems from which the subjects were asked to choose any 5 to answer. In individual sessions, which were tape recorded, the subjects were invited, though not required, to talk aloud as they dealt with each problem. The results pointed to distinct differences in the ways in which individuals of particular styles respond to problems.

As expected, the systematic subjects tended to be very concerned with getting into a problem by defining how to solve it. They were conscious of their planning and often commented on the fact that there were other specific ways of answering the problem.

In contrast, the intuitive subjects tended to jump in, try something, and see where it led them. They generally showed a pattern of rapid solution testing, abandoning lines of exploration that did not seem profitable.

More important, each mode of response was effective in solving different kinds of problems. In one instance, which required the decoding of a ciphered message, the intuitive subjects solved the problem—sometimes in a dazzling fashion—while none of the systematics were able to do so. In this particular case, there seemed to be a pattern among the intuitives: a random testing of ideas, followed by a necessary incubation period in which the implications of these tests were assimilated, and then a sudden jump to the answer.

There were often unexplained shifts in the reasoning of the intuitives, who were also much more likely to answer the problems orally. The latter tendency provided some confirmation for the idea that intuitive individuals use their own talking aloud to cue their activities and to alert themselves to possible lines of analysis.

There were distinct differences in the problems chosen by each of the groups, and their ratings of which problems they enjoyed most were remarkably consistent. The systematics preferred program-type problems, while the intuitives liked open-ended ones, especially those that required ingenuity or opinion.

The overall results of the initial experiments provided definite evidence to support both our model of cognitive style and the classification methods we developed through the main-sample test scores. The verbal answers in particular highlighted the degree to which these subjects consistently and distinctively respond to problems. There seems little doubt that, in these extreme cases at least, the individual maps himself onto the problem, rather than matching his behavior to the constraints and demands of the particular task.

SECONDARY SAMPLING. In another set of tests, again using the main sample of 107 subjects, we examined the relationship between cognitive style and personality. We did this through comparisons of our test results with the Myers-Briggs scales used to classify individuals in relation to Jungian theories of psychological type.[4]

The most striking result of our experiment was that, while the scores on the Myers-Briggs scales showed virtually no correlation with absolute performance on our tests, there was a relationship between cognitive style and those scales. In particular, the systematic subjects were very likely to be of the "thinking" type and the intuitives much more likely to be at the other end of the scale, "feeling." R. O. Mason and I. I. Mitroff provide a useful summary of the difference between the thinking-feeling types:

> A Thinking individual is the type who relies primarily on cognitive processes. His evaluations tend to run along the lines of abstract true/false judgments and are based on formal systems of reasoning. A preference for Feeling, on the other hand, implies the type of individual who relies primarily on affective processes. His evaluations tend to run along personalistic lines of good/bad, pleasant/unpleasant, and like/dislike. Thinking types systematize; feeling types take moral stands and are interested in and concerned with moral judgments.[5]

We found a more modest relationship between systematic style and "introversion" and, similarly, between intuitive style and "extroversion." Thus our findings mesh well with Mason and Mitroff's predictions (they did not report any experimental data) about psychological type and information systems.

FINAL STUDY. A year after the first two sets of experiments, we examined the relationship between style and career choice, using a sample of 82 MBA

---

[4]See Isabel Briggs Myers and Katharine C. Briggs, "The Myers-Briggs Type Indicator," Educational Testing Service, New Jersey, 1957.

[5]"A Program for Research on Management Information Systems," *Management Science*, January 1973, p. 475.

students. The results showed consistent differentiations between systematic and intuitive subjects. We compared the career preferences of the two groups and also looked at the test scores of those individuals who showed strong preference for particular careers.

In this experiment, the systematic students were attracted to administrative careers, to the military, and to occupations involving production, planning, control, and supervision. The intuitive group's choices centered around the more open-ended business functions; they preferred careers in psychology, advertising, library science, teaching, and the arts.

The overall result of the three sets of student experiments supports the validity of our conceptual model as a useful and insightful framework for examining the role of cognitive processes in decision making. More important, now that we have established such proof, we plan to extend our research to the study of business managers and especially to model builders and model users.

## Analytic Models

One of our major conjectures, which partly underlay the whole development of our model, has been that computer systems in general are designed by systematic individuals for systematic users. Although management science has lost its early tones of missionary zeal, of bringing "right" thinking to the ignorant, the implementation of analytic techniques not unreasonably reflects the scientist's own distinctive approach to problem solving.

Model building, from the viewpoint of the management scientist, involves making the causal relationships in a particular situation explicit and articulating the problem until he gets a reasonably predictive model; he will then generally refine that model. He has a faith in his own plan and process, and his specialized style of thinking enables him to literally build a model, shaping ideas and concepts into a methodological whole, and above all articulate relationships that the manager may understand but may not be able to make explicit.

The management scientist's skill is indeed a specialized one; the powerful organizing and systematizing capacity he brings to model building is his special contribution. But, obviously, that can be a vice rather than a virtue in specific situations. What Donald F. Heany calls the "have technique, will travel"[6] banner really amounts to the rigorously systematic individual's preference for a methodical approach to all problems in all contexts.

Fortunately, there are many systematic managers. Our assumption is that most general managers who use management science techniques

[6]See "Is TIMS Talking to Itself?" *Management Science*, December 1965, p. B-156.

are likely to be systematic in style. The techniques match their own innate approach to problems, and they gravitate to occupations that are suited to their style.

For example, since inventory control is a task that can be systematized, it will attract systematic managers, and it will therefore be an area in which management science techniques will find fruitful ground.

However, there are just as many management positions not filled by systematic thinkers. For example, advertising, which is not so easily systematized, will attract intuitive people. If management scientists want their techniques used in these more loosely structured business areas, they must try both to make their models less awesome to the intuitive managers they will be working with and to support the managers in their decision-making processes.

This requires understanding the intuitive approach to problem solving in general and developing models which will amplify and complement that approach.

CLASSES OF PROBLEMS. We have found it useful to categorize tasks—and problems in general—in terms of the problem solver's assessment of his ability to first recognize and then act on relevant information.[7] This process provides four basic classes of problems, as in Exhibit III.

The classes are easily illustrated. If, for example, a manager encounters a problem of inventory control in which he feels that he knows both what data are relevant and what mental operations and analysis are required to deal with that data, the problem is one of planning (Type 1 in Exhibit III). His whole effort then involves merely arranging the data into a form which can be used as input to a defined sequence of evaluation.

*Exhibit III: Classification of tasks and problems*

| | | Information acquisition, perceptual process | |
| | | Known | Unknown |
| --- | --- | --- | --- |
| Information manipulation, conceptual process | Known | Planning, Type 1 | Intelligence-search, Type 2 |
| | Unknown | Invention, Type 3 | Research, Type 4 |

[7]See James L. McKenney, "A Taxonomy of Problem Solving," working paper, Harvard Business School, 1973.

Another class of problem (Type 2) exists when the required operations and methods are known, but the data involved are not. Price forecasting in complex markets is an example of this situation. Before a forecast can be made, a mass of data on economic, price, and market variables must be organized and sifted. Once this has been done, the forecasting procedure is simple.

A very different state of affairs exists when the individual understands the data but does not know how to manipulate them. Many production-scheduling problems fall into this class, invention (Type 3). The relevant data are known and the problem consists of finding a way to achieve the desired end.

The fourth class of problem exists when both information and operations are unknown. In this situation, there is a conscious search for cues and a generation of explanatory concepts, together with the development of a method for manipulating the data thus organized. The development of new products is a typical research problem.

SPECIALIZED STYLES. Many management-science projects start as research. For example, modeling a complex environment such as the housing market in order to make industry or demand forecasts generally requires a complicated first step in which two areas of the problem are worked on in parallel: (1) the generation of concepts to "explain" reality and identify the most relevant variables, and (2) the definition of the outputs, aims, and implementation of the model.

*Systematic individual.* In our cafeteria experiment, the one problem rated most enjoyable by well over half the systematic group was a basic planning task. The systematic management scientist can often take a research problem and shift it to one of planning. The methodological formalization he provides helps translate unknown states of perception and conception into known ones.

However, there is sometimes the danger that he will force the translation; he may insist on some objective function that does not really fit the situation, partly because his preference for planning leaves him unwilling to accept "unknown" states. He needs to make the implicit explicit.

*Intuitive manager.* Just as the systematic management scientist's specialized style of thinking provides very definite strengths in specialized tasks, so too does the intuitive manager's. It is important to again stress that the intuitive mode is not sloppy or loose; it seems to have an underlying discipline at least as coherent as the systematic mode, but is less apparent because it is largely unverbalized.

There are many situations where the volume of information, the lack of structure in the task, and the uncertainty of the environment defy planning and programming. In such situations the intuitive manager's style can be highly effective.

For example, there is no way for any manager to systematically forecast consumer tastes for furniture styles. He can, however, build a set of cues and flexible premises that may alert him to shifts in taste. He may also use the rapid scanning and testing (the main characteristic of the intuitive) for a sense of fit among disparate items of information. More important, he need never make his concepts and methods explicit.

Unlike the model builder, the intuitive manager can act without making any conscious articulation of his premises. An amusing instance of this fact occurred in many of the early efforts to use process-control computers in paper making. The computer experts "knew" that paper makers knew how to make paper; the experts' only problem was articulating the decision processes that the paper makers used, which turned out to depend mainly upon the operators' "tasting the broth" and controlling the paper flow.

For a long time, this well-established and highly effective human decision process defied conversion into formal and explicit terms. The operators were not too helpful. They "knew" what worked; they had built up out of their experience a clear but not conscious sense of the process, but this sense often varied with the individual. Thus, when a shift changed, the new crew chief, for example, might reset the valves and modify the whole operation, asserting that the changes were needed because of the time of day. There was no articulated set of concepts or methods by which this assertion could even be tested.

The decision makers here—and they merit the term, since controlling the paper-making process is a constant series of evaluations, assessments, and actions—were able to act efficiently even though they could not articulate their own procedures. This lack of articulation became a problem only when it was necessary for the computer experts to build a model of that process.

APPROACH DIFFERENCES. Systematic and intuitive individuals often treat the same project as two entirely different problems. The systematic management scientist may try to structure the problem to reduce the unknowns and to define very explicitly all the constraints in the situation. He aims at a model that is complete and has predictive power, which he can then improve and refine. That, essentially, is how he regards problem solving.

However, consciously or not, the intuitive manager is most concerned with using the model to give him a better sense of the problem. He focuses on and enjoys playing with the unknowns until he gets a feeling for the necessary steps for completion. Then he is ready to delegate the process of dealing with the problem to some individual in his organization who can systematically handle it in a more routine fashion.

The intuitive manager may also approach a task for which a model is to be built not with a need to understand the analytic process, but with a desire to discover what he can trust in order to make useful predictions. This can be of value to the systematic scientist, in that, if he can build a model which "works," the manager may well be ready to use it even though he does not understand it.

The central issue, however, is the validation of the model. The scientist validates his model formally and methodologically; he can test it in relation to known inputs and outputs. In general, he will have faith in his plan and in his own systematic process. The manager will validate the model experientially and test it against some of his own concepts and expectations. He places much less faith in external "authority."

## Recommendations for Action

If our line of argument is valid, it is clear that the solution to the difficulties intuitive managers and systematic management scientists have in working together will not be obtained by trying to blur the differences. The intuitive manager may learn what network optimization is, but that is unlikely to make him think in the same systematic mode as the management scientist, who, in turn, is unlikely to develop intuitive responses through any form of education.

(This is not to assert that cognitive style is fixed, but to reinforce the point that individuals with very distinctive styles in specialized areas of activity have strengths that are directly related to their styles. It seems unlikely that the cognitive specialist will change easily—or that he should do so in any case.)

The real solution seems to lie in two areas: (1) in defining the model's role within the larger decision-making process of the particular situation, and (2) in determining how to validate the model.

From this, the manager and scientist together can better control both the process of building the model structure and their mutual expectations and actions. At the root of both these areas of concern is the whole question of trust and communication, less in the interpersonal than in the cognitive sense.

ROLE DEFINITION. The management scientist's role can be one of either product or service. It is important that he decide which it is in a particular situation.

On the one hand, if his model will mainly help clarify a manager's sense of the issues and options, then there is no point in the scientist's trying to provide a meticulous and complex simulation. The manager does not intend to use the model as the basis for any decision. In fact, the model may simply help him decide what the problem is and can then be thrown away.

On the other hand, the manager may need a product rather than a service; for example, a financial forecasting model, once validated, may be used by a manager as the main basis for ongoing decisions.

The degree and direction of the scientist's efforts will be very different, depending on how he perceives the manager's needs in the situation. The scientist can only identify those needs by asking questions: How does this manager approach problems? How does he define his problem, given the four different classifications in Exhibit III? Does he want the model to further his own learning or to help him make a specific decision?

The answer to each question has distinct consequences. For example, if the manager's response to problems is systematic, the model should explicitly reflect this fact. The scientist should explain to him the underlying assumptions as to method; the two can afford to invest substantial time and discussion on how to deal with the problem. Here, the manager is essentially looking for a technique and the scientist is the expert, with a catalog of methods.

However, if the manager is intuitive in style, the scientist should recognize that the model must allow the manager to range over alternatives and test solutions in the fashion that fits his natural mode of problem solving.

In this context, J. W. Botkin has used the paradigm of cognitive style in designing an interactive computer system for intuitive subjects.[8] He has identified five necessary features for such a model:

1. The user should have the ability to create an arbitrary order of processing; the system should not impose a "logical" or step-by-step sequence on him. In Botkin's words, "This lack of set sequence allows the intuitive user to follow his instinct for developing his ill-defined information plan directly from environmental cues."
2. The user should be able to define, explore, and play out "scenarios" that may either generate cues or test solutions.
3. The user should be able to shift between levels of detail and generality.
4. The user should have some control over the forms of output and should be able to choose visual, verbal and numeric displays at varying levels of detail.
5. The user should be able to extend his programming, providing input in an irregular and unspecific form (i.e., he should be able to provide commands such as, "Repeat the last step, increasing X by 10%").

Botkin's experiment showed fairly clearly that intuitive and systematic subjects used his model in greatly differing ways. The differences corresponded on the whole to those found in our cafeteria experiment. The intuitive group seemed to learn from the system and to enjoy using it as much as the systematic group.

[8]"An Intuitive Computer System: A Cognitive Approach to the Management Learning Process," unpublished doctoral dissertation, Harvard Business School, 1973.

Even though Botkin's model was a special case, his results suggest that an effort on the part of the model builder to consider how the manager will use the model—in terms of process rather than output—will provide large dividends.

Here again, there is a distinction between service and product. Where the manager is most concerned with the recommendations he can derive from the model, the sort of cognitive amplifiers Botkin provides are unnecessary. However, where the manager wants the model to help him clarify his own understanding of the situation, it may well be essential to build them into the formal structure of the model.

Thus the management scientist needs to consider what a "good" model is. For himself, goodness is largely a quality of predictive power and technical elegance. For the manager, it is more a concern of compatibility and comfort—that is, the fit between how he approaches the problem and how the model allows him to do so.

MODEL VALIDATION. Perhaps even more important than either recognizing the relevance of the user's own problem-solving process or determining how that person will use the model is the whole question of trust. Often, the manager does not get involved in the model itself; he simply asks for the outputs. He may well wish to validate the model by testing out some scenarios for which he has some expectations of the outcome.

However, John S. Hammond suggests that the model builder should recognize that in a large and complex model the user will have neither the desire nor the ability to understand its mechanics. The designer must, therefore, provide the user with some other way of testing out—of building trust in—the model. Hammond recommends, therefore, that the management scientist should aim—

> . . . to get something simple and useful up and running as soon as possible. By skillfully manipulating the resultant model, the management scientist should be able to obtain results that will give great insights about the problem, its nature, and its alternatives to the manager. These insights should cue the mind of the manager and cause him to perceive the problems and alternatives differently, which will in turn affect the priorities and direction of the management science effort. . . .

> Thus the management scientist, too, will learn about the nature of the problem and also about the nature of the manager's perception of it.[9]

This recommendation seems particularly relevant in cases where the manager's cognitive style is highly intuitive. For relatively little effort and minimal commitment to a particular definition and design, the man-

[9]"The Roles of the Manager and Analyst in Successful Implementation," paper presented to the XX International Meeting of the Institute of Management Sciences, Tel Aviv, Israel, 1973.

ager can obtain the initial exploration and trial testing that may enable him to articulate his assessments of the problem—or, better, that may enable the scientist to deduce them for him.

Our recommendations are fairly modest. Essentially, they argue that if both manager and scientist alike will look at the process instead of the output the techniques will look after themselves. It seems of central importance for the manager and scientist to recognize that each has a distinctive style of problem solving, and that each should accept the other's difference.

If the management scientist can anticipate the fact that the manager may not use in his decision-making process the conscious planning that is so natural for the scientist himself, he will be less likely to assume that the manager's reluctantly given statement of what the problem is has any permanent force. The intuitive manager can recognize a good plan, if he can validate it at some point on his own terms; the scientist's responsibility is to provide the plan and also the validation.

The manager's responsibility is to make very clear, first to himself and then to the scientist, what he wants the model to do and to be. If he asks for an optimization program for a facilities planning project, he should decide well in advance what he will do with the results. If he knows that he will not make his decision on the basis of the model's output, he should make sure that the design process and the model structure allow him to use the model to amplify his own thinking.

The intuitive manager is very happy to relinquish the mechanics of formal analytic techniques to the expert, but only after he has developed confidence and trust in that expert. It is in this sense that the common recommendation of educating the manager in quantitative skills seems so inadequate. The intuitive manager will learn to make use of these skills supplied by others; but this learning is internal, experiential, and informal.

More than anything, the manager needs to learn how to tell a good model from a bad one. For him, a good model is one that he can, by testing his own scenarios, make sense of. However sloppy this may seem to the systematic scientist, his model will be used only if it allows the manager to make such tests or if the process of designing it has done so on a more ongoing basis.


### Concluding Note

People in general tend to assume that there is some "right" way of solving problems. Formal logic, for example, is regarded as a correct approach to thinking, but thinking is always a compromise between the demands of comprehensiveness, speed, and accuracy. There is no best way of thinking. If the manager and the management scientist can recognize first that each has a different cognitive style, and thus a different way of solving the same problem, then their dialogue seems more likely to bear fruit.

Our model of cognitive style is not necessarily either complete or precise. We suggest, however, that it does provide a useful way of focusing on the implementation of analytic models for decision making and of developing strategies of action that are much more likely to succeed than those based on concepts of technique, education, and salesmanship.

# 2. MANAGERIAL WORK:
# ANALYSIS FROM OBSERVATION

*Henry Mintzberg*

What do managers do? Ask this question and you will likely be told that managers plan, organize, coordinate, and control. Since Henri Fayol [9] first proposed these words in 1916, they have dominated the vocabulary of management. (See, for example, [8], [12], [17].) How valuable are they in describing managerial work? Consider one morning's work of the president of a large organization:

> As he enters his office at 8:23, the manager's secretary motions for him to pick up the telephone. "Jerry, there was a bad fire in the plant last night, about $30,000 damage. We should be back in operation by Wednesday. Thought you should know."
>
> At 8:45, a Mr. Jamison is ushered into the manager's office. They discuss Mr. Jamison's retirement plans and his cottage in New Hampshire. Then the manager presents a plaque to him commemorating his thirty-two years with the organization.
>
> Mail processing follows: An innocent-looking letter, signed by a Detroit lawyer, reads: "A group of us in Detroit has decided not to buy any of your products because you used that anti-flag, anti-American pinko, Bill Lindell, upon your Thursday night TV show." The manager dictates a restrained reply.
>
> The 10:00 meeting is scheduled by a professional staffer. He claims that his superior, a high-ranking vice-president of the organization, mistreats his staff, and that if the man is not fired, they will all walk out. As soon as the meeting ends, the manager rearranges his schedule to investigate the claim and to react to this crisis.

Which of these activities may be called planning, and which may be called

Editors' Note: Reprinted with permission from *Management Science*, October 1971, pp. B97–B110, published by The Institute of Management Sciences.

organizing, coordinating, and controlling? Indeed, what do words such as "coordinating" and "planning" mean in the context of real activity? In fact, these four words do not describe the actual work of managers at all; they describe certain vague objectives of managerial work. " . . . they are just ways of indicating what we need to explain" [1, p. 537].

Other approaches to the study of managerial work have developed, one dealing with managerial decision-making and policy-making processes, another with the manager's interpersonal activities. (See, for example, [2] and [10].) And some empirical researchers using the "diary" method, have studied, what might be called, managerial "media"—by what means, with whom, how long, and where managers spend their time.[1] But in no part of this literature is the actual content of managerial work systematically and meaningfully described.[2] Thus, the question posed at the start— what do managers do?—remains essentially unanswered in the literature of management.

This is indeed an odd situation. We claim to teach management in schools of both business and public administration; we undertake major research programs in management; we find a growing segment of the management science community concerned with the problems of senior management. Most of these people—the planners, information and control theorists, systems analysts, etc.—are attempting to analyze and change working habits that they themselves do not understand. Thus, at a conference called at M.I.T. to assess the impact of the computer on the manager, and attended by a number of America's foremost management scientists, a participant found it necessary to comment after lengthy discussion [20, p. 198]:

> I'd like to return to an earlier point. It seems to me that until we get into the question of what the top manager does or what the functions are that define the top management job, we're not going to get out of the kind of difficulty that keeps cropping up. What I'm really doing is leading up to my earlier question which no one really answered. And that is: Is it possible to arrive at a specification of what constitutes the job of a top manager?

His question was not answered.

[1]Carlson [6] carried out the classic study just after World War II. He asked nine Swedish managing directors to record on diary pads details of each activity in which they engaged. His method was used by a group of other researchers, many of them working in the U.K. (See [4], [5], [15], [25].)

[2]One major project, involving numerous publications, took place at Ohio State University and spanned three decades. Some of the vocabulary used followed Fayol. The results have generated little interest in this area. (See, for example, [13].)

In late 1966, I began research on this question, seeking to replace Fayol's words by a set that would more accurately describe what managers do. In essence, I sought to develop by the process of induction a statement of managerial work that would have empirical validity. Using a method called "structured observation," I observed for one-week periods the chief executives of five medium to large organizations (a consulting firm, a school system, a technology firm, a consumer goods manufacturer, and a hospital).

Structured as well as unstructured (i.e., anecdotal) data were collected in three "records." In the *chronology record*, activity patterns throughout the working day were recorded. In the *mail record*, for each 890 pieces of mail processed during the five weeks, were recorded its purpose, format and sender, the attention it received, and the action it elicited. And, recorded in the *contact record*, for each 368 verbal interactions, were the purpose, the medium (telephone call, scheduled or unscheduled meeting, tour), the participants, the form of initiation, and the location. It should be noted that all categorizing was done during and after observation so as to ensure that the categories reflected only the work under observation. [19] contains a fuller description of this methodology and a tabulation of the results of the study.

Two sets of conclusions are presented below. The first deals with certain characteristics of managerial work, as they appeared from analysis of the numerical data (e.g., How much time is spent with peers? What is the average duration of meetings? What proportion of contacts are initiated by the manager himself?). The second describes the basic content of managerial work in terms of ten roles. This description derives from an analysis of the data on the recorded *purpose* of each contact and piece of mail.

The liberty is taken of referring to these findings as descriptive of managerial, as opposed to chief executive, work. This is done because many of the findings are supported by studies of other types of managers. Specifically, most of the conclusions on work characteristics are to be found in the combined results of a group of studies of foremen [11], [16], middle managers [4], [5], [15], [25], and chief executives [6]. And although there is little useful material on managerial roles, three studies do provide some evidence of the applicability of the role set. Most important, Sayles' empirical study of production managers [24] suggests that at least five of the ten roles are performed at the lower end of the managerial hierarchy. And some further evidence is provided by comments in Whyte's study of leadership in a street gang [26] and Neustadt's study of three U.S. presidents [21]. (Reference is made to these findings where appropriate.) Thus, although most of the illustrations are drawn from my study of chief executives, there is some justification in asking the reader to consider when he sees the terms "manager" and his "organization" not only "presidents" and their "companies," but also "foremen" and their "shops," "directors" and their "branches," "vice-presidents" and their "divisions." The term *manager* shall be used with reference to all those people in charge of formal organizations or their subunits.

## Some Characteristics of Managerial Work

Six sets of characteristics of managerial work derive from analysis of the data of this study. Each has a significant bearing on the manager's ability to administer a complex organization.

CHARACTERISTIC 1. THE MANAGER PERFORMS A GREAT QUANTITY OF WORK AT AN UN-RELENTING PACE. Despite a semblance of normal working hours, in truth managerial work appears to be very taxing. The five men in this study processed an average of thirty-six pieces of mail each day, participated in eight meetings (half of which were scheduled), engaged in five telephone calls, and took one tour. In his study of foremen, Guest [11] found that the number of activities per day averaged 583, with no real break in the pace.

Free time appears to be very rare. If by chance a manager has caught up with the mail, satisfied the callers, dealt with all the disturbances, and avoided scheduled meetings, a subordinate will likely show up to usurp the available time. It seems that the manager cannot expect to have much time for leisurely reflection during office hours. During "off" hours, our chief executives spent much time on work-related reading. High-level managers appear to be able to escape neither from an environment which recognizes the power and status of their positions nor from their own minds which have been trained to search continually for new information.

CHARACTERISTIC 2. MANAGERIAL ACTIVITY IS CHARACTERIZED BY VARIETY, FRAGMEN—TATION, AND BREVITY. There seems to be no pattern to managerial activity. Rather, variety and fragmentation appear to be characteristic, as successive activities deal with issues that differ greatly both in type and in content. In effect the manager must be prepared to shift moods quickly and frequently.

A typical chief executive day may begin with a telephone call from a director who asks a favor (a "status request"); then a subordinate calls to tell of a strike at one of the facilities (fast movement of information, termed "instant communication"); this is followed by a relaxed scheduled event at which the manager speaks to a group of visiting dignitaries (ceremony); the manager returns to find a message from a major customer who is demanding the renegotiation of a contract (pressure); and so on. Throughout the day, the managers of our study encountered this great variety of activity.

Most surprisingly, the significant activities were interspersed with the trivial in no particular pattern.

Furthermore, these managerial activities were characterized by their brevity. Half of all the activities studied lasted less than nine minutes and only ten percent exceeded one hour's duration. Guest's foremen averaged 48 seconds per activity, and Carlson [6] stressed that his chief executives were unable to work without frequent interruption.

In my own study of chief executives, I felt that the managers demonstrated a preference for tasks of short duration and encouraged interruption. Perhaps the manager becomes accustomed to variety, or perhaps the flow of "instant communication" cannot be delayed. A more plausible explanation might be that the manager becomes conditioned by his workload. He develops a sensitive appreciation for the opportunity cost of his own time. Also, he is aware of the ever present assortment of obligations associated with his job—accumulations of mail that cannot be delayed, the callers that must be attended to, the meetings that require his participation. In other words, no matter what he is doing, the manager is plagued by what he must do and what he might do. Thus, the manager is forced to treat issues in an abrupt and superficial way.

CHARACTERISTIC 3. MANAGERS PREFER ISSUES THAT ARE CURRENT, SPECIFIC, AND AD HOC. Ad hoc operating reports received more attention than did routine ones; current, uncertain information—gossip, speculation, hearsay—which flows quickly was preferred to historical, certain information; "instant communication" received first consideration; few contacts were held on a routine or "clocked" basis; almost all contacts concerned well-defined issues. The managerial environment is clearly one of stimulus-response. It breeds, not reflective planners, but adaptable information manipulators who prefer the live, concrete situation, men who demonstrate a marked action-orientation.

CHARACTERISTIC 4. THE MANAGER SITS BETWEEN HIS ORGANIZATION AND A NETWORK OF CONTACTS. In virtually every empirical study of managerial time allocation, it was reported that managers spent a surprisingly large amount of time in horizontal or lateral (nonline) communication. It is clear from this study and from that of Sayles [24] that the manager is surrounded by a diverse and complex web of contacts which serves as his self-designed external information system. Included in this web can be clients, associates and suppliers, outside staff experts, peers (managers of related or similar organizations), trade organizations, government officials, independents (those with no relevant organizational affiliation), and directors or superiors. (Among these, directors in this study and superiors in other studies did *not* stand out as particularly active individuals.)

The managers in this study received far more information than they emitted, much of it coming from contacts, and more from subordinates

*Part II: Premodeling*

who acted as filters. Figuratively, the manager appears as the neck of an hourglass, sifting information into his own organization from its environment.

CHARACTERISTIC 5. THE MANAGER DEMONSTRATES A STRONG PREFERENCE FOR THE VERBAL MEDIA. The manager has five media at his command—mail (documented), telephone (purely verbal), unscheduled meeting (informal face-to-face), scheduled meeting (formal face-to-face), and tour (observational). Along with all the other empirical studies of work characteristics, I found a strong predominance of verbal forms of communication.

*Mail.* By all indications, managers dislike the documented form of communication. In this study, they gave cursory attention to such items as operating reports and periodicals. It was estimated that only thirteen percent of the input mail was of specific and immediate use to the managers. Much of the rest dealt with formalities and provided general reference data. The managers studied initiated very little mail, only twenty-five pieces in the five weeks. The rest of the outgoing mail was sent in reaction to mail received—a reply to a request, an acknowledgment, some information forwarded to a part of the organization. The managers appeared to dislike this form of communication, perhaps because the mail is a relatively slow and tedious medium to use.

*Telephone and Unscheduled Meetings.* The less formal means of verbal communication—the telephone, a purely verbal form, and the unscheduled meeting, a face-to-face form—were used frequently (two-thirds of the contacts in the study) but for brief encounters (average duration of six and twelve minutes respectively). They were used primarily to deliver requests and to transmit pressing information to those outsiders and subordinates who had informal relationships with the manager.

*Scheduled Meetings.* These tended to be of long duration, averaging sixty-eight minutes in this study, and absorbing over half the managers' time. Such meetings provided the managers with their main opportunities to interact with large groups and to leave the confines of their own offices. Scheduled meetings were used when the participants were unfamiliar to the manager (e.g., students who request that he speak at a university), when a large quantity of information had to be transmitted (e.g., presentation of a report), when ceremony had to take place, and when complex strategy-making or negotiation had to be undertaken. An important feature of the scheduled meeting was the incidental, but by no means irrelevant, information that flowed at the start and end of such meetings.

*Tours.* Although the walking tour would appear to be a powerful tool for gaining information in an informal way, in this study tours accounted for only three percent of the managers' time.

In general, it can be concluded that the manager uses each medium for particular purposes. Nevertheless, where possible, he appears to gravitate to verbal media since these provide greater flexibility, require less effort, and bring faster response. It should be noted here that the manager does not leave the telephone or the meeting to get back to work. Rather, communication is his work, and these media are his tools. The operating work of the organization—producing a product, doing research, purchasing a part—appears to be undertaken infrequently by the senior manager. The manager's productive output must be measured in terms of information, a great part of which is transmitted verbally.

CHARACTERISTIC 6. DESPITE THE PREPONDERANCE OF OBLIGATIONS, THE MANAGER APPEARS TO BE ABLE TO CONTROL HIS OWN AFFAIRS. Carlson suggested in his study of Swedish chief executives that these men were puppets, with little control over their own affairs. A cursory examination of our data indicates that this is true. Our managers were responsible for the initiation of only thirty-two percent of their verbal contacts and a smaller proportion of their mail. Activities were also classified as to the nature of the managers' participation, and the active ones were outnumbered by the passive ones (e.g., making requests vs. receiving requests). On the surface, the manager is indeed a puppet, answering requests in the mail, returning telephone calls, attending meetings initiated by others, yielding to subordinates' requests for time, reacting to crises.

However, such a view is misleading. There is evidence that the senior manager can exert control over his own affairs in two significant ways: (1) It is he who defines many of his own long-term commitments, by developing appropriate information channels which later feed him information, by initiating projects which later demand his time, by joining committees or outside boards which provide contacts in return for his services, and so on. (2) The manager can exploit situations that appear as obligations. He can lobby at ceremonial speeches; he can impose his values on his organization when his authorization is requested; he can motivate his subordinates whenever he interacts with them; he can use the crisis situation as an opportunity to innovate.

Perhaps these are two points that help distinguish successful and unsuccessful managers. All managers appear to be puppets. Some decide who will pull the strings and how, and they then take advantage of each move that they are forced to make. Others, unable to exploit this high-tension environment, are swallowed up by this most demanding of jobs.


### The Manager's Work Roles

In describing the essential content of managerial work, one should aim to model managerial activity, that is, to describe it as a set of programs. But an undertaking as complex as this must be preceded by the development of a useful typological description of managerial work. In other words, we must first understand the distinct components of managerial work. At the present time we do not.

In this study, 890 pieces of mail and 368 verbal contacts were categorized as to purpose. The incoming mail was found to carry acknowledgments, requests and solicitations of various kinds, reference data, news, analytical reports, reports on events and on operations, advice on various situations, and statements of problems, pressures, and ideas. In reacting to mail, the managers acknowledged some, replied to the requests (e.g., by sending information), and forwarded much to subordinates (usually for their information). Verbal contacts involved a variety of purposes. In 15% of them activities were scheduled, in 6% ceremonial events took place, and a few involved external board work. About 34% involved requests of various kinds, some insignificant, some for information, some for authorization of proposed actions. Another 36% essentially involved the flow of information to and from the manager, while the remainder dealt specifically with issues of strategy and with negotiations. (For details, see [19].)

In this study, each piece of mail and verbal contact categorized in this way was subjected to one question: Why did the manager do this? The answers were collected and grouped and regrouped in various ways (over the course of three years) until a typology emerged that was felt to be satisfactory. While an example, presented below, will partially explain this process to the reader, it must be remembered that (in the words of Bronowski [3, p. 62]): "Every induction is a speculation and it guesses at a unity which the facts present but do not strictly imply."

Consider the following sequence of two episodes: A chief executive attends a meeting of an external board on which he sits. Upon his return to his organization, he immediately goes to the office of a subordinate, tells of a conversation he had with a fellow board member, and concludes with the statement: "It looks like we shall get the contract."

The purposes of these two contacts are clear—to attend an external board meeting, and to give current information (instant communication) to a subordinate. But why did the manager attend the meeting? Indeed, why does he belong to the board? And why did he give this particular information to his subordinate?

Basing analysis on this incident, one can argue as follows: The manager belongs to the board in part so that he can be exposed to special information which is of use to his organization. The subordinate needs the information but has not the status which would give him access to it. The chief executive does. Board memberships bring chief executives in contact with one another for the purpose of trading information.

Two aspects of managerial work emerge from this brief analysis. The manager serves in a "liaison" capacity because of the status of his office, and what he learns here enables him to act as "disseminator" of information into his organization. We refer to these as *roles*—organized sets of behaviors belonging to identifiable offices or positions [23]. Ten roles were chosen to capture all the activities observed during this study.

All activities were found to involve one or more of three basic behaviors—interpersonal contact, the processing of information, and the making of decisions. As a result, our ten roles are divided into three corresponding groups. Three roles—labelled *figurehead*, *leader*, and *liaison*—deal with behavior that is essentially interpersonal in nature. Three others—*nerve center*, *disseminator*, and *spokesman*—deal with information-processing activities performed by the manager. And the remaining four—*entrepreneur*, *disturbance handler*, *resource allocator*, and *negotiator*—cover the decision-making activities of the manager. We describe each of these roles in turn, asking the reader to note that they form a *gestalt*, a unified whole whose parts cannot be considered in isolation.

THE INTERPERSONAL ROLES. Three roles relate to the manager's behavior that focuses on interpersonal contact. These roles derive directly from the authority and status associated with holding managerial office.

*Figurehead.* As legal authority in his organization, the manager is a symbol, obliged to perform a number of duties. He must preside at ceremonial events, sign legal documents, receive visitors, make himself available to many of those who feel, in the words of one of the men studied, "that the only way to get something done is to get to the top." There is evidence that this role applies at other levels as well. Davis [7, pp. 43–44] cites the case of the field sales manager who must deal with those customers who believe that their accounts deserve his attention.

*Leader.* Leadership is the most widely recognized of managerial roles. It describes the manager's relationship with his subordinates—his attempts to motivate them and his development of the milieu in which they work. Leadership actions pervade all activity—in contrast to most roles, it is possible to designate only a few activities as dealing exclusively with leadership (these mostly related to staffing duties). Each time a manager encourages a subordinate, or meddles in his affairs, or replies to one of his requests, he is playing the *leader* role. Subordinates seek out and react to these leadership clues, and, as a result, they impart significant power to the manager.

*Liaison.* As noted earlier, the empirical studies have emphasized the importance of lateral or horizontal communication in the work of managers at all levels. It is clear from our study that this is explained largely in terms of the *liaison* role. The manager establishes his network of contacts essentially to bring information and favors to his organization. As Sayles notes in his study of production supervisors [24, p. 258], "The one enduring objective [of the manager] is the effort to build and maintain a predictable, reciprocating system of relationships. . . ."

Making use of his status, the manager interacts with a variety of peers and other people outside his organization. He provides time, information, and favors in return for the same from others. Foremen deal with staff groups and other foremen; chief executives join boards of directors, and maintain extensive networks of individual relationships. Neustadt notes this behavior in analyzing the work of President Roosevelt [21, p. 150]:

> His personal sources were the product of a sociability and curiosity that reached back to the other Roosevelt's time. He had an enormous acquaintance in various phases of national life and at various levels of government; he also had his wife and her variety of contacts. He extended his acquaintance-ships abroad; in the war years Winston Churchill, among others, became a "personal source." Roosevelt quite deliberately exploited these relationships and mixed them up to widen his own range of information. He changed his sources as his interests changed, but no one who had ever interested him was quite forgotten or immune to sudden use.

THE INFORMATIONAL ROLES.  A second set of managerial activities relate primarily to the processing of information. Together they suggest three significant managerial roles, one describing the manager as a focal point for a certain kind of organizational information, the other two describing relatively simple transmission of this information.

*Nerve Center.*  There is indication, both from this study and from those by Neustadt and Whyte, that the manager serves as the focal point in his organization for the movement of nonroutine information. Homans, who analyzed Whyte's study, draws the following conclusions [26, p. 187]:

> Since interaction flowed toward [the leaders], they were better informed about the problems and desires of group members than were any of the fol-lowers and therefore better able to decide on an appropriate course of action. Since they were in close touch with other gang leaders, they were also better informed than their followers about conditions in Cornerville at large. Moreover, in their positions at the focus of the chains of interaction, they were better able than any follower to pass on to the group decisions that had been reached.

The term *nerve center* is chosen to encompass those many activities in which the manager receives information.

Within his own organization, the manager has legal authority that formally connects him—and only him—to *every* member. Hence, the manager emerges as *nerve center* of internal information. He may not know as much about any one function as the subordinate who specializes in it, but he comes to know more about his total organization than any other member. He is the information generalist. Furthermore, because of the manager's status and its manifestation in the *liaison* role, the manager gains unique access to a variety of knowledgeable outsiders including peers who are themselves *nerve centers* of their own organizations. Hence, the manager emerges as his organization's *nerve center* of external information as well.

As noted earlier, the manager's nerve center information is of a special kind. He appears to find it most important to get his information quickly and informally. As a result, he will not hesitate to bypass formal information channels to get it, and he is prepared to deal with a large amount of gossip, hearsay, and opinion which has not yet become substantiated fact.

*Disseminator.* Much of the manager's information must be transmitted to subordinates. Some of this is of a *factual* nature, received from outside the organization or from other subordinates. And some is of a *value* nature. Here, the manager acts as the mechanism by which organizational influencers (owners, governments, employee groups, the general public, etc., or simply the "boss") make their preferences known to the organization. It is the manager's duty to integrate these value positions, and to express general organizational preferences as a guide to decisions made by subordinates. One of the men studied commented: "One of the principal functions of this position is to integrate the hospital interests with the public interests." Papandreou describes this duty in a paper published in 1952, referring to management as the "peak coordinator" [22].

*Spokesman.* In his *spokesman* role, the manager is obliged to transmit his information to outsiders. He informs influencers and other interested parties about his organization's performance, its policies, and its plans. Furthermore, he is expected to serve outside his organization as an expert in its industry. Hospital administrators are expected to spend some time serving outside as public experts on health, and corporation presidents, perhaps as chamber of commerce executives.

THE DECISIONAL ROLES. The manager's legal authority requires that he assume responsibility for all of his organization's important actions. The *nerve center* role suggests that only he can fully understand complex decisions, particularly those involving difficult value tradeoffs. As a result, the manager emerges as the key figure in the making and interrelating of all significant decisions in his organization, a process that can be referred to as *strategy-making*. Four roles describe the manager's control over the strategy-making system in his organization.

*Entrepreneur.* The *entrepreneur* role describes the manager as initiator and designer of much of the controlled change in his organization. The manager looks for opportunities and potential problems which may cause him to initiate action. Action takes the form of *improvement projects*— the marketing of a new product, the strengthening of a weak department, the purchasing of new equipment, the reorganization of formal structure, and so on.

The manager can involve himself in each improvement project in one of three ways: (1) He may *delegate* all responsibility for its design and approval, implicitly retaining the right to replace that subordinate who takes charge of it. (2) He may delegate the design work to a subordinate, but retain the right to *approve* it before implementation. (3) He may actively *supervise* the design work himself.

Improvement projects exhibit a number of interesting characteristics. They appear to involve a number of subdecisions, consciously sequenced over long periods of time and separated by delays of various kinds. Furthermore, the manager appears to supervise a great many of these at any one time—perhaps fifty to one hundred in the case of chief executives. In fact, in his handling of improvement projects, the manager may be likened to a juggler. At any one point, he maintains a number of balls in the air. Periodically, one comes down, receives a short burst of energy, and goes up again. Meanwhile, an inventory of new balls waits on the sidelines and, at random intervals, old balls are discarded and new ones added. Both Lindblom [2] and Marples [18] touch on these aspects of strategy-making, the former stressing the disjointed and incremental nature of the decisions, and the latter depicting the sequential episodes in terms of a stranded rope made up of fibres of different lengths each of which surfaces periodically.

*Disturbance Handler.* While the *entrepreneur* role focuses on voluntary change, the *disturbance handler* role deals with corrections which the manager is forced to make. We may describe this role as follows: The organization consists basically of specialist operating programs. From time to time, it experiences a stimulus that cannot be handled routinely, either because an operating program has broken down or because the stimulus is new and it is not clear which operating program should handle it. These situations constitute disturbances. As generalist, the manager is obliged to assume responsibility for dealing with the stimulus. Thus, the handling of disturbances is an essential duty of the manager.

There is clear evidence for this role both in our study of chief executives and in Sayles' study of production supervisors [24, p. 162]:

> The achievement of this stability, which is the manager's objective, is a never-to-be-attained ideal. He is like a symphony orchestra conductor, endeavoring to maintain a melodious performance in which contributions of the various instruments are coordinated and sequenced, patterned and paced, while the orchestra members are having various personal difficulties, stage hands are moving music stands, alternating excessive heat and cold are creating audience and instrument problems, and the sponsor of the concert is insisting on irrational changes in the program.

Sayles goes further to point out the very important balance that the manager must maintain between change and stability. To Sayles, the manager seeks "a dynamic type of stability" (p. 162). Most disturbances elicit short-term adjustments which bring back equilibrium; persistent ones require the introduction of long-term structural change.

*Resource Allocator.* The manager maintains ultimate authority over his organization's strategy-making system by controlling the allocation of its resources. By deciding who will get what (and who will do what), the manager directs the course of his organization. He does this in three ways:

1. *In scheduling his own time*, the manager allocates his most precious resource and thereby determines organizational priorities. Issues that receive low priority do not reach the *nerve center* of the organization and are blocked for want of resources.
2. In designing the organizational structure and in carrying out many improvement projects, the manager *programs the work of his subordinates*. In other words, he allocates their time by deciding what will be done and who will do it.
3. Most significantly, the manager maintains control over resource allocation by the requirement that he *authorize all significant decisions* before they are implemented. By retaining this power, the manager ensures that different decisions are interrelated—that conflicts are avoided, that resource constraints are respected, and that decisions complement one another.

Decisions appear to be authorized in one of two ways. Where the costs and benefits of a proposal can be quantified, where it is competing for specified resources with other known proposals, and where it can wait for a certain time of year, approval for a proposal is sought in the context of a formal *budgeting* procedure. But these conditions are most often not met—timing may be crucial, nonmonetary costs may predominate, and so on. In these cases, approval is sought in terms of an *ad hoc request for authorization*. Subordinate and manager meet (perhaps informally) to discuss one proposal alone.

Authorization choices are enormously complex ones for the manager. A myriad of factors must be considered (resource constraints, influencer preferences, consistency with other decisions, feasibility, payoff, timing, subordinate feelings, etc.). But the fact that the manager is authorizing the decision rather than supervising its design suggests that he has little time to give to it. To alleviate this difficulty, it appears that managers use special kinds of *models* and *plans* in their decision-making. These exist only in their minds and are loose, but they serve to guide behavior. Models may answer questions such as, "Does this proposal make sense in terms of the trends that I see in tariff legislation?" or "Will the EDP department be able to get along with marketing on this?" Plans exist in the sense that, on questioning, managers reveal images (in terms of proposed improvement projects) of where they would like their organizations to go: "Well, once I get these foreign operations fully developed, I would like to begin to look into a reorganization," said one subject of this study.

*Negotiator.* The final role describes the manager as participant in negotiation activity. To some students of the management process [8, p. 343], this is not truly part of the job of managing. But such distinctions

*Part II: Premodeling*

are arbitrary. Negotiation is an integral part of managerial work, as this study notes for chief executives and as that of Sayles made very clear for production supervisors [24, p. 131]: "Sophisticated managers place great stress on negotiations as a way of life. They negotiate with groups who are setting standards for their work, who are performing support activity for them, and to whom they wish to 'sell' their services."

The manager must participate in important negotiation sessions because he is his organization's legal authority, its *spokesman* and its *resource allocator*. Negotiation is resource trading in real time. If the resource commitments are to be large, the legal authority must be present.

These ten roles suggest that the manager of an organization bears a great burden of responsibility. He must oversee his organization's status system; he must serve as a crucial informational link between it and its environment; he must interpret and reflect its basic values; he must maintain the stability of its operations; and he must adapt it in a controlled and balanced way to a changing environment.

## Management as a Profession and as a Science

Is management a profession? To the extent that different managers perform one set of basic roles, management satisfies one criterion for becoming a profession. But a profession must require, in the words of the Random House Dictionary, "knowledge of some department of learning or science." Which of the ten roles now requires specialized learning? Indeed, what school of business or public administration teaches its students how to disseminate information, allocate resources, perform as figurehead, make contacts, or handle disturbances? We simply know very little about teaching these things. The reason is that we have never tried to document and describe in a meaningful way the procedures (or programs) that managers use.

The evidence of this research suggests that there is as yet no science in managerial work—that managers do not work according to procedures that have been prescribed by scientific analysis. Indeed, except for his use of the telephone, the airplane, and the dictating machine, it would appear that the manager of today is indistinguishable from his predecessors. He may seek different information, but he gets much of it in the same way— from word-of-mouth. He may make decisions dealing with modern technology but he uses the same intuitive (that is, nonexplicit) procedures in making them. Even the computer, which has had such a great impact on other kinds of organizational work, has apparently done little to alter the working methods of the general manager.

How do we develop a scientific base to understand the work of the manager? The description of roles is a first and necessary step. But tighter forms of research are necessary. Specifically, we must attempt to model managerial work—to describe it as a system of programs. First, it will be necessary to decide what programs managers actually use. Among a great number of programs in the manager's repertoire, we might expect to find a time-scheduling program, an information-disseminating program, and a disturbance-handling program. Then, researchers will have to devote a considerable amount of effort to studying and accurately describing the content of each of these programs—the information and heuristics used. Finally, it will be necessary to describe the interrelationships among all of these programs so that they may be combined into an integrated descriptive model of managerial work.

When the management scientist begins to understand the programs that managers use, he can begin to design meaningful systems and provide help for the manager. He may ask: Which managerial activities can be fully reprogrammed (i.e., automated)? Which cannot be reprogrammed because they require human responses? Which can be partially reprogrammed to operate in a man-machine system? Perhaps scheduling, information collecting, and resource allocating activities lend themselves to varying degrees of reprogramming. Management will emerge as a science to the extent that such efforts are successful.

### Improving the Manager's Effectiveness

Fayol's fifty year old description of managerial work is no longer of use to us. And we shall not disentangle the complexity of managerial work if we insist on viewing the manager simply as a decision-maker or simply as a motivator of subordinates. In fact, we are unlikely to overestimate the complexity of the manager's work, and we shall make little headway if we take overly simple or narrow points of view in our research.

A major problem faces today's manager. Despite the growing size of modern organizations and the growing complexity of their problems (particularly those in the public sector), the manager can expect little help. He must design his own information system, and he must take full charge of his organization's strategy-making system. Furthermore, the manager faces what might be called the *dilemma of delegation*. He has unique access to important information but he lacks a formal means of disseminating it. As much of it is verbal, he cannot spread it around in an efficient manner. How can he delegate a task with confidence when he has neither the time nor the means to send the necessary information along with it?

Thus, the manager is usually forced to carry a great burden of responsibility in his organization. As organizations become increasingly large and complex, this burden increases. Unfortunately, the man cannot significantly increase his available time or significantly improve his abilities to manage. Hence, in the large, complex bureaucracy, the top manager's time assumes an enormous opportunity cost and he faces the real danger of becoming a major obstruction in the flow of decisions and information.

Because of this, as we have seen, managerial work assumes a number of distinctive characteristics. The quantity of work is great; the pace is unrelenting; there is great variety, fragmentation, and brevity in the work activities; the manager must concentrate on issues that are current, specific, and ad hoc, and to do so, he finds that he must rely on verbal forms of communications. Yet it is on this man that the burden lies for designing , and operating strategy-making and information processing systems that are to solve his organization's (and society's) problems.

The manager can do something to alleviate these problems. He can learn more about his own roles in his organization, and he can use this information to schedule his time in a more efficient manner. He can recognize that only he has much of the information needed by his organization. Then, he can seek to find better means of disseminating it into the organization. Finally, he can turn to the skills of his management scientists to help reduce his workload and to improve his ability to make decisions.

The management scientist can learn to help the manager to the extent he can develop an understanding of the manager's work and the manager's information. To date, strategic planners, operations researchers, and information system designers have provided little help for the senior manager. They simply have had no framework available by which to understand the work of the men who employed them, and they have had poor access to the information which has never been documented. It is folly to believe that a man with poor access to the organization's true *nerve center* can design a formal management information system. Similarly, how can the long-range planner, a man usually uninformed about many of the *current* events that take place in and around his organization, design meaningful strategic plans? For good reason, the literature documents many manager complaints of naïve planning and many planner complaints of disinterested managers. In my view, our lack of understanding of managerial work has been the greatest block to the progress of management science.

The ultimate solution to the problem—to the overburdened manager seeking meaningful help—must derive from research. We must observe, describe, and understand the real work of managing; then and only then shall we significantly improve it.

### REFERENCES

1. Braybrooke, David. "The Mystery of Executive Success Re-examined." *Administrative Science Quarterly*, Vol. 8 (1964): pp. 533–560.
2. ——— and Lindblom, Charles E. *A Strategy of Decision*. New York: Free Press, 1963.
3. Bronowski, J. "The Creative Process." *Scientific American*, Vol 199 (September 1958): pp. 59–65.

4. Burns, Tom. "The Directions of Activity and Communications in a Departmental Executive Group." *Human Relations*, Vol. 7 (1954): pp. 73–97.

5. ———. "Management in Action." *Operational Research Quarterly*, Vol. 8 (1957): pp. 45–60.

6. Carlson, Sune. *Executive Behaviour*. Stockholm: Strömbergs, 1951.

7. Davis, Robert T. *Performance and Development of Field Sales Managers*. Division of Research, Graduate School of Business Administration, Harvard University, Boston, 1957.

8. Drucker, Peter F. *The Practice of Management*. New York: Harper and Row, 1954.

9. Fayol, Henri. *Administration Industrielle et Générale*. Paris: Dunods, 1950 (first published 1916).

10. Gibb, Cecil A. "Leadership." Chapter 31 in *The Handbook of Social Psychology*, Vol. 4, Second edition, edited by Gardner Lindzey and Elliot A. Aronson. Reading, Mass: Addison-Wesley, 1969.

11. Guest, Robert H. "Of Time and the Foreman." *Personnel*, Vol. 32 (1955–56): pp. 478–486.

12. Gulick, Luther H. "Notes on the Theory of Organization." In *Papers on the Science of Administration*, edited by Luther Gulick and Lyndall Urwick. New York: Columbia University Press, 1937.

13. Hemphill, John K. *Dimensions of Executive Positions*. Bureau of Business Research Monograph Number 98. Columbus: The Ohio State University, 1960.

14. Homans, George C. *The Human Group*. New York: Harcourt, Brace, 1950.

15. Horne, J. H. and Lupton, Tom. "The Work Activities of Middle Managers—An Exploratory Study." *The Journal of Management Studies*, Vol. 2 (February 1965): pp. 14–33.

16. Kelly, Joe. "The Study of Executive Behavior by Activity Sampling." *Human Relations*, Vol. 17 (August 1964): pp. 277–287.

17. MacKenzie, R. Alex. "The Management Process in 3D." *Harvard Business Review* (November-December 1969): pp. 80–87.

18. Marples, D. L. "Studies of Managers—A Fresh Start?" *The Journal of Management Studies*, Vol. 4 (October 1967): pp. 282–299.

19. Mintzberg, Henry. "Structured Observation as a Method to Study Managerial Work." *The Journal of Management Studies*, Vol. 7 (February 1970): pp. 87–104.

20. Myers, Charles A. (ed) *The Impact of Computers on Management*. Cambridge, Mass.: The M.I.T. Press, 1967.

21. Neustadt, Richard E. *Presidential Power: The Politics of Leadership*. New York: The New American Library, 1964.

22. Papandreou, Andreas G. "Some Basic Problems in the Theory of the Firm." In *A Survey of Contemporary Economics*, Vol. II, edited by Bernard F. Haley. Homewood, Illinois: Irwin, 1952, pp. 183–219.

23. Sarbin, T. R. and Allen, V. L. "Role Theory." In *The Handbook of Social Psychology*, Vol. I, Second edition, edited by Gardner Lindzey and Elliot A. Aronson. Reading, Mass.: Addison-Wesley, 1968, pp. 488–567.

24. Sayles, Leonard R. *Managerial Behavior: Administration in Complex Enterprises*. New York: McGraw-Hill, 1964.

25. Stewart, Rosemary. *Managers and Their Jobs*. London: Macmillan, 1967.

26. Whyte, William F. *Street Corner Society*, Second edition. Chicago: University of Chicago Press, 1955.

# 3. MANAGERIAL ACCEPTANCE OF SCIENTIFIC RECOMMENDATIONS

## C. West Churchman

Those who have thought and written about management often refer to management "know-how" as an essential ingredient of success. By "know-how" they apparently mean the ability of the manager to understand what is going on in his environment. It is the chief concern of the management scientist to translate these vague stipulations about management knowledge into precise and verifiable assertions about how decisions are made and how decisions ought to be made.

One of the central problems of management science is the understanding of the role of information in decision-making. The reason this problem is so difficult is that we have failed to pay enough attention to the very subtle concept of the *use of information*. The much maligned, classical economic man was supposed to act in accordance with his self-interest, given complete information. But what does "given" mean in this context? What the economist meant was that the information was automatically fed into the rational decision process, and the correct answer was thereby derived. If the manager of a firm can be adequately represented as a computer, this concept of "given" may be adequate for then we merely mean by "given" information the inputs to a computer program.

However, when we consider real managers in their real environments, the concept of "given" is not clear at all. Let us picture a manager busily at work making a number of decisions. Suppose by some lucky chance that sufficient information is "available" for him to make a perfect decision in each case. We need some operational definition of "available," and the one that comes most readily to mind is that information is "available" if it is stored in the form of retrievable symbols in the environment of the manager. More precisely, a piece of information is available to a manager if he can retrieve it at virtually zero cost (e.g., by asking someone, or looking it up, or retrieving it from computer memory). Even this more precise meaning of "available" leaves much to be desired, but the definition will suffice for the purpose of stating the problem of this article, which is: There is sufficient evidence to show that a manager may have perfect information "available" to him and yet not make the correct decision. What is the explanation of this phenomenon? Why don't managers act on the information stored in their environments?

Before proceeding to discuss this problem in depth, something more needs to be said about the concept of a "right choice," i.e., about knowledge of the correct action. A man may choose the right action by accident, so to speak, when in his clumsy way he stumbles upon the correct way to act. Thus, an archer who hits the bull's eye does not necessarily know how to shoot. What makes the expert archer is the ability to adjust his method of controlling the arrow so that, no matter what the motion of his target, within limits he can perform successfully. Hence, knowledge about a decision consists of choosing the correct action even though the conditions change. Knowledge is a sensitivity to changes in one's environment.

## Inventory Control

The point can be illustrated very well by referring to inventory control within industry. Most companies do reasonably well with their inventories during periods of stable demand. This is because the managers responsible for controlling inventory learn from experience that ordering too large or too small quantities is bad policy, and they have also learned to prepare for normal shifts in demand in terms of buffer stocks. But we would not say that the management has knowledge of the control of inventory unless it had developed a method of adjusting to large shifts in demand or in costs.

Hence, when an operations research team comes in and tries to develop models, it often finds that its recommendations do not deviate very far from the current practice of the management. This does not imply, however, that the work of the operations research team has been wasted. On the contrary, once a model is developed, the parameters of the model can be adjusted to take care of variations in the environment, such as the upswing or downswing of demand, the costs of carrying inventory, placing orders, or shortages. Thus, the great advantage of modeling industrial operations is that the manager is then in an excellent position to adjust for changes. In other words, according to the definition of "knowledge" introduced above, the manager is provided with awareness of the right action rather than mere display of the right action.

The point cannot be overemphasized. Often in companies we find that men with years of experience have arrived at methods of managing operations which cannot be matched by analysis. For example, a vice-president of sales of a large company would forecast sales of the company's products based on reports received from the field, economic data, and other types of information, coupled with his own judgment. He seemed to have an un-canny way of coming up with accurate estimates that we could not dupli-cate by any statistical methods known to us. In this case the company could be said to have arrived at the correct action, but again I doubt if we would want to say that the company had *knowledge* of forecasting. If the vice-president were to leave, the environment would be changed and the com-pany would have no obvious way to adapt to the change. Thus, our statisti-cal methods, though perhaps slightly inferior to those of the vice-president under current conditions, constituted something more like knowledge than the vice-president's intuitively based decisions.

## A Matter of Ability

In the discussion above, it is clear that I have been describing knowledge as a matter of ability. It is the ability of a decision-maker to adjust his deci-sions to changes in the situations that confront him. We could go on to describe deeper forms of knowledge. For example, we might want to con-sider the way in which knowledge of decision-making in one area assists decision-making in another area or the way in which knowledge of decision-making can be refined, so that finer and finer distinctions can be made between types of decisions. I think these deliberations would lead us to a consideration of "understanding" as opposed to mere knowledge, because understanding is essentially the process by which the decision-maker knows why his method of decision-making is correct. To know "why" is to go beyond the present situation to a larger world, to understand why the decisions in the present situation are justified by considerations of the larger world. Essentially, understanding represents the highway from knowledge to wisdom; wisdom is the highest form of understanding.

Assuming that enough has been said about knowledge, let us return to the problem stated at the outset. We have pictured a man in an environment where sufficient information is "available" to provide him with knowledge of how to make decisions. Why doesn't knowledge occur?

One ready answer is that the information is too costly to obtain. Indeed, we have hidden in the definition of "available" the very difficult concept of "cost of information," and we could devote many pages to discussing this concept as is done, for example, in the work of Marschak and Radner[1] on the theory of teams. Instead, in order to put the problem of this article into sharp relief, we will assume for the moment that we are talking about a manager who can retrieve information readily at no cost. Why does this manager fail to use the information so readily available to him?

[1]Roy Radner and J. Marschak, "Economic Theory of Teams."

## Use of Information

The obvious answer is that he does not know how to transform the available information into a knowledge of action. In other words, he does not have a program built into his mind that will transform the inputs into correct outputs. Thus, operations researchers have suggested to the manager the wisdom of using personnel who do know how to do just exactly this: They know how to take the information available and calculate a decision system which, in effect, provides the manager with the knowledge of how to behave. We generally refer to this type of activity as analysis. Hence, the suggestion is that the missing gap for many managers is the lack of someone or some device capable of performing the necessary analysis.

Unfortunately, we have overwhelming evidence that available information plus analysis does not lead to knowledge. A management science team can properly analyze a situation and present recommendations to the manager, but no change occurs. The situation is so familiar to those of us who try to practice management science that I hardly need to describe the cases. Some of my graduate students undertook to write to the authors of cases reported in *Operations Research* over the first six years of its publication to determine to what extent the recommendations of the studies had been carried out by management. In no case was there sufficient evidence that the recommendations had been accepted.

At the University of California, Professor Ratoosh and I have been conducting some experiments in which we have been able to establish in controlled situations that analysis plus available information does not lead to knowledge. In our experiments, five subjects run a small firm. The instructions given to the subjects provide complete "available" information about the firm's operations. That is, it is possible so to analyze the information that the managers of our laboratory firm can adopt the right action. Furthermore, by analysis it is possible to generate a model which will provide the managers with a method of making decisions, even though demands and costs and other factors change. In other words, the model can provide the managers with a knowledge of how to act. In some of our groups we have placed a person who has gone through the analysis beforehand. He is then given the task of persuading the rest of the management team. Therefore, in our laboratory we have constructed a situation in which there is available information plus analysis. The result has almost uniformly been one in which knowledge does not occur. The managers do not accept the recommendations and are far from gaining any knowledge from the analysis.[2]

[2]Philburn Ratoosh and C. W. Churchman, "Innovation in Group Behavior," Working Paper No. 10, Center for Research in Management Science, University of California, Berkeley, January 1960; "Report on Further Implementation Experiments," Working Paper No. 26, *loc. cit.*, March 1961.

Of course, one could say that the difficulty is that the available information is in one location (the instructions given to the subjects), the analysis is in a second (in the head of one person), and the decision-making is in a third. One might feel that if all three of these components could be combined into one unit, the problem could be solved.

This suggestion is a reasonable one and brings us back to the original definition of "available" information for the purpose of revising it somewhat. The original definition made "available" a very passive kind of thing and ignored the very important concept of transmittal of information. How is the information to be retrieved? If the channels of retrieval are obscured by linguistic ambiguities and other noises, the information may not be "available," no matter how precisely it is stored.

## Concept of Communication

The concept we seem to require is "communication." Communication is a device for taking several minds and making them act more like one mind.

Thus, many people have suggested that the missing variable in the equation is proper communication, that available information *plus* analysis *plus* communication leads to knowledge. They say that if only operations researchers could learn to talk in a language the managers can understand, there would be no further difficulties in implementing operations research recommendations. Thus articles on the implementation of recommendations speak over and over again about the need for better communication between the scientist and the manager. These articles point to the fact that the scientist talks in a semi-formal language (mathematics) and the manager talks in his own management terms, which are not exactly those of normal discourse. The problem, say these articles, is to make the proper translation.

## Mode of Communication

Of course, to prove the invalidity of the new formula (information + analysis + communication leads to knowledge) is very difficult because there are so many modes of communication. However, in our experiments we have found no adequate mode. We have presented the solution in simple graphical form, in simple arithmetical form, in ordinary discourse, as well as in the form of more complicated mathematical expressions. We can find no evidence that the mode of communication makes any difference. We have presented the solution in pieces and in a total report, and, again, we have found no difference. I am aware of the fact that the sociological literature, and especially the work of Hovland,[3] has dealt at length with the importance of mode of communication with respect to persuasion, but we have not been able to translate these findings into our own work.

Of course, I am not saying that the mode of communication has no effect whatsoever. It is not very difficult, even in our experiments, to prepare messages which are so incomprehensible that they have no effect whatsoever, except to annoy the managers. What I am saying is that the formula will not do. More precisely, the prescription for "better" communication ends up by being no more than a restatement of the problem: to find some set of activities so that with complete information "available," the manager will come to know the correct action. It is the attempt to find such a set of activities that makes the problem very difficult because by now we have exhausted all the obvious possibilities.

The next suggestion is one with which I am sure most managers and scientists are familiar. One must bear in mind the distinction between the personal goals of the manager and the organizational goals. Even if the corporate goals are explicit and clear, the manager's own personal ambitions may be at variance at times with the interests of the corporation. Therefore, if the scientist generates a method of making decisions that best serves the corporate aims, he may encounter resistance because the recommendations do not fit into the manager's personal goals. In other words, it is possible that a manager who really wanted to accomplish the organizational goals would come to know the correct action.

For example, it is a well-known fact that managers feel threatened by modern techniques of analysis. They have reason to believe that analysis, with the help of high-speed computers, may take over their roles. In order to preserve their status, they resist the recommendations that analysis provides. At this point one usually distinguishes between a perceived threat and a real threat. The perceived threat is one that may be incorrect; for example, it may happen that sophisticated analysis strengthens rather than weakens the manager's role. The task of the researcher in this case is one of clarifying the situation for the manager, though how this is to be done is often very obscure. A real threat is one that does in fact threaten the manager's role, making it either obsolete or less important.

## Reaction to Change

A more general way to describe the problem is as follows. When a change is suggested to a manager, he reacts in ways that are typical to his own personality. Part of him will resist the suggestion, and often the resistance is so strong that he will reject the suggestion altogether. Nevertheless, the per-

[3]Carl I. Hovland, Irving L. Janis, and Harold H. Keeley, "Communication and Persuasion," (New Haven: Yale University Press, 1954); Carl I. Hovland, *et al.*, *The Order of Presentation in Persuasion* (New Haven: Yale University Press, 1957).

*Part II: Premodeling*

sons responsible for making the suggestion may learn enough about the manager's personality so that they know what to say to him to break down his resistance. Thus, they recognize that there is a part of the manager's personality that will adjust to change. On the other hand, there may be a part that remains invariant, no matter what the environment. Indeed, psychological literature leads us to believe that most men display invariant characteristics over most of their lives: they rarely change from an extrovert to an introvert, or from a thinking type to a feeling type, for example.

These reflections imply that the missing ingredient in the process of implementation is the understanding of the manager. Any research team that fails to study the manager and his personality may very well fail to bring about a recommended change. Furthermore, any research team that believes it can implement a recommendation by the same process, regardless of who is managing, is simply naive.

Because he often lacks a methodology of understanding people, the researcher may give up any attempt to implement broad changes of policy. Instead, he may be satisfied to work in areas where the status and role of the manager remain invariant no matter what is changed. A manager may not feel threatened if the equipment in his shop is redesigned or if physical sequences of actions are changed. But if someone asks whether his shop should manufacture the items it does, in the quantities it customarily makes, he cannot help but regard this question as one that is directed to his own role. If he is a reflective type, he may enjoy the question; if he is an anxious type, he may not. Even if he enjoys the question, he may believe that a solution arrived at by analysis stifles his imagination. His personality may be such that he must act instinctively and creatively or not act at all.

### Coalitions in Management

Perhaps the most important invariances of personality occur in the formation of coalitions in organizations. These are the so-called political aspects of management in firms. A coalition may arise because the members of the coalition recognize certain common economic advantages. But it is well known that coalitions also come about because of the personalities of their members; some mix of attitude, trait, and opinion creates a loyalty that is hard to dissolve. The loyalty is strengthened by opposition. Thus, various obscure and complicated coalition frameworks occur among managers; they are obscure because no one ever writes down their bylaws and articles of confederation, or ever announces them publicly. Indeed, most managers are not clearly aware of them. For a further discussion of this point, see Cyert and March.[4]

[4]Richard M. Cyert and James G. March, *Behavioral Theory of the Firm* (Englewood Cliffs: Prentice-Hall, Inc., 1963).

These coalitions of managers are like the "invisible colleges" of scientists; see, for example, Derek Price.[5] They are the sources the manager consults; they are the basis of the language he uses; they provide the criteria of what is important and what is unimportant. They are made up of persons, books, journals, and other communication devices in the manager's environment.

Thus, in the context of managerial politics, the researcher is apt to find that his recommendations are viewed from the point of view of their effect on a coalition, and not from the point of view of the whole organization. Since the researcher usually doesn't know who belongs to what coalition, and is far from understanding what holds the coalition together, he cannot determine how to overcome coalition biases. He finds himself in a confusing welter of contradictory reactions of managers.

## A Scarce Commodity

The most significant outputs of the hidden managerial coalition are the importance of issues and the ways in which important issues should be considered. Managers control a very scarce commodity: their own time and attention. Their most conscious problem is one of determining to what they should pay attention. A researcher who claims he can save them a few thousands or millions of dollars may immediately lose their attention, because the managers believe that a new market or a threat to the corporation's existence are far more demanding of their attention than cost savings, especially if the method of analysis is alien to them.

In other words, one aspect of the formula suggested earlier was quite faulty. It may be true that information + analysis ideally leads to knowledge, but analysis takes up a significant portion of the manager's time and energy. One measure of the cost of analysis for him is the distance of the analytic method from his typical way of thinking about problems. His typical way of thinking comes from his coalition. A very striking example of a manager's reaction to "scientism," i.e., alien thinking, is to be found in a recent article of Lilienthal's.[6]

Thus, to discover what a manager thinks is important and how he believes he should think about important issues, one must determine to whom he listens, and to determine to whom he listens one must understand the coalitions to which he belongs. Some of these coalitions are external to the company; they are the other members of the managerial community whom the manager respects. These large coalitions of managers in specific industries account for the managerial styles and fads. If these coalitions come to believe that science, and especially mathematics and computers, are impor-

[5]Derek J. de Solla Price, *Science since Babylon* (New Haven: Yale University Press, 1961).
[6]D. E. Lilienthal, "Skeptical Look at 'Scientific Experts'," *New York Times*, September 29, 1963.

*Part II: Premodeling*

tant, managers will pay attention to scientists. If not, they won't pay attention, no matter how elegant the recommendations the scientists make.

## Problem of Attention

I have purposefully been vague about the meaning of a coalition, in order to emphasize a point. But the definition is really quite simple: A manager's coalition is the group of people who influence what the manager attends to. I do not say that they are the group that influences what he does, because this is too narrow a concept. The manager of a competing firm may hire an operations research group. If this influences another manager to learn about operations research, the first manager belongs to the second's coalition.

There is little doubt that in the experiments we have run at the University of California at Berkeley, the problem is one of attention. The subjects quickly form one or more coalitions, and then become much too busy to want to attend to the recommendations that are made to them, even though these recommendations are correct. The analysis offered may be foreign to the way in which they have taught themselves to think about their task. In some mysterious way, the subjects agree that the way they are organized, "not going into the red," and various other secondary aspects of the task are the most important.

If we are to learn more about the implementation of recommendations, we must learn more about how people decide where to direct their attention. It is for this reason that at System Development Corporation, Herbert Eisenberg, Martin Shubik, and I have started a few very simple experiments on deliberation and its role in decision-making. Deliberation is the process by which the mind in reaching a decision scans various aspects of the problem. In our experiments, we present one subject with alternative points of view to which he may pay attention, and other subjects try to influence him towards one viewpoint or another. We are attempting to learn more about the way in which managers come to pay attention to issues.

This essay is a mystery novel, with the added frustration that the culprit remains unidentified even at the end. Perhaps the advantage of such a devilish novel is that it may suggest a better plot for the next one to be written. With this in mind, let me end by introducing some broad philosophical generalities, not supported by the "available" evidence, but nonetheless helpful in future research.

We started by looking for the ingredients that a research staff would seek to supply in order to bring about a recommended change: available information, analysis, and communication. We argued in the end that none of these ingredients matters at all unless the manager pays attention to the problem, and that paying attention is an obscure process of the managerial mind, little understood by management scientists.

## An Obscure Concept

The obscurity we face in this regard is simply the obscurity of the concept of decision-making itself. We do not yet understand how to describe a human decision. The descriptions usually offered reflect the psychological traits of the describers. A thinking type believes that the mathematical theories of games and of optimization will provide all the concepts necessary to define a decision clearly, as well as a correct decision. He is arrogant enough to label his efforts "decision theory," without any uneasy pang of conscience. The feeling type asserts that a decision is essentially a unique expression of human values, and that the meaning of a decision cannot be captured by generalized mathematical expressions. An intuitive type believes that decisions are insights, quick flashes of understanding how to solve a problem. They frequently assert that the manager leaps to his conclusion without benefit of or even need for analysis. Finally, there are those who assume that the whole business of decision-making is contained in available information: what decision is made depends solely on what facts are known.

## A Manager's World

Philosophy attempts to take one step back from the issues that divide scientists into intellectual camps. All the points of view mentioned above are valid. They amount to saying that decision-making can be conceptualized in many ways. What seems to be common to these ways of describing decisions is the concept of focus.[7] A specific decision is the focus of a mathematical model, a general value structure, of insightful behavior, of masses of data. The focusing that leads to decision-making takes the manager's whole world and displays a subarea where he must seek a solution. Within this subarea the coalitions that influence this behavior lead him to confine his attention to certain aspects. Eventually he is led to one alternative, to *the* choice.

The rational mind of the scientist would like to remove all irrationality from this focusing of attention of the manager. The trouble is that in order to do this, we scientists must understand the world of the manager: not a piece of it, but the whole world. If we only understand a piece of the manager's world, we have no justification for asserting that he should pay attention to the piece that we present to him.

Thus, in order to recommend important changes to a manager, we must understand the process by which this whole world becomes focused on certain issues and aspects of his environment. Any decision is a snapshot of the

---

[7]Thomas A. Cowan, address delivered at the American Association for the Advancement of Science meetings in Denver, December 1961.

universe of the manager. An optimal decision is a snapshot of a rational universe.

# 4. MANAGEMENT MISINFORMATION SYSTEMS

*Russell L. Ackoff*

The growing preoccupation of operations researchers and management scientists with Management Information Systems (MIS's) is apparent. In fact, for some the design of such systems has almost become synonymous with operations research or management science. Enthusiasm for such systems is understandable: it involves the researcher in a romantic relationship with the most glamorous instrument of our time, the computer. Such enthusiasm is understandable but, nevertheless, some of the excesses to which it has led are not excusable.

Contrary to the impression produced by the growing literature, few computerized management information systems have been put into operation. Of those I've seen that have been implemented, most have not matched expectations and some have been outright failures. I believe that these near- and far-misses could have been avoided if certain false (and usually implicit) assumptions on which many such systems have been erected had not been made.

There seem to be five common and erroneous assumptions underlying the design of most MIS's, each of which I will consider. After doing so I will outline an MIS design procedure which avoids these assumptions.

### Give Them More

Most MIS's are designed on the assumption that the critical deficiency under which most managers operate is the *lack of relevant information*. I do not deny that most managers lack a good deal of information that they should have, but I do deny that this is the most important informational deficiency from which they suffer. It seems to me that they suffer more from an *over abundance of irrelevant information*.

This is not a play on words. The consequences of changing the emphasis of an MIS from supplying relevant information to eliminating irrelevant information is considerable. If one is preoccupied with supplying relevant in-

Editors' Note: Reprinted with permission from *Management Science*, December 1967, pp. B147–B156, published by The Institute of Management Sciences.

formation, attention is almost exclusively given to the generation, storage, and retrieval of information: hence emphasis is placed on constructing data banks, coding, indexing, updating files, access languages, and so on. The ideal which has emerged from this orientation is an infinite pool of data into which a manager can reach to pull out any information he wants. If, on the other hand, one sees the manager's information problem primarily, but not exclusively, as one that arises out of an overabundance of irrelevant information, most of which was not asked for, then the two most important functions of an information system become *filtration* (or evaluation) and *condensation*. The literature on MIS's seldom refers to these functions let alone considers how to carry them out.

My experience indicates that most managers receive much more data (if not information) than they can possibly absorb even if they spend all of their time trying to do so. Hence they already suffer from an information overload. They must spend a great deal of time separating the relevant from the irrelevant and searching for the kernels in the relevant documents. For example, I have found that I receive an average of forty-three hours of unsolicited reading material each week. The solicited material is usually half again this amount.

I have seen a daily stock status report that consists of approximately six hundred pages of computer print-out. The report is circulated daily across managers' desks. I've also seen requests for major capital expenditures that come in book size, several of which are distributed to managers each week. It is not uncommon for many managers to receive an average of one journal a day or more. One could go on and on.

Unless the information overload to which managers are subjected is reduced, any additional information made available by an MIS cannot be expected to be used effectively.

Even relevant documents have too much redundancy. Most documents can be considerably condensed without loss of content. My point here is best made, perhaps, by describing briefly an experiment that a few of my colleagues and I conducted on the OR literature several years ago. By using a panel of well-known experts we identified four OR articles that all members of the panel considered to be "above average," and four articles that were considered to be "below average." The authors of the eight articles were asked to prepare "objective" examinations (duration thirty minutes) plus answers for graduate students who were to be assigned the articles for reading. (The authors were not informed about the experiment.) Then several experienced writers were asked to reduce each article to 2/3 and 1/3 of its original length only by eliminating words. They also prepared a brief abstract of each article. Those who did the condensing did not see the examinations to be given to the students.

A group of graduate students who had not previously read the articles were then selected. Each one was given four articles randomly selected, each of which was in one of its four versions: 100%, 67%, 33%, or abstract.

Each version of each article was read by two students. All were given the same examinations. The average scores on the examinations were then compared.

For the above-average articles there was no significant difference between average test scores for the 100%, 67%, and 33% versions, but there was a significant decrease in average test scores for those who had read only the abstract. For the below-average articles there was no difference in average test scores among those who had read the 100%, 67%, and 33% versions, but there was a significant *increase* in average test scores of those who had read only the abstract.

The sample used was obviously too small for general conclusions but the results strongly indicate the extent to which even good writing can be condensed without loss of information. I refrain from drawing the obvious conclusion about bad writing.

It seems clear that condensation as well as filtration, performed mechanically or otherwise, should be an essential part of an MIS, and that such a system should be capable of handling much, if not all, of the unsolicited as well as solicited information that a manager receives.

## The Manager Needs the Information That He Wants

Most MIS designers "determine" what information is needed by asking managers what information they would like to have. This is based on the assumption that managers know what information they need and want it.

For a manager to know what information he needs he must be aware of each type of decision he should make (as well as does) and he must have an adequate model of each. These conditions are seldom satisfied. Most managers have some conception of at least some of the types of decisions they must make. Their conceptions, however, are likely to be deficient in a very critical way, a way that follows from an important principle of scientific economy: the less we understand a phenomenon, the more variables we require to explain it. Hence, the manager who does not understand the phenomenon he controls plays it "safe" and, with respect to information, wants "everything." The MIS designer, who has even less understanding of the relevant phenomenon than the manager, tries to provide even more than everything. He thereby increases what is already an overload of irrelevant information.

For example, market researchers in a major oil company once asked their marketing managers what variables they thought were relevant in estimating the sales volume of future service stations. Almost seventy variables were identified. The market researchers then added about half again this many variables and performed a large multiple linear regression analysis of sales of existing stations against these variables and found about thirty-five to be statistically significant. A forecasting equation was based on this analysis. An OR team subsequently constructed a model based on only one of these variables, traffic flow, which predicted sales better than the thirty-five variable regression equation. The team went on to *explain* sales at service stations in terms of the customers' perception of the amount of time lost by stopping for service. The relevance of all but a few of the variables used by the market researchers could be explained by their effect on such perception.

The moral is simple: one cannot specify what information is required for decision making until an explanatory model of the decision process and the system involved has been constructed and tested. Information systems are subsystems of control systems. They cannot be designed adequately without taking control in account. Furthermore, whatever else regression analyses can yield, they cannot yield understanding and explanation of phenomena. They describe and, at best, predict.


### Give a Manager the Information He Needs and His Decision Making Will Improve

It is frequently assumed that if a manager is provided with the information he needs, he will then have no problem in using it effectively. The history of OR stands to the contrary. For example, give most managers an initial tableau of a typical "real" mathematical programming, sequencing, or network problem and see how close they come to an optimal solution. If their experience and judgment have any value they may not do badly, but they will seldom do very well. In most management problems there are too many possibilities to expect experience, judgment, or intuition to provide good guesses, even with perfect information.

Furthermore, when several probabilities are involved in a problem the unguided mind of even a manager has difficulty in aggregating them in a valid way. We all know many simple problems in probability in which untutored intuition usually does very badly (e.g., What are the correct odds that 2 of 25 people selected at random will have their birthdays on the same day of the year?). For example, very few of the results obtained by queuing theory, when arrivals and service are probabilistic, are obvious to managers; nor are the results of risk analysis where the managers' own subjective estimates of probabilities are used.

The moral: it is necessary to determine how well managers can use needed information. When, because of the complexity of the decision process, they can't use it well, they should be provided with either decision rules or performance feedback so that they can identify and learn from their mistakes. More on this point later.

## More Communication Means Better Performance

One characteristic of most MIS's which I have seen is that they provide managers with better current information about what other managers and their departments and divisions are doing. Underlying this provision is the belief that better interdepartmental communication enables managers to coordinate their decisions more effectively and hence improves the organization's overall performance. Not only is this not necessarily so, but it seldom is so. One would hardly expect two competing companies to become more cooperative because the information each acquires about the other is improved. This analogy is not as farfetched as one might first suppose. For example, consider the following very much simplified version of a situation I once ran into. The simplification of the case does not affect any of its essential characteristics.

A department store has two "line" operations: buying and selling. Each function is performed by a separate department. The Purchasing Department primarily controls one variable: how much of each item is bought. The Merchandising Department controls the price at which it is sold. Typically, the measure of performance applied to the Purchasing Department was the turnover rate of inventory. The measure applied to the Merchandising Department was gross sales; this department sought to maximize the number of items sold times their price.

Now by examining a single item let us consider what happens in this system. The merchandising manager, using his knowledge of competition and consumption, set a price which he judged would maximize gross sales. In doing so he utilized price-demand curves for each type of item. For each

*Figure 1: Price demand curve*

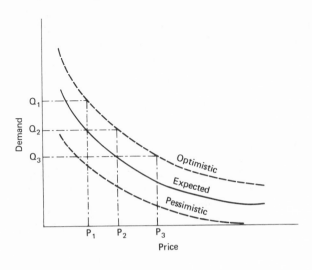

price the curves show the expected sales and values on an upper and lower confidence band as well. (See Figure 1.) When instructing the Purchasing Department how many items to make available, the merchandising manager quite naturally used the value on the upper confidence curve. This minimized the chances of his running short which, if it occurred, would hurt his performance. It also maximized the chances of being overstocked but this was not his concern, only the purchasing manager's. Say, therefore, that the merchandising manager initially selected price $P_1$ and requested that amount $Q_1$ be made available by the Purchasing Department.

In this company the purchasing manager also had access to the price-demand curves. He knew the merchandising manager always ordered optimistically. Therefore, using the same curve he read over from $Q_1$ to the upper limit and down to the expected value from which he obtained $Q_2$, the quantity he actually intended to make available. He did not intend to pay for the merchandising manager's optimism. If merchandising ran out of stock, it was not his worry. Now the merchandising manager was informed about what the purchasing manager had done so he adjusted his price to $P_2$. The purchasing manager in turn was told that the merchandising manager had made this readjustment so he planned to make only $Q_3$ available. If this process—made possible only by perfect communication between departments—had been allowed to continue nothing would have been bought and nothing would have been sold. This outcome was avoided by prohibiting communication between the two departments and forcing each to guess what the other was doing.

I have obviously caricatured the situation in order to make the point clear: when organizational units have inappropriate measures of performance which put them in conflict with each other, as is often the case, communication between them may hurt organizational performance, not help it. Organizational structure and performance measurement must be taken into account before opening the flood gates and permitting the free flow of information between parts of the organization. (A more rigorous discussion of organizational structure and the relationship of communication to it can be found in [1].)

### A Manager Does Not Have to Understand How an Information System Works, Only How to Use It

Most MIS designers seek to make their systems as innocuous and unobtrusive as possible to managers lest they become frightened. The designers try to provide managers with very easy access to the system and assure them that they need to know nothing more about it. The designers usually succeed in keeping managers ignorant in this regard. This leaves managers unable to evaluate the MIS as a whole. It often makes them afraid to even try to do so lest they display their ignorance publicly. In failing to evaluate their MIS, managers delegate much of the control of the organization to the system's designers and operators who may have many virtues, but managerial competence is seldom among them.

Let me cite a case in point. A Chairman of a Board of a medium-size company asked for help on the following problem. One of his larger (decentralized) divisions had installed a computerized production-inventory control and manufacturing-manager information system about a year earlier. It had acquired about $2,000,000 worth of equipment to do so. The Board Chairman had just received a request from the Division for permission to replace the original equipment with newly announced equipment which would cost several times the original amount. An extensive "justification" for so doing was provided with the request. The Chairman wanted to know whether the request was really justified. He admitted to complete incompetence in this connection.

A meeting was arranged at the Division at which I was subjected to an extended and detailed briefing. The system was large but relatively simple. At the heart of it was a reorder point for each item and a maximum allowable stock level. Reorder quantities took lead-time as well as the allowable maximum into account. The computer kept track of stock, ordered items when required and generated numerous reports on both the state of the system it controlled and its own "actions."

When the briefing was over I was asked if I had any questions. I did. First I asked if, when the system had been installed, there had been many parts whose stock level exceeded the maximum amount possible under the new system. I was told there were many. I asked for a list of about thirty and for some graph paper. Both were provided. With the help of the system designer and volumes of old daily reports I began to plot the stock level of the first listed item over time. When this item reached the maximum "allowable" stock level it had been reordered. The system designer was surprised and said that by sheer "luck" I had found one of the few errors made by the system. Continued plotting showed that because of repeated premature reordering the item had never gone much below the maximum stock level. Clearly the program was confusing the maximum allowable stock level and the reorder point. This turned out to be the case in more than half of the items on the list.

Next I asked if they had many paired parts, ones that were only used with each other; for example, matched nuts and bolts. They had many. A list was produced and we began checking the previous day's withdrawals. For more than half of the pairs the differences in the numbers recorded as withdrawn were very large. No explanation was provided.

Before the day was out it was possible to show by some quick and dirty calculations that the new computerized system was costing the company almost $150,000 per month more than the hand system which it had replaced, most of this in excess inventories.

The recommendation was that the system be redesigned as quickly as possible and that the new equipment not be authorized for the time being.

The questions asked of the system had been obvious and simple ones. Managers should have been able to ask them but—and this is the point— they felt themselves incompetent to do so. They would not have allowed a hand-operated system to get so far out of their control.

No MIS should ever be installed unless the managers for whom it is intended are trained to evaluate and hence control it rather than be controlled by it.

## A Suggested Procedure for Designing an MIS

The erroneous assumptions I have tried to reveal in the preceding discussion can, I believe, be avoided by an appropriate design procedure. One is briefly outlined here.

1. ANALYSIS OF THE DECISION SYSTEM. Each (or at least each important) type of managerial decision required by the organization under study should be identified and the relationships between them should be determined and flow-charted. Note that this is *not* necessarily the same thing as determining what decisions *are* made. For example, in one company I found that make-or-buy decisions concerning parts were made only at the time when a part was introduced into stock and was never subsequently reviewed. For some items this decision had gone unreviewed for as many as twenty years. Obviously, such decisions should be made more often; in some cases, every time an order is placed in order to take account of current shop loading, underused shifts, delivery times from suppliers, and so on.

Decision-flow analyses are usually self-justifying. They often reveal important decisions that are being made by default (e.g., the make-buy decision referred to above), and they disclose interdependent decisions that are being made independently. Decision-flow charts frequently suggest changes in managerial responsibility, organizational structure, and measure of performance which can correct the types of deficiencies cited.

Decision analyses can be conducted with varying degrees of detail, that is, they may be anywhere from coarse to fine grained. How much detail one should become involved with depends on the amount of time and resources that are available for the analysis. Although practical considerations frequently restrict initial analyses to a particular organizational function, it is preferable to perform a coarse analysis of all of an organization's managerial functions rather than a fine analysis of one or a subset of functions. It is easier to introduce finer information into an integrated information system than it is to combine fine subsystems into one integrated system.

2. AN ANALYSIS OF INFORMATION REQUIREMENTS. Managerial decisions can be classified into three types:

(a) Decisions for which adequate models are available or can be constructed and from which optimal (or near optimal) solutions can be derived. In such cases the decision process itself should be incorporated into the information system thereby converting it (at least partially) to a control system. A decision model identifies what information is required and hence what information is relevant.

(b) Decisions for which adequate models can be constructed but from which optimal solutions cannot be extracted. Here some kind of heuristic or search procedure should be provided even if it consists of no more than computerized trial and error. A simulation of the model will, as a minimum, permit comparison of proposed alternative solutions. Here too the model specifies what information is required.

(c) Decisions for which adequate models cannot be constructed. Research is required here to determine what information is relevant. If decision making cannot be delayed for the completion of such research or the decision's effect is not large enough to justify the cost of research, then judgment must be used to "guess" what information is relevant. It may be possible to make explicit the implicit model used by the decision maker and treat it as a model of type (b).

In each of these three types of situation it is necessary to provide feedback by comparing actual decision outcomes with those predicted by the model or decision maker. Each decision that is made, along with its predicted outcome, should be an essential input to a management control system. I shall return to this point below.

3. AGGREGATION OF DECISIONS. Decisions with the same or largely overlapping informational requirements should be grouped together as a single manager's task. This will reduce the information a manager requires to do his job and is likely to increase his understanding of it. This may require a reorganization of the system. Even if such a reorganization cannot be implemented completely what can be done is likely to improve performance significantly and reduce the information loaded on managers.

4. DESIGN OF INFORMATION PROCESSING. Now the procedure for collecting, storing, retrieving, and treating information can be designed. Since there is a voluminous literature on this subject I shall leave it at this except for one point. Such a system must not only be able to answer questions addressed to it; it should also be able to answer questions that have not been asked by reporting any deviations from expectations. An extensive exception-reporting system is required.

5. DESIGN OF CONTROL OF THE CONTROL SYSTEM. It must be assumed that the system that is being designed will be deficient in many and significant ways. Therefore, it is necessary to identify the ways in which it may be deficient, to design procedures for detecting its deficiencies, and for correcting the

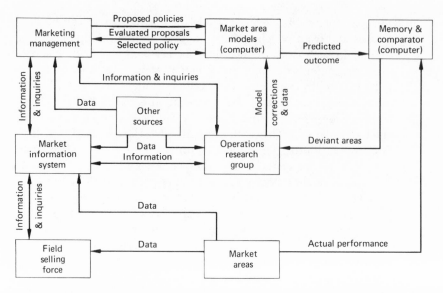

*Figure 2: Simplified diagram of a market-area control system*

system so as to remove or reduce them. Hence the system should be designed to be flexible and adaptive. This is little more than a platitude, but it has a not-so-obvious implication. No completely computerized system can be as flexible and adaptive as can a man-machine system. This is illustrated by a concluding example of a system that is being developed and is partially in operation. (See Figure 2.)

The company involved has its market divided into approximately two hundred marketing areas. A model for each has been constructed as is "in" the computer. On the basis of competitive intelligence supplied to the service marketing manager by marketing researchers and information specialists, he and his staff make policy decisions for each area each month. Their tentative decisions are fed into the computer which yields a forecast of expected performance. Changes are made until the expectations match what is desired. In this way they arrive at "final" decisions. At the end of the month the computer compares the actual performance of each area with what was predicted. If a deviation exceeds what could be expected by chance, the company's OR group then seeks the reason for the deviation, performing as much research as is required to find it. If the cause is found to be permanent the computerized model is adjusted appropriately. The result is an adaptive man-machine system whose precision and generality are continuously increasing with use.

Finally it should be noted that in carrying out the design steps enumerated above, three groups should collaborate: information systems specialists, operations researchers, *and managers.* The participation of managers in the design of a system that is to serve them assures their ability to evalu-

*Part II: Premodeling*

ate its performance by comparing its output with what was predicted. Managers who are not willing to invest some of their time in this process are not likely to use a management control system well, and their system, in turn, is likely to abuse them.

### REFERENCE

1. Sengupta, S. S., and Ackoff, R. L. "Systems Theory from an Operations Research Point of View." *IEEE Transactions on Systems Science and Cybernetics*, Vol. 1 (Nov. 1965): pp. 9–13.

# B. *Interpersonal Relationships with the Client*

## 5. MANAGEMENT INFORMATION SYSTEMS: THE CHALLENGE TO RATIONALITY AND EMOTIONALITY

*Chris Argyris*

---

Management science theorists and practitioners would tend to agree that some day management information systems (MIS) will probably be designed that perform many critical managerial functions. Many also would agree that the realization of this potential is a long way off.

What would happen if an MIS system were developed that could achieve

Editors' Note: Reprinted with permission from *Management Science*, February 1971, pp. B275-B292, published by The Institute of Management Sciences.

this potential? How would individuals react to increased rationality in their lives? Will they think as many humanists believe, namely that information science rationality can lead to a mechanistic and rigid world which, because of its narrow concept of efficiency, will dominate man and eclipse his humanness (Argyris [9])? Will individuals believe, as many futurists argue, that the scope of our society has become so great and the interdependence so pervasive, that without the rationality possible from sophisticated information systems we run the risk of losing control over our everyday life and our destiny?

These critical questions require much research from many different perspectives. We have chosen to focus on these issues by conducting empirical research in actual settings where they are being played out (or, more accurately, fought out). The setting is the study of a management services division in a multibillion dollar corporation. One objective of the division is to introduce new management information systems into certain management processes, that are now possible with the advent of more sophisticated management information systems, within the firm. The professionals in the management services division see themselves as consultants to the entire corporation with the mission of unfreezing "This colossus and pushing it into the twenty-first century." They genuinely believe, like the futurists noted above, that organizations have become so complex and cumbersome that the only (best?) answer for effectiveness is management through the expanded and deepened rationality possible from sophisticated information systems.

What has caused organizations to develop internal processes that lead to increased ineffectiveness? In order to shed light on this question, we need to focus on the pyramidal structure which is the most dominant organizational design in use. It assumes that within respectable tolerances man will behave rationally, that is, as the design requires him to behave (Argyris [4]).

## The Formal Organization and Its Impact on the Participants

There are three aspects of the formal organizational design that are important in generating work requirements for the participants at all levels. They are (1) work specialization, (2) chain of command, and (3) unity of direction. These properties of formal organization have been shown to place (especially the lower level employees) in situations where they tend to be dependent upon and submissive to their superiors; where they experience a very short time perspective and low feelings of responsibility about their work.

Those employees who prefer to experience some degree of challenge, to have some control, to make some decisions will tend to feel frustration and a sense of psychological failure. They may adapt to the frustration and failure by such activities as apathy, indifference, work slow downs, goldbrick-

*Part II: Premodeling*

ing, the creation of unions, absenteeism and turnover. Those employees who do not prefer challenging work or control over their work activities will not tend to feel frustrated. They will tend to report satisfaction and involvement, but the latter will not be deep or enduring.

The impact of task specialization, chain of command, and unity of direction is different at the upper levels. At the upper levels the formal design tends to require executives who need to manage an intended rational world, to direct, control, reward and penalize others, and to suppress their own and others' emotionality (Argyris [5]). Executives with these needs and skills tend to be ineffective in creating and maintaining effective interpersonal relationships; they fear emotionality and are almost completely unaware of ways to obtain employee commitment that is internal and genuine. This results in upper level systems that have more conformity, mistrust, antagonism, defensiveness, and closedness than individuality, trust, concern and openness.

As these dysfunctional activities become embedded in the system and as the defenses that hide their original causes are rigidified and locked into place, there is a tendency in the system to reduce the probability that accurate information will flow through the system. Top management reacts by establishing further controls which feed back to reinforce the original condition that began this causal sequence.

These reactions again tend to reinforce the initial conditions, and so there is a closed loop creating a system with increasing ineffectiveness in problem solving, decision making, and implementation. *In the social universe, where presumably there is no mandatory state of entropy, man can claim the dubious distinction of creating organizations that generate entropy, that is, slow but certain processes toward system deterioration.*

To some readers this analysis may seem overly pessimistic; to others overly optimistic. John Gardner [20], for example, has gone so far as to suggest that the "dry rot" in organizations will become so bad that they eventually will collapse (a view shared by the writer). Admittedly, empirical research is needed if the analysis is to become convincing.

The relevant point for the operations researcher-management scientist, however, is that his field has been born at the very time our institutions are becoming increasingly ineffective. This will place his professional wares in high demand. It will also have the (temporary) advantage of increasing the probabilities that even his early and primitive modelling attempts will be useful. To put it somewhat coarsely, things are so bad that the only way is up. The success, however, may come as much as a result of the hard thinking and the facing of reality that is required if one attempts to model the world as it does from the use of the models developed. This advantage is not to be disparaged. All of us working in these new fields need all the honeymoon period that we can get.

The difficulty in being born at this time stems from the very advantage just described. As organizations become increasingly ineffective, they tend to produce *valid* information for the *unimportant* and programmed problems and *invalid* information for the important and nonprogrammed problems (Argyris [11]). The development and successful introduction of a sophisticated MIS is an example of an important and nonprogrammed problem. Thus the climate of rationality needed for the effective construction of an MIS may be very difficult to create.

THE PROPERTIES OF MANAGEMENT INFORMATION SYSTEMS, (MIS), AND THEIR IMPACT ON MANAGEMENT.[1] We are concerned with MIS whose usage can alter significantly the way top managers make important decisions (not those that deal with trivial data that are easily programmable). These are the MIS that help the executive to order and understand the complexity of the present. They are the systems that provide the executive with an opportunity to experiment with different possible future states of his environment and to learn what might be the possible consequences for each state. These are the systems therefore that a top executive may use to simulate the future so that he can increase the probability that his decision processes will produce outcomes which are in some sense fulfilling prophecies.

It is agreed that such systems may be a long way off. However, it seems useful to study these systems as if they existed in order to identify some of the problems that may accompany their introduction and use. Thus the MIS studied in this project, as is the case for many such models, is far from constituting complete systems of this kind. The state of the art is too primitive for such claims. However, in studying the human problems associated with the introduction and acceptance of MIS to management, it is acceptable to focus on the potential of the MIS and the extent of its realization in an application such as this because executives react to the potential as much as (if not more than) to our present delivery capabilities.

MIS, like formal pyramidal organizations, are based upon the assumption that organizations are, and should continue to be, intendedly rational. Whereas the traditional scientific management designer of organization attempts to construct organizational structures as they ought to be (forgetting provisionally, at least, the personality interpersonal and group factors), the designer of MIS is more interested in modelling the system in accordance with how individuals actually behave. He focuses on aspects of the functional *and* dysfunctional activities described above. In doing this he acknowledges the relevant formal *and* informal activities. The important criterion for inclusion is that the factors are relevant to solving the problem at hand.

*(1) Reduction of space of free movement.* Whereas the traditional management expert limits his plans to the formal system, the MIS expert enlarges his domain of interest to all relevant factors. Consequently, the MIS

---

[1]Because the research focused primarily on management, the data to be reported will be related to management.

expert may ask that behavior, policies, practices, and norms that have been operating covertly be surfaced so that their contributions to the problem be made explicit. This requirement can be threatening because what has been hidden may be incriminating to some participants.

Equally important, however, is that, as the informal is made explicit, it comes under the control of the management. The result may be that the participants will feel increasingly hemmed-in. In psychological language the participants will experience a great restriction of their space of free movement. Research suggests that a restriction of the (psychological) space of free movement tends to create feelings of lack of choice, pressure and psychological failure. These feelings, in turn, can lead to increasing feelings of helplessness, and decreasing feelings of self-responsibility resulting in the increasing tendency to withdraw or to become dependent upon those who created or approved the restriction of space of free movement.

*(2) Psychological failure and double bind.* The second impact of MIS upon management is related to the eventual thrust of the MIS on what Carroll has called "global real time" or "on-line, real-time" (Carroll [17]). The salient characteristics of this structure are formal and continuous flows of global information throughout the system and machine involvement in all decision making. The system makes all the important decisions. If the local decision maker sees an opportunity to alter the plan, he asks the console to evaluate his idea and give him a yes or no response. The real-time decisions are made centrally. Ultimately, the real-time decisions will be automated completely (Carroll [17, p. 402]). Moreover future planning will be a continual activity primarily carried out by MIS as it is fed information about possible changes.

The impact of such a system can be eventually to create a world for the local decision maker where his daily goals are defined for him, the actions to achieve these goals will be specified, and the level of aspiration will be determined, and the performance evaluated, by a system that is external to him. These conditions may lead individual managers to perform as expected. However, they will also lead to a sense of psychological failure (Lewin, Dembo, Festinger, and Sears [21]). Psychological failure occurs whenever someone else defines the individual's goals, path to his goals, his level of aspiration, and criteria for success. Psychological failure, in turn, leads those managers who aspire toward challenging work that requires self-responsibility to be frustrated while those who prefer less challenge and less responsibility are satisfied. The former may leave, fight, or psychologically withdraw; the latter usually stay and withdraw. The manager, in short, because of the MIS, will now tend to experience the frustrations that the employees have experienced in the past as a result of the industrial and quality control engineers who have designed their work and monitored their performance.

The sense of psychological failure is distasteful to human beings such as successful managers who have been accustomed to psychological success.

The manager is now in a double bind. If he follows the new rationality he will succeed as a manager and fail as a human being. He is damned if he refuses to obey, and he damns himself if he does obey.

*(3) Leadership based more on competence than on power.* A third impact that the MIS can have upon management is its emphasis upon the use of valid information and technical competence, rather than formal power, to manage organizations. It is not accidental that in models of the actual flow of work events there is rarely a hierarchy of power positions independent of the work flow. If a decision maker exists, he is in the diagram along the work flow and not above it, as is the case in the traditional models. McDonough and Garrett have described this characteristic of MIS as emphasizing what and how things are done (McDonough and Garrett [22, p. 18]), whereas in traditional models there was an equal, if not greater, emphasis upon who did it.

The MIS is not, however, completely devoid of emphasis on power. In defining a "good criterion" Hitch has been quoted as saying, "The criterion for good criteria is consistency with a good criterion at a higher level" (McDonough and Garrett [22, p. 19]). With this definition the MIS expert places himself under the control of the upper levels of management; an action that probably helps to account for his "acceptance" by the upper levels given the problems that we have discussed above and will discuss below.

The difficulties with making valid information and technical competence the new currency for power are several. First, one greatly reduces the probability that managers can order others simply because they have power. This may be threatening to executives who have, up till now, been free to make the organization "move" even if they had incomplete or invalid information.

Second, as we have seen above, is the tendency for organizations to produce invalid information about important issues. An effective MIS will ask the executives to produce precisely that information that they may have learned to withhold (until the appropriate moment) in order to survive.

Third, organizations with properties described above require those executives who enjoy ambiguity, the manipulation of others, and the making of self-fulfilling prophecies. The latter skill is a particularly important one. One of the marks of a successful executive has been that he was able to marshal human and financial resources to make his decisions come true even if others felt that the decision could not be accomplished. These executives enjoyed, indeed needed, to feel that they were fighting and confronting and overcoming a system (Argyris [6], Bennis [14], Dalton [19]).

*(4) Decreasing feelings of essentiality.* As MIS becomes more sophisticated there will be less need for ambiguity and self-fulfilling prophecies; there will be less need for "taking hold of the goddam place and turning it around and tightening it up." These activities will now be carried out in a planned and rational way by the MIS.

In other words success, in the past, may have come from selecting an admittedly ambiguous course of action but, with resources and power, making it come to reality. The manager, therefore, had good reason to feel essential and powerful. If a decision was successful, he could point to where his influence was important. With optimal ambiguity and fluidity he could also reduce the probability of being convicted of incompetence if the decision was not successful. The ambiguity and fluidity could have helped him to protect himself from his competitors *and*, when successful, made it possible to assign the feelings of success to himself. The use of sophisticated quantitative models therefore could tend to reduce this protection and the feelings of essentiality on the part of the line manager. One might argue that a line manager could take more risks with an MIS because he could blame the model or those who develop it. Our research suggests such an action is not a psychological risk to the individual. Moreover, a line executive would not enhance his position with those above him if his strategy is to blame others.

*(5) Reduction of intra- and inter-group politics.* A mature MIS reduces the need for organizational politics within but especially among departments. The basic assumption of traditional organizational theory is that the subordinate should focus on fulfilling his departmental responsibilities. It is the superior's task to integrate the several departments into a meaningful whole. Because of such factors as competition, lack of trust, and win-lose dynamics, the subordinate tends to build walls around his department to protect it from competing peers or arbitrary superiors. Given the interdepartmental rivalries and barriers, interdependence becomes only partially effective, and success may come primarily from constant monitoring by the superior.

Researchers have documented the existence of interdepartmental rivalries where one side must lose and the other win (Blake, Shepard, Mouton [15]). Competition for scarce resources is high. Indeed many managers believe that interdepartmental competition is healthy. They see it as the best way to assure that departments will make the best possible demands upon the management. This "rabble hypothesis" of management can be shown to have many dysfunctional effects upon interdepartmental cooperation. It is probably the major cause of subordinates developing and maintaining a departmental view whereas their superiors wish that they had a concern for the whole.

The reduction of organizational politics for managing the whole system requires that the relevant departments provide valid information and abide by decisions made by the MIS. The sophisticated MIS no longer views the organization as an aggregate of "hungry, competitive, and angry" units but as a set of interrelated activities that have to be meshed into a whole. In order to do this, the MIS follows a principle that most managers agree with in theory but seldom follow in practice. "The idea is that the activity of any part of an organization has some effect on the activity of every other part. . . . Therefore, in order to evaluate any decision of action . . . it is necessary to identify all the significant interactions and to evaluate their *combined* impact on the performance of the organization as a whole, not merely on the part originally involved" (Ackoff [1]). In order to capture the wholeness of the problem, the technology must deal not only with the behavior of each department, but also with the interrelationships among the departments. This leads the information scientist to seek information from the parts about their relationship with each other and the whole. He hopes to build a model that will show how the departments can be integrated into a fully functioning whole. To succeed means that the departments which have been locked into win-lose conflicts will have to learn to cooperate with each other. Departments with a long history of survival through combat will understandably be skeptical and cautious about being "required" to cooperate.

*(6) New requirements for conceptual thinking.* Finally, the sophisticated MIS will require of managers a different level of intellectual and conceptual competence. However, the historical emphasis upon power over competence and fuzziness over explicitness has naturally attracted executives with qualities and competence that are different than those needed if one is to manage with a sophisticated management information technology.

One major difference is the level of conceptualization they are able to employ. In the past, when data was very incomplete much of the intuition used by a manager was to fill in the many blanks with possible valid data. This meant that managers focused on immersing themselves "in the facts" especially as revealed by past practice.

A sophisticated management information system is able to develop a much richer set of data or facts. Past and present experience can be efficiently summarized and presented. The new skill that may be required is for the manager to deal with the interdependence among the facts. But since he has many facts and these produce complex interdependencies and since the human mind is a finite information processing system, the demand will be for more effective conceptualization of the data in higher order concepts (Miller [23]). This skill typically has been lacking with many managers (Anshem [3]).

Management science specialists might wish to point out, at this time, that the ultimate goal of a valid information science system is to free the manager from the routine data and permit him to focus on being creative and innovative. Indeed, as Ackoff states, the objective of a valid management information system is to reduce the overabundance of irrelevant information because many managers suffer from information overload. The writer agrees.

Unfortunately, our studies so far indicate that the majority of managers still do not know how to use models as the basis for creative experiments. This is partly due to the fact that experimentation, risk taking, and trust, as we say above, have been largely drummed out of managerial systems. This, in turn, tends to assure that men who do not enjoy experimenting will become managers. And for those few brave souls who prefer to experiment, they will probably be faced with an array of control systems to keep their innovations "within bounds."

To summarize: Line management and MIS experts probably agree upon the necessity for organizations being essentially rational phenomena. However, the MIS experts' view of rationally designing systems could lead to some basic changes in the present world of management. The managers may find themselves (1) experiencing increasing amounts of psychological failure yet system success and therefore more double binds; (2) being required to reduce interdepartmental warfare and intradepartmental politics; and (3) finding that the concept of managerial success changes its base from one of power, ambiguity, and self-fulfilling prophecy to valid information, explicitness, and technical competence.

Therefore, sophisticated MIS that introduce in organizations a quantum jump in rationality represent a stressful and emotional problem to the participants.

THE "NEW" DEGREE OF RATIONALITY CREATES A "DEEPER" DEGREE OF EMOTIONALITY. How would MIS professionals tend to react to stress and emotions?

Before an attempt is made to answer this question a caveat seems in order. The analysis, to date, has attempted to predict the world if and when MIS were fully mature. No claim is made that we have reached such a state or indeed ever will. The position is that as MIS become more sophisticated, they will tend to create the conditions described above. However, as we shall point out below, man need not be reactive and submissive to a system. Indeed, it will be our argument that if the MIS were used effectively, they could actually free the manager rather than restrict him. Our pessimistic prediction is that man will not tend to use MIS effectively because of the norms of the existing world and the way he has programmed himself to be more incompetent than competent in dealing with people.

THE BEHAVIOR OF THE MIS PROFESSIONALS. Recently I conducted a study that hopefully will shed some light on parts of the analysis above as well as the assertion that man may have programmed himself to tend toward interpersonal incompetence rather than competence. I studied a management science-operations research team (MSOR team) operating as a management information group in a multibillion dollar corporation. The number of professionally trained core members on the MSOR team was about twenty. They were housed in modern facilities and were located as part of a management services department which reported in a staff relationship (and through five layers of management) to the top corporate management. The team was headed by a professionally trained mathematical statistician who, for years, had been championing the relevance of quantitative analytical methods to management.

Although the group had been given a generous budget and excellent facilities, top management's receptivity to quantitative analytical thinking had left much to be desired. Several reasons may be offered. First, as mentioned above, the executives had succeeded because they had the capacity to make choices, based upon intuitive heuristic understanding. Once a decision had been made, they were experts at marshalling human and financial resources to implement the decisions. They were skilled at making their decisions "come true"; they were skilled at turning a decision into a self-fulfilling prophecy.

Second, the organization had developed quantitative financial analyses which were used to manage the corporation. These financial systems which seemed, to the MSOR team, to be inadequate, antiquated, and tied to reporting history were buttressed by a powerful organization that had influence with the top management.

Finally, the state of the art in management science information systems is still primitive compared to the demands of the management. Thus the MSOR team could not, in all honesty, make promises of major innovations with spectacular results (which would be required to unfreeze the financial department from its position).

The head of the MSOR team plus his superiors used the admittedly primitive state of the field to "sell" the MSOR team as developing modest experiments which would not rock the boat while hopefully providing new insights and methods for management. The opportunity to develop an MSOR team in terms of experimentation and research attracted the team members because it would reduce the probabilities of creating unrealistically high expectations on the part of the clients while giving the team members more time to develop valid models.

## The Research Methods Used

The writer interviewed (in individual and group sessions) all of the MSOR team members plus the superiors two layers above the head of the group. The interviews were semistructured and tape recorded. They lasted about an hour with a few being as short as thirty minutes and some (primarily the group sessions) about four hours. The interviews served to provide the background information and the perceptions of the team members of their problems.

The major research method however was observation of actual work meetings plus analysis of tape recordings of meetings. Tape recordings of twenty-five meetings were obtained and analyzed. Fifteen of these meetings were analyzed in great detail. It is these fifteen meetings that provide the core of our data for this paper.

The meetings were tape recorded and analyzed by using a set of categories whose reliability and predictive validity are described in detail elsewhere and presented briefly in Table I (Argyris [7]). Those above the middle or zero line are hypothesized to facilitate, and those below to inhibit, inter-personal relationships and problem solving. The further away from the zero line, the more difficult is the behavior to perform. Thus, openness to ideas (*i*) or feelings (*f*) is hypothesized to be more difficult than owning ideas or feelings (i.e., stating one's ideas or feelings), and experimenting is more difficult than openness. Each unit of behavior is scored on two levels. Level I represents the individual and interpersonal. Level II represents norms of the group. For example:

| *Sample Statement* | *Would Be Scored As* | |
|---|---|---|
| 1. "I believe that we should reject the idea even though we are told not to." | Own *i* | Individuality *i* |
| 2. "I feel tense." | Own *f* | Individuality *f* |
| 3. "Would you please tell me more about your theory?" | Open *i* | Concern *i* |
| 4. "This is not easy for me to talk about. I feel like my whole life has been a shambles. I feel frightened and bewildered." | Experimenting *f* | Trust *f* |

When both scores represent categories above the zero line or below, the

*Table I: Categories of behavior*

| Level I | | | | Level II | |
|---|---|---|---|---|---|
| Individual | | Interpersonal | | Norms | |
| Experimenting | *i* | Help others to | *i* | Trust | *i* |
| | *f* | experiment | *f* | | *f* |
| Openness | *i* | Help others to | *i* | Concern | *i* |
| | *f* | be open | *f* | | *f* |
| Owning | *i* | Help others to | *i* | Individuality | *i* |
| | *f* | own | *f* | | *f* |
| *Zero* | | | | | |
| Not owning | *i* | Not help others | *i* | Conformity | *i* |
| | *f* | to own | *f* | | *f* |
| Not open | *i* | Not help others | *i* | Antagonism | *i* |
| | *f* | to be open | *f* | | *f* |
| Rejecting experimenting | *i* | Not help others | *i* | Mistrust | *i* |
| | *f* | to experiment | *f* | | |

behavior may be said to be *consistent*. For example, in the four cases above, the categories representing the personal and norms levels are all positive. If behavior was positive and negative, it would be viewed as *inconsistent* (e.g., owning *i*—conformity *i* or open *i*—antagonism *i*). Inconsistent behavior presents a special class of problems which is very important in understanding individual or group attempts to be effective.

THE RESULTS OF OBSERVATIONS. The results of six meetings are presented (Table II). The first three compose a pattern to be identified as A (which represents 7 of the 15 meetings). The second three compose pattern B (and are representative of the remaining 8 meetings).

Pattern A was characterized by a high degree of stating or *owning* up to ideas. Ideas were stated in such a way as to contribute most frequently to the norm of *concern* for ideas. The second most frequently scored norm was *conformity* to ideas (but that was significantly lower). These results may be interpreted to mean that the discussion was straightforward where the facts spoke for themselves.

*Openness to* ideas occurred significantly lower than owning up to ideas. An analysis of these scores indicated that openness was found mostly (1) when a member wanted to learn something from a superior or a client and (2) when presentations were being made of quantitative models and the people listening asked questions to understand them.

There was little behavior of the members helping or not helping each other to own up to, be open, and experiment with ideas. The members seemed to be on their own, concerned with their contribution and less with helping others. Inconsistent behavior tended to be somewhat more frequent than the openness, but the scores were not very high.

Behavior that was *rarely* observed was (a) expressing feelings; (b) openness to feelings; (c) experimenting with ideas or feelings; (d) helping others to own up to feelings; (e) helping others to experiment with their ideas and feelings; (f) the positive norms of trust or individuality and the negative norm of antagonism and mistrust; and (g) overtly refusing to express, to be open, to experiment with ideas or feelings and overtly and directly trying to prevent or inhibit others.

These results suggest several characteristics of the dynamics of the groups.

1. Behavior that facilitates or directly inhibits others' behavior and feelings was rarely expressed. The norms for openness to new ideas, for expressing feelings, and for taking risks were very weak. These groups, therefore, should *not* be settings where creative and innovative work is done. Also, any risk taking or conformation should tend to be inhibited (Argyris [12]).

   Such a conclusion may seem to be at variance with the findings reported by several recent studies (Churchman and Schainblatt [18],

Mumford and Ward [24], Pettigrew [25]) to the effect that MIS people perceive themselves as wanting to be, and as being, creative or innovative. These data are based upon individual reports. Indeed, most of our population reported similar needs and self-perceptions. The conclusions above are focused on group behavior. We are, in short,

Table II: Group scores for six meetings

| | | 1 n = 90 | | 2 n = 80 | | 3 n = 100 | | 4 n = 200 | | 5 n = 200 | | 6 n = 15 | |
|---|---|---|---|---|---|---|---|---|---|---|---|---|---|
| | | n | % | n | % | n | % | n | % | n | % | n | % |
| PERSONAL | | | | | | | | | | | | | |
| own | i | 67 | 74 | 56 | 70 | 74 | 74 | 116 | 58 | 132 | 66 | 112 | 74 |
| own | f | | | | | | | | | | | | |
| open | i | 22 | 24 | 16 | 20 | 21 | 21 | 50 | 25 | 29 | 14 | 16 | 10 |
| open | f | | | | | | | | | | | | |
| exper | i | | | | | | | | | | | | |
| exper | f | | | | | | | | | | | | |
| INTERPERSONAL | | | | | | | | | | | | | |
| ho* own | i | | | | | | | | | | | | |
| not ho own | i | | | 8 | 10 | 4 | 04 | 50 | 25 | 39 | 20 | 21 | 14 |
| GROUP NORMS | | | | | | | | | | | | | |
| conc | i | 75 | 83 | 47 | 53 | 66 | 66 | 108 | 54 | 75 | 39 | 51 | 34 |
| conc | f | | | | | | | | | | | | |
| indiv | i | 7 | 08 | 3 | 05 | 6 | 06 | 8 | 04 | 3 | 02 | 2 | 01 |
| indiv | f | | | | | | | | | | | | |
| trust | i | | | | | | | | | | | | |
| trust | f | | | | | | | | | | | | |
| conf | i | 8 | 08 | 30 | 70 | 30 | 30 | 83 | 41 | 104 | 53 | 73 | 48 |
| conf | f | | | | | | | | | | | | |
| antag | i | | | | | | | 1 | 01 | 18 | 07 | 22 | 14 |
| antag | f | | | | | | | | | | | | |
| mistrust | i | | | | | | | | | | | | |
| mistrust | f | | | | | | | | | | | | |
| INCONSISTENT BEHAVIOR | | | | | | | | | | | | | |
| own i conf | i | 7 | 08 | 22 | 27 | 23 | 23 | 50 | 25 | 59 | 30 | 53 | 36 |
| own i antag | i | | | | | 3 | 03 | | | 13 | 06 | 23 | 16 |
| open i conf | i | | | | | | | | | | | 6 | 04 |
| open i antag | i | | | | | | | | | 4 | 02 | 8 | 06 |
| Total Imbalance | | 7 | 08 | 22 | 27 | 26 | 26 | 50 | 25 | 86 | 43 | 90 | 60 |

*Helping others.

predicting that if these individuals are creative they will tend to have their creativity cancelled out or reduced when they are operating in these groups.

2. Individuals rarely express positive or negative feelings in the group setting while striving to achieve their tasks. This may be due to several possibilities:

   a. The individuals rarely generate positive or negative feelings.
   b. The individuals do generate positive and negative feelings but are inhibited in expressing these feelings (e.g., their view of effective problem solving may include the suppressing of feelings or their personality inhibits them from expressing their feelings).
   c. The individuals develop positive and negative feelings but feel group and cultural norms exist about expressing them.

These findings are very similar to the ones found to exist for top and middle management groups (Argyris [8]). Thus, the MSOR team members tend to behave in ways that are similar to line executives. Although the similarity of behavior may lead one to infer that feelings of commonality and effective communication should exist, our observations suggest a different outcome. The reason may be found by observing what actually happens when the MSOR team meets managers. These conditions tended to be stressful and tension producing because here were the times when the MSOR team was trying to convince line executives to accept an MIS. Here is where the new rationality produced the deeper emotionality.

The behavior of the MSOR team under stress changed significantly. The results are identified as pattern B. We note that pattern B is again characterized by a high degree of *owning up* to ideas. However, *conformity* to ideas becomes the predominant norm. People are doing much more persuading and "selling." *Openness* to ideas is reduced but not altered significantly. *Helping others* is sharply reduced to zero. *Not helping* others increases dramatically. People may be observed cutting each other off. *Antagonism* increases significantly in two of the three meetings. Inconsistent behavior also increases dramatically.

Again, feelings are hardly ever expressed; experimenting, trust, or mistrust are rarely observed.

Under stress, the MSOR team loses some of its composure; it produces more behavior scored as conformity and antagonism; it suppresses its feelings of tension by intellectualizing them; it does little to help its own members or others to become more open, to explore new issues, and to take risks.

The research of top management behavior cited previously concludes that they too react in similar ways when under stress. *We have two groups who react to stress and tension in ways that will tend to inhibit effective problem solving.*

Thus, MIS professional and line managers have a comparable degree of interpersonal competence. Under stress, people with this degree of interpersonal competence tend to react in ways that inhibit effective problem solving. These conclusions are supported by Pettigrew's results. Operations researchers report that they run into interpersonal and interdepartmental problems when they are trying to do the job the way they think it should be done (68%). "The biggest single difficulty lay in communicating with and convincing 'user' departments that a change or a series of changes was in fact in their and their company's interests" (Pettigrew [25, p. 211]).

To summarize:

| Under Minimal Stress both Groups Will Tend to | Under Stress both Groups Will Tend to |
|---|---|
| 1. Encourage the expression of non-risk-taking ideas. | 1. Encourage the expression of non-risk ideas. |
| 2. Encourage concern for non-risk-taking. | 2. Discourage concern for ideas and encourage conformity, encourage inconsistent behavior (as much as it encourages concern under minimal stress), and antagonism more than helping others. |
| 3. Encourage mild expression of selling and persuasion. | 3. Encourage strong expression of selling, persuasion. Listening to others is primarily in terms of winning arguments, supporting colleagues, or agreeing with what is being said. |
| 4. Encourage mild competitive behavior of not helping others. | 4. Encourage strong competitive or withdrawal behavior and increase not helping others. |
| 5. Encourage individuals not to be concerned about group effectiveness. | 5. Encourage individual members not to be concerned about group effectiveness. |
| 6. Discourage the expression of risk taking, deviant news, issues loaded with conflict, trust or mistrust, feelings of any kind. | 6. Discourage the expression of risk taking, issues loaded with conflict, trust, or mistrust, feelings of any kind. |

The overemphasis on persuasion and selling, the increase in competition or withdrawal, the discouragement of openness and risk taking, the discouragement of helping others and of showing concern for group effectiveness *are basically emotional responses, even though the feelings may be intellectualized.* Thus, two groups whose members prefer to be intendedly rational, who prefer to manage rationally, who seek new intendedly rational designs of managing human behavior develop a design for dealing with confrontation of the introduction of a new MIS that is basically emotional and threatening to them.

ADAPTATION BY THE CLIENTS TO THREAT. The clients' reactions to threat can be predicted from the analysis to date. First, the feelings of mistrust, suspicion, and fears of inadequacy will rarely be discussed openly. If information science groups are destroyed or slowly permitted to atrophy, the announced reasons will be consistent with present managerial practice. For example, not enough clients can be persuaded to pay for the services. Or management still does not understand the value of the new systems and therefore does not know how to use an operations research group effectively (Burack [16]).

If the specialists are kept, management may react by assigning them projects that are of low level importance or of critical urgency. In both cases, the attending conditions help to assure the poor use of management information concepts and models. In the former case, since the status of the project in the client's eyes will be low, the specialists may find it difficult to get the cooperation from all levels of the organization in supplying the necessary data or in permitting observations of the activities to be modelled. In the case of the latter, the pressures are so great and tensions so high that deadlines are usually defined that make it difficult for the specialist to study the problem thoroughly and to develop a systematic model. The clients, who typically do not understand the time required to collect the data and, more importantly, to develop abstract models that are relevant to their particular requirements, become impatient, frustrated, and disappointed. The specialists develop the same feelings for having their ultimate value assessed on the basis of the sophistication of these admittedly incomplete models.

ADAPTATION OF THE TEAM. Team members developed several ways to cope with their dilemmas. First they convinced themselves that it was their mission "to force people to become more explicit in their thinking in order to be more effective." Another put it this way, "It is my job to make people think through what the hell their objectives are." Given that their task is now conceived as *coercing* others to become more explicit and rational, then any coercion on their part becomes consistent with their mission.

Another mode of adaptation was to be as diplomatic as possible. This came in the form of translating their ideas into "simple" (but "sloppy") managerial language, by suppressing (they thought) their disrespect for the low calibre of intellectual capacity among managers, and by not confronting any issue that might be threatening to the line.

To be sure, there came moments when the team members could no longer be diplomatic. At that moment, they either withdrew (behavior that tended to upset aggressive line managers because an important reason for their aggressiveness was a fear of being rejected) or they too became aggressive and competitive. To make matters worse, once the latter occurred, whatever success the team members had in hiding their feelings of intellectual superiority was greatly reduced, and they came across (in the eyes of line management) as arrogant. For example, one computer expert responded to a line manager (who had just asked him to explain his proposals), "Do you understand the concept of the half life in physics?" (Mumford and Ward [24, p. 247]).

Another way to adapt was to meet in their private rooms and complain loudly to each other and to their superiors about the inhibiting behavior of their clients. This not only provided an opportunity for catharsis, but it created pressures on the supervisors to calm the group down, to assure them that the project was going well, and to promise to do their best to meet with some senior line representatives to ask for better cooperation. The team members tended to feel cheered and left the meeting thanking the superior and asking him to make their requests to the higher levels without upsetting them. If the top line people became upset, they could upset the lower level line people who, in turn, could make it very difficult for the lower level management scientists. One can imagine the tension felt by superiors. They were asked to complain "carefully" to already defensive line managers, but to do so with enough "force" to assure some action on their part "against" their subordinates.

These contradictory demands made of their superiors were compounded by the contradictory games they tended to play with their clients. For example, the clients experienced the information science technologists to want:

| | | |
|---|---|---|
| 1. All relevant information made explicit and subject to correction | yet | 1. they kept many of their change strategies about the clients secret. |
| 2. Organizations should be based more on competence than power | yet | 2. they used power and manipulation to get their work accepted. |
| 3. Management to reduce their intuitive and seat-of-the-pants thinking | yet | 3. they used primarily intuitive thinking in developing their strategies to introduce their technology to the clients. |

These basic inconsistencies between stated philosophy and actual behavior helped the clients who were defensive to rationalize their myopia and resistance as necessary protective activity. Under these conditions the distance between the clients and the technologists became greater.

Attempts could be made to reduce the distance by having as head of the specialists someone who "understands, gets along with, and speaks the language of the line." This may mean that the head of a management science-operations research group would be selected primarily for his abilities to succeed with line executives rather than for his technical competence.

Unfortunately, this frequently used strategy tends to fail in several ways. Since the head of the technical group also will not tend to deal with the emotional dimensions openly, he will find himself becoming increasingly diplomatic and cautious with line management. This, in turn, may create increased anxiety in the team members who could interpret this as a potential sellout to the line.

To make matters more difficult, the head may also feel that in order to obtain paying customers for his group, he may have (1) to accept, for the group, assignments that are not challenging; (2) to oversell the capabilities of information science technology and thereby create unreal expectations; (3) to agree with the line that information technology specialists are somewhat odd and difficult; (4) to agree to reductions in the quality of effort and in the time available; or (5) to remain indefinitely vague about what can be accomplished, thereby preventing the clients from having realistic expectations.

The more the subordinates find themselves caught up in the consequences of such behavior, the more hopeless and frustrated they may become. The first-rate men may leave while the others may stay but come to condemn their superior for the problems of ineffectiveness.

One can predict that if the MSOR team members attempted to resolve the issues among themselves, there would be a high probability that the meeting would be a highly stressful one. Consequently, the behavior described at the outset would tend to predominate. For example, those who valued the competitive, win-lose dynamics would tend to make their contributions as articulately and persuasively as possible. They would generate a pervasive mode of "selling." Selling would tend to make the speaker feel that he was being articulate and intellectually powerful. However, this very power may act to reduce the probabilities that the "customer" would buy because the customer would sense (a) that the emotional component was stronger than the rational, yet (b) the speaker was insisting that he was being rational and asking others to be the same. (Let's look at the facts.) The listener would tend to mistrust the "sales pitch." He would see it more as the speaker trying to win him over, to protect his own interests, rather than to help create a climate where the best solutions or a new idea could be created.

Under these conditions the participants would also tend to immunize themselves from being infected by the enthusiasm of the seller by (a) turning him off, (b) not listening but preparing their own sales pitch, or (c) if they did listen, it would lead the original seller to feel less effective. He may react by increasing his selling and by evaluating the others as somewhat stubborn for defending their "narrow departmental or personal view."

Thus, there would be a recycling which would tend to increase the selling and competitiveness. This, in turn, would make individuals feel they were rarely heard or understood, which, in turn, would make them be very careful and articulate in verbalizing their thoughts. Thus, they may focus more on preparing their contributions than on listening to others. Moreover, once they spoke, they would continue until all of their accumulated ideas had been heard. The time available to be "on the air" would become scarce. This would result in ineffective group meetings and problem solving.

SOME THOUGHTS ON COPING WITH THE PROBLEMS IDENTIFIED. The reader may ask what can the MSOR team members and the line executives do to reduce the problems identified above and to increase the probabilities of effective introduction of MIS? The first step is that both groups become aware that the MIS per se is *not* the basic problem. The basic problem is that modern organizations, as we indicated at the outset, are designed with power centralized at the top, with specialization of tasks which results in many concealed dysfunctional components that are revealed by a MIS and that MIS implies a different design for organizations, one where competence is more important than power, and collaboration and interdependence are more important than competition. This tends to create many fears and resistances on the part of individuals, groups, and intergroups.

In order for valid advice to become available, much empirical research is needed on the differential impact of the different degrees of these consequences. Rubenstein et al. [26] has identified ten variables that could be used in such studies. They are

1. Level of management support
2. Client receptivity
3. Organizational and technical capability of the OR/MS person or group
4. Organizational location
5. Influence upon organization
6. Reputation
7. Adequacy of the resources
8. Relevance of projects
9. Level of opposition
10. General perception of the level of success

Many researchers have suggested that one way to reduce these problems is to teach managers the basic knowledge about management information science technology. Others suggest that both managers and MIS professionals need to be taught to hold a position of "mutual understanding." Under such conditions both react to each other in order to enhance their personal gains (Churchman and Schainblatt [18]). The difficulty with these suggestions is that no one, to the writer's knowledge, has ever shown that if such learning is achieved it transfers to real situations when the individuals are fighting a win-lose game and are under high stress. Indeed, our data show that the MIS people, who are well educated in information sciences, have similar emotional problems with each other. They frequently challenge each other's work which leads to the same kinds of strains that exist between themselves and the line managers.

Suggestions to bridge the two cultures by placing line managers in MIS groups and vice versa may help. However, in the writer's experience, when these "fully" educated men enter the arena of conflict and win-lose, they may use their knowledge about the other side to decrease the probability that they will win.

In the organization studied, the strategy used was to place a member of the line management on the MIS team to act as a liaison. He was in constant touch with both groups. He made significant inputs into the development of the model. However, these men reported great role strain. They described themselves as men-in-the-middle trying to please and help both sides only to wind up as a hero or a traitor (depending upon which way the decision went).

Others have suggested that MIS may be helped if the team is housed in a management services division, if it has easy access to influential top management, and if it has adequate funds to support some of its activities on a research basis. This group was housed in a management services division and was encouraged by top management to take on a few jobs, primarily on a research basis. The access to the top management, however, was not easy. But it is not clear what such an access could have achieved. Perhaps both sides would hesitate to go to the top because the nature of their win-lose intergroup dynamics and lack of communication would become evident to the highest officers.

The primary difficulty with all these strategies is that they assume the problem can be solved rationally. Education and structural rearrangements assume that people will respond rationally to the new stimuli these learnings and changes create. This assumption is valid up to the point where people begin to threaten each other and are in conflict. Then both sides regress and respond ineffectively. Rational solutions may delay the moment of conflict, but they do not get at the underlying problem, namely, no one has been able to program human activity significantly to eliminate or reduce conflict and threat. Moreover, in the cases where it has been attempted, the "success" has been due to the fact that the protagonists got the message and suppressed the expression of conflict in front of top management.

This does *not* mean that rational solutions such as education and structural changes will never work. The strategy being suggested is that the competence of *both* managers and MIS professionals in dealing with emotionality and strain in interpersonal and intergroup problems must be raised. As their interpersonal competence in these areas increases they will naturally turn to education and structural changes. We would predict, on the basis of other research, that their commitment to education and the changes will then be internal, not merely external (imposed) (Argyris [7], [8]). Under these conditions the participants would also tend to develop a responsibility of continually monitoring their solutions to correct the failures. In short, the team members may need to be helped to modify their behavior.

Behavioral science research suggests that in order to increase one's interpersonal competence the individual needs to be aware of his self and his defenses. Next, it is helpful if the individual strives to attain a minimum of psychological conflict and an acceptance of his self so that he can create conditions that lead to trust, openness, risk taking, and effective confrontation of conflict (Argyris [13]).

The focus on interpersonal relations and the expression of feelings should *not* be interpreted to mean that rationality should be substituted for emotionality and interpersonal competence for technical competence. As Rubenstein et al. [26] pointed out, a reputation for professional excellence is central to the success of an MIS unit. Openness requires a particular combination of rational *and* emotional communication. Openness does *not* mean that each individual should express whatever is on his mind regardless of any concern for the feelings of others. The aim is to create a situation in which the MSOR team members can express how they feel in such a manner as to help the line executives express themselves in a similar open manner. The theory is that emotional problems within organizations do not simply disappear when they are not faced; rather they tend to obstruct the carrying out of rational plans.

Also, the utilization of behavioral science technology requires an awareness of, and competence in, the use of a different set of concepts and conceptual schemes. These schemes, primitive as they may be, are presently either unknown or incompletely known to the MSOR team members. Moreover, to learn these concepts in such a way that the individual can use them he would be required to undergo learning experiences that may be somewhat painful to him. Concepts about human behavior are most effectively learned by first experiencing them and later relating the concepts to the experience (Schein and Bennis [27]). This means that the learning situations can be designed to help individuals experience and openly talk about their feelings regarding many different complex emotions. But, as we have seen, the expression and exploration of feelings was not one of the strengths of the MSOR team members.

Developing and increasing interpersonal competence includes becoming aware that high competence is maintained by constant feedback of valid information from others about one's own impact on the others. In order to get relatively valid feedback from others, one must help to create conditions for minimal defensiveness for one's self and the others. These conditions include (1) reducing the formal power of the superior, (2) focusing more on interpersonal competence as a basis for influence, and (3) creating conditions where others can feel free to confront one's self and others on the difficult interpersonal and substantive issues. Such a relationship is significantly different from the way the various team members dealt with authority and influence. They were consistent with their line executives who tend to be controlling and directive.

Finally, there is a necessity to recognize and deal openly with interpersonal interdependence. Individuals are incomplete without others. Again this tends to be at variance with the feeling and beliefs of most of the MSOR team members. They felt "completed" by relating themselves to a world of symbols, models, and concepts. They tended to resist getting into interpersonal interdependence.

The point being made is that the introduction of a sophisticated information technology is as much an emotional human problem that requires interpersonal competence (as well as technical competence) and that requires knowledge about the human aspects of organizations such as personality, small groups, intergroups, and living systems of organization norms. Those of us working in these fields are painfully aware of the inadequacy and primitive state of our knowledge. We need help from the management scientist-operations research professional if the relationships between thought and action, as played out in this world, are to be understood and made more effective.

#### REFERENCES

1. Ackoff, R. L. (ed) *Progress in Operations Research*, Vol. 1. New York: John Wiley & Sons, 1961, p. 26.
2. ———. "Management Misinformation Systems." Management Science Center, Wharton School of Finance and Commerce, University of Pennsylvania, 1968, Mimeograph.
3. Anshem, M. "The Management of Ideas." *Harvard Business Review* (July-August 1969): pp. 99–107.
4. Argyris, C. *Personality and Organization*. New York: Harper and Row, 1957.
5. ———. *Interpersonal Competence and Organizational Effectiveness*. Homewood, Ill.: R. D. Irwin and Co., 1962.
6. ———. *Integrating the Individual and the Organization*. New York: John Wiley & Sons, 1964.
7. ———. *Organization and Innovation*. Homewood, Ill.: R. D. Irwin, Inc., 1965.
8. ———. "Interpersonal Barriers to Decision-Making." *Harvard Business Review* 44(2) (1966): pp. 84–97.
9. ———. "How Tomorrow's Executives Will Make Decisions." *Think* 33(6) (1967a): pp. 18–26.
10. ———. "Today's Problems with Tomorrow's Organizations." *Journal of Management Studies* 4(1) (February 1967b): pp. 31–55.
11. ———. "On the Effectiveness of Research and Development Organizations." *American Scientist* 56(4) (1968): pp. 344–355.
12. ———. "The Incompleteness of Social Psychological Theory." *American Psychologist* 24(1) (October 1969): pp. 893–908.
13. ———. *Intervention Theory and Method: A Behavioral Science View* (in press).
14. Bennis, W. G. *Changing Organizations*. New York: McGraw-Hill, 1966.
15. Blake, R. R.; Shepard, H. A. and Mouton, J. S. *Managing Intergroup Conflict in Industry*. Houston: Gulf Publishing, 1964.
16. Burack, E. H. "Operations Research: Its Future Place in Business Organization." *Michigan State University, Business Topics* 17(4) (Spring 1969): pp. 9–16.

17. Carroll, D. C. "On the Structure of Operational Control Systems." In *Operations Research and the Design of Management Information Systems*, edited by John F. Pierce, Jr. Special Tech. Association Publication Stap. No. 4, Chapter 23 (1965): pp. 398–402.
18. Churchman, C. W. and Schainblatt, A. H. "The Researcher and the Manager: A Dialectic of Implementation." *Management Science*, Vol. 11 (February 1965): pp. B-69–B-87.
19. Dalton, M. *Men Who Manage*. New York: John Wiley & Sons, 1958.
20. Gardner, J. "America in the Twenty-Third Century." *New York Times*, July 27, 1968.
21. Lewin, K.; Dembo, T.; Festinger, L. and Sears, P. S. "Level of Aspiration." In *Personality and the Behavior Disorders*, edited by J. M. V. Hunt. New York: Ronald Press, 1944, pp. 333–378.
22. McDonough, A. M. and Garrett, L. J. *Management Systems*. Homewood, Ill.: R. D. Irwin and Co., 1965, pp. 18–19.
23. Miller, G. A. "The Magical Number Seven Plus or Minus Two." *Psychological Review*, Vol. 63 (1956): pp. 81–97.
24. Mumford, E. and Ward, T. "Computer Technologists." *Journal of Management Studies* 3(3) (October 1966): pp. 244–255.
25. Pettigrew, A. "Inter-Group Conflict and Role Strain." *Journal of Management Studies* 5(2) (May 1968): pp. 205–218.
26. Rubenstein, A. H.; Radnor, M.; Baker, N. R.; Heiman, D. R. and McColly, J. B. "Some Organizational Factors Related to the Effectiveness of Management Science Groups in Industry." *Management Science*, Vol. 13, No. 8 (April 1967): pp. B-508–B-518.
27. Schein, E. H. and Bennis, W. G. *Personal and Organizational Change Through Group Methods: The Laboratory Approach*. New York: John Wiley & Sons, 1965.

# 6. HOW DO YOUR QUANTITATIVE SPECIALISTS STACK-UP?

*Thad B. Green and Dennis F. Ray*

Consulting in the quantitative area involves both technical and consulting skills. Success is not an either-or proposition. Both skills are necessary. The abundance of literature dealing with the technical skills is staggering. Unfortunately, the opposite condition exists for quantitative consulting skills. For both internal and external consulting, relatively few articles are published (except for the efforts of Gene Woolsey)—and less on theory is available. To put it differently, many—perhaps too many—scholars have pub-

Editors' Note: Reprinted with permission from *Business and Economic Perspectives*, Spring 1977, pp. 41–47.

lished technical research findings dealing with the left eyebrow of a gnat perched on the right cheek of an elephant in the African jungle. Frankly, consultants are not too interested in eyebrows or gnats; and they certainly don't confine their attention to the area in the immediate vicinity of the gnat. What they would like to know is how to survive in the jungle! Trouble is, the ones that are surviving aren't taking time to publish their experiences.

This problem exists in part because the professor-consultants who are capable of researching and publishing find it difficult to develop an academically sound research design. There is a technical design problem because variables in the jungle simply will not cooperate by remaining constant, or varying in the direction or degree desired. Furthermore, there is the practical problem of research design which is just as insurmountable. The consultant is hired to solve problems, not conduct research. In view of this research design dilemma, the professor-consultant chooses not to publish his valuable observations and conclusions for fear of tarnishing the scholarly reputation which he so genuinely assumes other scholars ascribe to him. As Jay Lorsch argues, the value of rigorous research cannot be denied; yet we must not abandon needed investigations simply because the variables cannot be controlled. We must, as Russell Ackoff suggests, tackle the "messes" and not confine our efforts solely to the neat and definable problems.

There is another type of professor-consultant who contributes to the problem, though in a different way. He is the type who does publish but, invariably and unintentionally, makes it obvious that his jungle experience is confined to either a one-hour safari at Disney World or watching last week's "Wild Kingdom" on NBC.

As Jackson Grayson says, we need to bridge this gap between two cultures. The jungle consultants must walk hand-in-hand with the jungle "livers"—and then share their experience with those students and consultants who can't or won't. This article is one such attempt at sharing—sharing some concepts and guidelines believed to be essential for success as a quantitative consultant. The thoughts presented here are based on experiences derived by the authors from regularly visiting the jungle. No attempt has been made to lend credibility by quoting academic publications authored by scholarly persons who have written about a world in which they do not live. Though the sample is small by some standards, this article reflects a combined total of 17 years of consulting experience (including management, quantitative, and systems consulting) by the authors in approximately 30 organizations.

### Expectations

In beginning a quantitative consulting assignment it is imperative to first understand what the client expects. This seems obvious—even trivial. But don't be misled. Ignoring the need to identify expectations is a major cause of failure. Why was a consultant brought in? Is he to perform magic? Is he unrealistically expected to develop complete and perfect solutions to all problems? Or, are the client's expectations more realistic? Does he "simply" expect (1) solutions that are good, but not perfect; (2) solutions that are pragmatic; (3) solutions that are not grandiose, but realistic; (4) solutions he can "live with"; (5) solutions compatible with financial, manpower, and other system constraints; or (6) solutions generally acceptable to persons affected by them? Is the client hopeful but highly skeptical? Or is he doubtful that the consultant can really help? Is he overly pessimistic about positive results? Has the consultant been hired as a "scapegoat"? Will the client accept anything proposed so long as the consultant is around to accept the blame?

Knowing what the client expects is sometimes elusive and difficult to detect. What he says often is not what he means. His actions frequently do not reveal true feelings. His real expectations may well be disguised. Regardless of the reasons for this behavior, the consultant must develop the skill to see through it all, and accurately detect what the client really desires.

Client expectations obviously influence the consultant's approach. If the client is very pessimistic, it is necessary first to gain his confidence. If he has expectations impossible to attain, the consultant must employ a different approach. An understanding of the client's motives may even convince the consultant that he should not accept the project. Consequently, it is important initially to focus on determining the client's expectations rather than hastily becoming engrossed in the assignment.

### Attitudes

The consultant's sensitivity to the client's expectations is influenced by the attitude or frame of mind with which he approaches the consulting task. The assignment should not be viewed primarily as an opportunity to test some new theory or experiment with a sophisticated model. The consultant should have a service-oriented attitude. This emanates from his realization that in exchange for the consulting fee, valuable services are to be provided to the client. The attitude of the consultant must be compatible with serving and fulfilling the client's needs.

The consultant should also have an attitude of respect for the client. Since the client seldom is knowledgeable about quantitative techniques, he often appears to have less than a firm grip on the situation, and a general feeling of incompetence may pervade. But the consultant must realize that the client has lived in the environment that initially is very new to the consultant. As a quantitative specialist, the consultant may know more about technical solutions to problems than the client. But the client surely knows more about his own jungle than anyone else. Give him the credit and respect due. Especially realize that he is a prime asset in facilitating the consultant's efforts to understand problems and relationships, to develop workable solutions, and to design successful implementation strategies. The consultant doesn't have to stay a step ahead of the client and have all the answers to impress him. He will be impressed far more if he is shown the kind of respect he feels is justified. But simply showing an attitude of respect is not enough. The point is this. The talented quantitative consultant truly views the client as an invaluable resource.

### Behavior, Behavior, Behavior

This emphasis on attitude, like the focus on client expectations, is part of a behavioral consciousness that is indispensable for the quantitative consultant. In spite of this importance, the consultant shares a similar guilt with those who are non-quantitative. Whereas the latter fail to recognize the quantitative elements of a problem, the quantitative consultant fails to recognize the behavioral ingredients. Viewing the organization and its problem areas behaviorally and humanistically as well as viewing them as a quantifiable set of interrelated system components is absolutely necessary. This view facilitates the consultant's task in several ways because all systems, models, and procedures proposed, and the process of designing them, involve and have an impact on the working lives of the people in the organization.

Client acceptance of the consultant's efforts is a prerequisite to success, and getting the proposal accepted is enhanced by considering the behavioral ramifications. It is necessary to ask how the proposal affects the client. What's in it for him? How is he benefited? Or, how is he hurt? Does it, for example, reduce his power and prestige? Every proposal has behavioral implications. They must be considered along with the technical aspects of the project. It is important to understand the client and why he behaves as he does. It is especially crucial to realize that he is not in a snow white, ivory-tower environment. Rather he lives in a jungle where decisions are made instinctively, and often non-rationally, based on feelings, emotions, whims, and prejudices. Awareness of these behavioral aspects can help the consultant better understand the client's dilemma in accepting or rejecting the proposal.

Closely related is the necessity to identify and incorporate the behavioral considerations in all proposed solutions and their corresponding implementation strategy. One special concern is to design solutions to reflect behavioral constraints as well as the financial and technical ones. For example, the client may insist that whatever form the solution takes, it must not adversely affect employee morale. In every phase of the development of solutions and implementation strategies, the consultant should not only anticipate adverse behavior but should design mechanisms to either prevent or cope with it. To do this, the consultant must understand human behavior. A proposal that includes these behavioral considerations unquestionably is more acceptable to the client.

A behavioral awareness is important to the quantitative consultant in at least one other area. In the initial stages of the consulting effort, when the analysis and preliminary investigation are being conducted, a good working relationship with people in the organization is an important ingredient of success. Although much of the gathered data comes from records of varying types, much also comes from the client and his employees. It is necessary to realize that each individual represents his own personal interests and in doing so he often shields information and in some cases may even deliberately falsify it. Interestingly, the client who hired the consultant is often the most guilty.

He, like others, wants to make a good impression. He feels a compulsion to disguise any incompetence. And he is especially concerned that the consultant's proposal not reveal any of his inadequacies. Vital information may also be withheld because the consultant is not fully accepted as an "insider." Company secrets regarding future plans may be well guarded. From the clients' point of view, there may be good reason for withholding certain information since a consultant is free to consult with any organization, even a competitor. Yet, the consultant is at an extreme disadvantage when, for whatever reasons, information is deliberately withheld or falsified.

This reluctance to communicate may be present from the outset in some organizations, but more typically it develops later. This invariably occurs in a seemingly innocent and even ironic way. Contrary to what one might first believe, the reception and cooperation given the consultant generally seem quite positive initially. Everyone acts as if they are anxious to "get the facts on the table." Numerous individuals often seem eager to take the consultant aside to pass along confidential information. The consultant is usually delighted that information is surfacing so abundantly, especially because people are coming to him. But beware! A caveat is in order.

When this confidential sharing is allowed to happen, the consultant often becomes alienated from the individuals who first seemed so anxious to help. As they see others also confidentially communicating, they may feel that their own weaknesses have been exposed. This is followed by a tendency to no longer trust the consultant since he could now betray them with the "other" information he has received. Therefore, the consultant is viewed as a threat. To further cooperate with him is considered a magnification of this threat. Thus, innocently but suddenly, the consultant finds himself in a precarious predicament. The most damaging outcome of this situation is not the sudden reduction of communication, but rather the increasing resistance toward his proposals. The confidential communicators are no longer on his team. Worse yet, they may even be on an opposing team. The consultant can often combat this kind of problem by discouraging the communication of information that is irrelevant to the project although it may be interesting. An additional approach is to schedule all interviews with two or more persons. This discourages much of the undesirable kind of confidential communication, and it reduces the suspicion that it is taking place.

## The Environment

In addition to the behavioral considerations of the internal environment, it is absolutely necessary for the consultant to understand the organization's external environment. What are the external variables that influence and constrain the models and systems to be proposed by the consultant? For example, what effect do pollution control laws have on the mathematical constraints in a linear programming model designed to minimize the cost of ingredients in a particular chemical solution? When consulting in the defense industry, do federal requirements to employ specified planning and control techniques dictate the models and systems to propose? Is the business firm in a highly competitive industry that demands safe, low-risk, low-cost solutions? Or can the firm afford to implement sophisticated approaches of moderate risk without jeopardizing its viability? Because these external factors may (1) require selection of alternative models or (2) necessitate substantial alterations in model formulation, the consultant's success is a function of his ability to secure external environmental information and appropriately incorporate it. Accordingly, recommendations must be compatible and consistent with both the external and internal environment.

## Jargon

One final point is worth noting—even though it is frequently mentioned. Whether the consultant is surveying the environment, selling his proposal or implementing a solution, he is continuously communicating with key personnel. Communicating in an understandable way is many times the difference between success and failure as a consultant. And the quantitative consultant is at an unavoidable disadvantage. He lives in a jargon jungle where sophisticated, technical language is second-nature to him. While words like PERT, Monte Carlo, and simplex may be impressive to the client, he is usually turned off with the foreign language of the consultant. It follows, therefore, that there is a direct correlation between the consultant's success and his ability and willingness to talk in laymen's language.

## Compendium

We in the quantitative area have an important role to play as consultants in both public and private organizations. It is important that we acquire the

*Part II: Premodeling*

necessary skills to meet this responsibility. By combining consulting skills with the technical know-how, quantitative consulting can indeed become more effective.

# 7. DEVELOPING A SUCCESSFUL CLIENT-CONSULTANT RELATIONSHIP

*Charles H. Ford*

The next time you are with a group of, say, 10 businessmen and the conversation begins to lag, try slipping in the word, "Consultant," and watch the conversation pick up as passions heat. No doubt, the words "crooks" and "incompetents" and "con-men" will be the more printable ones used. One of the participants is bound to throw in the old cliche, "A consultant is nothing more than an unemployed executive with a briefcase." Almost everyone will have had either an unfortunate experience with a consultant or, more likely, will have *heard* of someone who has.

In short, as more businesses operating in today's complicated, ultra-competitive, shortage-ridden business climate can profitably use a consultant's services, the profession's reputation is sliding down hill.

Let's try to add some perspective to the situation: Business has become and is becoming even more compartmentalized in terms of specialized functions. Ten years ago, for example, few businesses were concerned with the ecological impact of their operations. Equality of employment opportunity was on the basis of race; today sex must be considered as well. OSHA is a new force to contend with. New computer applications appear almost daily. Shortages have introduced both new production problems and marketing problems.

Couple all this with the on-going situation of new marketing and new product opportunities and new manufacturing techniques both procedural and equipmental; throw into the equation the pervasive problem of in-bred management whose perspective is sometimes obscured by being too close to a problem and whose frames of reference are based on "What we've always done" and a pretty good case can be made for the outsider who has a high level of expertise in one or more fields; whose experience is based on the experience of a multiplicity of companies and whose frames of reference are not bound by in-bred company habits and attitudes.

Editors' Note: Reprinted with permission from *Human Resources Management*, volume 13, number 2, Summer 1974, pp. 2–11, Graduate School of Business Administration, University of Michigan, Ann Arbor, MI 48109.

Why, then, the rancor? The answer is twofold. First, an increasing number of client-consultant relationships have simply not worked out. And as the cost of most everything has gone up, so has the cost of this failure. In very simple terms, in those cases which did not work out, either the consultant did not do what he should have done or the client did not do what he should have done. More likely, the answer lies in a combination of mutual culpability.

Second, one does not hear with the same expression of heat and passion of successful client-consultant relationships for the same reason that newspapers do not bother to print good news. Thus, the failures take on added significance and tend to tarnish the whole aspect of consulting.

We here, of course, are concerned with why these relationships are not successful and what a client should do to insure that they will be.

We cannot help, unfortunately, the fact that most of the reasons for failure once stated appear painfully obvious. Even though the reader might conclude that "This couldn't happen to me," one must remember that client-consultant relationships are often new experiences for the client and thus he lacks the perspective of previous experience. The obviousness of failure becomes first a product of 20-20 hindsight and second, is often lost in the welter of recrimination that follows an unsuccessful relationship.

The examples we will use are typical of what has and is happening. They will not tax the reader's imagination—nor are they meant to. Rather, they seek to serve by illustration the pitfalls that client companies fall into and how they can be avoided. Let the reader be assured that if the causes of failure were profound, we would illustrate our points by profundities, but to do so in the light of reality would only serve to obscure the real simplicities of the problem. Now let us examine the causes of failure based on what the consultant should have done or did not do.

## About the Consultant

1. THE CONSULTANT FAILS TO IDENTIFY THE REAL PROBLEM. A large ladies lingerie manufacturer found its sales slipping. Its salesmen complained that its high prices were making the line noncompetitive.

"Not so," humphed the president. "These guys have had it too soft too long. Now that things have gotten rough competitively, they've forgotten how to sell. We'll get them back to fundamentals."

Enter the Sales Engineering Consultant. After analyzing the situation he agreed with the president's conclusion. He went to work holding sales meetings, setting up incentive programs and quotas, holding classes in salesmanship. "We don't need him to teach us how to sell," the salesman complained. "Some of us were selling before he was out of diapers." For emphasis, four of the company's twelve salesmen promptly quit. Sales continued to slide. Exit the sales engineer.

"Perhaps," thought the president, "I'd better look into my costing procedures." Enter the Cost Consultant. He was appalled at the simplicity and looseness of the present costing system and agreed that the problem must be there.

He proceeded to set up an elaborate costing and cost control system that would have required two extra people to administer. No one could fault his in-depth approach but when his unit costs came out approximately the same as what the company was already using, he too got his walking papers.

"That's it for consultants," said the president. "All I've got to show for them is four less salesmen and a bigger hole in my bank account." "Try one more," suggested his worried banker. "Let's try a manufacturing specialist." Enter the manufacturing specialist. "Your plants are ten years behind the times," he suggested. He laid out a program for modernizing equipment, methods and cost controls. The company and the bank went along with the program. Result: Costs came down, prices followed; sales went up.

Two consultants (and the company president) had attacked the symptoms of the problem rather than the root cause. Regardless of their competence within their fields, their failure was preordained simply because they failed to look sufficiently beyond their specialties to determine whether they (their specialties) were really the problem areas that needed solving in order to achieve the client's objective, namely, to increase sales.

2. THE CONSULTANT PROMISES TOO MUCH TOO SOON. No one calls in a consultant unless he has a problem. This in itself generally creates a susceptibility to the consultant's expansive expression of confidence in his ability to solve the problem.

Many problem solutions look easy when discussed across a desk. The problem is often stated in such a way as to make the solution seem text book. At this point, in the absence of specifics and problem nuances, it is often discussed in abstract terms. As a result, the consultant sometimes tends to tie his promise of success to the obvious simplicity of the solution. The client, often desperate, is eager to accept it. Thus, we have the elements of a potential explosion.

In actually addressing himself to the solution, however, the consultant often finds nuances that he hadn't expected—and the possibility of which he hadn't advised the client—perhaps elements of the problem that were not discussed at the interview because of the client's prejudicial point of view or because of his failure to attach significance to them. Perhaps the consultant finds other problems that flow into the main problem which gives it a different complexion from what he expected. As a result, he finds that the easy solution upon which he based his promises has changed along with his ability to deliver.

For example, a consultant was called in to help reorganize a metal works company. The average age of the top 12 executives was 59. The president, 64, felt that the company's decline was due to the rigid thinking of his deeply patterned executives. He asked the consultant to run an executive evaluation of each department head and to recommend executive replacement where necessary. "I just can't get these people to move. The industry is passing us by and we just sit and look at each other. These people have been with me a long time. Too long perhaps."

Not an unusual situation, thought the consultant. Finding the weak sisters ought not to be too difficult, he assured the president. He'd soon have things turned around. The president was blissfully reassured. The consultant accepted the president's premise that the latter's dynamism was being sabotaged by the conservativeness of his key people. "It's like punching a balloon," complained the president. "My inputs just don't come out the other side when they're filtered through my key people."

The deeper the consultant probed, however, the more apparent it became that the problem lay principally with the president himself and the executive vice president—a presidential brother-in-law, a relationship which had not been explained at the interview. Both were in reality quite antagonistic to change ("I built this company, dammit, and I know what built it") and in a position to shift the responsibility of the company's resultant decline to the department heads.

Virtually every executive the consultant interviewed could pull programs and ideas out of his desk that had been submitted and rejected. To the consultant, most of these made sense.

Final result? The consultant suggested that it might be a good idea if the president turned the reins over to someone else and went fishing. And while he was doing it, he might take his brother-in-law with him. The reaction, predictably, was explosive. Consulting had incurred another vocal enemy simply because the consultant promised expansively what he couldn't deliver. Even though he had the answer, it was not the one he had promised.

3. THE CONSULTANT FAILS TO SPECIFY HIS ROLE. Often a consultant will accept an assignment and not indicate clearly to the client what form his help will take.

A consultant was hired by a large stereo equipment manufacturer to reorganize the company. The company felt it needed to regear itself to meet new changes in consumer buying habits and increased foreign-made competition. "Our organization functioned well during the growth years because we developed a good product line and the market was waiting for us. Now we're being hurt by a contracting market and not only is our domestic competition importing components from abroad but foreign competition itself is exporting to this country. We need to shift gears both organizationally to cut our costs and functionally to meet the shift in consumer buying habits."

The consultant agreed with the need. In came his associates with pencils and clipboards. Surveys were made, executives were evaluated, new production methods and techniques were developed. Two months later, the consultant submitted his report—all 104 pages of it single-spaced. He followed this up with his final bill.

The client hit the ceiling. "The report is fine," he said, "if I had the time to read it, digest it and could understand it. I thought the consultant would hold us by the hand during the reorganization and follow up on it to make sure it worked—and to make adjustments where it didn't. By the time I got through reading this report, I could have done the job myself."

The report now reposes in the president's desk drawer. The company is out nearly $44,000 and the company's executives have very unkind things to say about consultants and consulting.

4. THE CONSULTANT FAILS TO ADAPT TO THE INDIVIDUALITY OF THE CLIENT'S PROBLEMS. Consultants, as anyone else, often develop patterns of approaches based on their experiences. Often they view situations as they should rather than as they are.

An "expert" on organization was called in by a growing conglomerate to help the company work in the newly acquired management teams it was absorbing. Coincidentally, he (the consultant) had just performed the same job for another conglomerate. The previous company had a strong operations-oriented management team. Its philosophy was to buy ailing companies at bargain prices and turn them around. With this company, the consultant had strengthened the bonds of corporate management and weakened the authority of the absorbed managements. It worked. The strong-willed competent corporate management made itself felt with success on the less competent absorbed managements.

The consultant was delighted. In his enthusiasm, he wrote an article on the subject based on his successful experience. Conglomerates, he concluded, should have strong central managements. With his previous success as a blueprint, he promptly proceeded to reorganize the latest client the same way. The result was chaos.

Theoretically, it should have worked and he would die, if necessary, defending his approach. After all, it *had* worked before. He had the experience to prove it. The client must be doing something wrong, he contended.

Unfortunately, although the circumstances appeared to be the same, obviously they were not. The top management of the latter client was financially oriented—not operationally oriented. Its philosophy was to buy moderately successful companies and infuse additional capital necessary to help them grow further. The absorbed managements were far more competent to operate their companies, to assess the risks, etc., than corporate management.

The company saved itself by *reversing* the consultant's blueprint and delegating more authority to the absorbed managements—the same managements that had built the successful subsidiaries in the first place and needed only the motivation of increased authority to make them continue to grow. The company's president made a vow never again to hire a consultant even if, at a later date, the firm faced disaster.

The consultant often fails to tailor his approach to the unique and different circumstances of his client. And every company is unique and different, with different people, different attitudes, operating under different pressures. The gap in communication so frequently complained about between the client's people and the consultant is most often due to the consultant's failure to adapt his approach to the specifics of the client company.

5. THE CONSULTANT'S RECOMMENDATIONS ARE NOT FEASIBLE. There is a marked difference, obviously, between a good theoretical recommendation and a feasible practical one. And one consequential difference is a satisfied client and an unsatisfied one.

A medium-sized toy manufacturer had grown rapidly in the past few years. Its staff was located in three buildings in two different cities, forty miles apart. Two of these buildings also housed its two factories. The third building housed only part of its staff. All three buildings were older types and low rental. Like Topsy, the company had just grew. It had concentrated its capital efforts in new equipment and product development to the point where it was skating on a thin edge of working capital.

It discovered that as it grew, staff coordination became a problem. It called in an organization specialist to help solve the problem. He analyzed the communications breakdown and concluded that the obvious and best solution was to house the staff in one building. This noble bit of intelligence cost the client $3,100.

"I didn't need to spend $3,100 for that answer," said the company president, not without heat. "If we had the money to build or lease a new headquarters, we'd have already done it. We're not that stupid." Discarding the consultant's report, the company, although disenchanted with consultants, was prevailed upon to hire a communications specialist. He promptly proceeded to set up a time-controlled system of interoffice, interplant communications. Although it was not the optimum solution, everyone agreed, at least it "will help us grease the wheels to keep things moving until we retrench our capitalization to the point where we can consolidate our staff into one building."

Optimum solutions, defensible on paper, are often not the "best" solutions for a particular time. When the consultant fails to distinguish this difference, the client-consultant relationship is doomed to failure.

6. THE CONSULTANT LACKS COMPETENCE. And here, reluctantly, we must include the "Con man." Many consultants simply lack the expertise or temperament with which to solve a company's problem. The "con man" is the one who, despite this, attempts to sell his services—and, unfortunately, often does. He relies on glibness, rash promises, name dropping, and often a working knowledge of the language used in his field of "expertise."

For example, the principal of a consulting firm visited a glove plant. He had never before been in one. Before going in he asked one of his senior consultants, who had made the contact and who had toured the plant, to name an operation. "Thumb setting." "How many do they do an hour?" "About 120."

When he too was given the tour, he stopped at the thumb-setting operation, turned to the company's vice president of manufacturing and noted, "Hmm, thumb setting. What do you run an hour, about 120?" This established him as an "expert" on manufacturing gloves.

Incompetence, of course, goes beyond the realm of deceit. A consultant may have worked for one or two companies, specializing in one area of operations. His successful experience, he feels, qualifies him to give counsel and advice. It may—and it may not. The problems he faced previously may not be the same problems, even within the same field of specialty, that the client company faces. Or he may not be accountable in the same way as he was when he worked for an employer, and his solutions to problems may be more conservative or more radical than those he would have made when he was accountable.

Or his previous method of problem solving may have been through trial and error—a luxury a client can ill afford if he's paying for outside expertise. Or his employment experience may have been such that he had had competent guidance—a factor that may be missing when he goes out on his own.

The reasons for incompetence are many and diverse and we need not dwell on them any further except to note in summary that consultants, as any other group of people, range from good to bad.

## Some General Observations

Before getting into the client's contributions to the failure of a client-consultant relationship, we should make some observations. The reader will note that some of these contributions are so basic as to belong in an elementary primer on management. In substance, for example, we will point out that the client should exercise care in selecting a consultant and should know how the consultant will operate before he starts. Most readers, sophisticated and hard-headed, will smite their foreheads in anguish over this basic advice. "Come on, now," is apt to be the plea. "We didn't come this far only to be told this."

Unfortunately, between the smite and practice something frequently happens. While admittedly many prospective clients are likely to establish the client-consultant relationship on some pretty firm ground, we are concerned here with the failure of these relationships, not the successes—and how these failures can be reduced.

With this in mind, let's look at why an experienced manager may commit a fundamental error which seems quite obvious when viewed in retrospect or when committed to paper.

1. Most consultants "sell" very well. They have to. They are selling an expensive intangible service to a very sophisticated market—top managements—and the cultivation of a good selling approach is a must. Virtually every consultant makes a good appearance. He generates an enthusiasm and climate of confidence that is often infectious—especially to a man who has lived with and brooded over a problem and who perhaps has reached the point where he's given up on it and recognizes the need for outside help. The consultant is almost always well spoken with a glibness in the language of the trade. He is generally well read and can cite the latest concepts in management technique that may or may not be applicable to the prospective client's problem—but which are impressive nonetheless.

He is often familiar with the problems of other companies (either through his experience, his reading, or his conversations with others) and how they did or did not solve their problems. This increases the client's receptivity to the consultant's "selling" because he is made to feel that the consultant knows a whole lot more about his problem than he (the prospective client) because the consultant either explicitly or implicitly indicates a familiarity with this type of problem.

Thus, what may appear to the prospective client a crisis problem often feeds back as just another easily soluble run-of-the-mill job for the consultant. The relief in being able to turn this over to the latter, to be able to turn his attention to other problems and opportunities with the feeling that the present problem is in capable, knowledgeable hands, can often make the prospective client a little careless in laying the proper groundwork for the resultant relationship.

2. The prospective client is often isolated from the specific problems of other companies and their company peculiarities. He recognizes the insularity produced by his company's in-bred attitudes and limited frames of reference. There is the feeling (and generally true) that the consultant because of his third-party perspective can bridge the gap between these attitudes and the rest of the industry "out there." Most companies' top executives harbor the subconscious feeling that someone else may be doing

something better and they won't find out about it until it's too late.

The consultant's experience may crisscross the industry and can provide this information—especially when the consultant drops the right tactical hints. This too tends to make some prospective clients, if caught at the right time, less prone to do their homework.

3. Many prospective clients don't delve as much as they should into how the consultant will operate. The reason is simple. They assume the consultant knows his business and they (prospective clients) are often results oriented. Most top managements adhere pretty strongly to the principle of delegation, e.g., delegate responsibilities and evaluate results (even though in practice this principle is all too often ignored) and carry it over to the operation of a client-consultant relationship. This type of delegation is fine and desirable if the delegatee is an executive of the company building a career and risking this career constantly by his success or failure to achieve results. However, the consultant does not risk this. Obviously, he wants to succeed. But his relationship with the prospective client is not a career one. It may, and most likely will be, a one-time shot. Therefore, his mode of operation should become an important evaluative consideration to the client in determining whether to consummate the client-consultant relationship. All too often, unhappily, it is not.

With this background in mind, let's now look at the client's contributions to the failure of a client-consultant relationship and more specifically, what he can do to reduce the incidence of failure.

### Now, About the Client

As we stated previously, this coin has two sides. From the consultant's side of responsibility, we've covered some of the reasons why the client-consultant relationship doesn't work. We cannot leave the client out of this negative equation because he too may share the culpability. At the same time that we analyze his contribution to it, we will also note what steps he can take to insure that his experience with a consultant is both profitable and nonexplosive.

1. THE CLIENT FAILS TO PROPERLY SCREEN A PROSPECTIVE CONSULTANT. Consultants come in all shapes and forms—from the one-man generalist to the one-man specialist; from the large firm with many consultants and many specialties to the moonlighting academician. Their specialties may vary from organization to data processing; from decision-making courses to fair employment practices; from labor relations to definition of management goals. The list is endless and if one probed deeply enough, one would even find consultants to consultants.

The prospective client, therefore, has a wide field to choose from. In selecting one, the client should exercise the same caution he uses in selecting a top executive. What is the consultant's experience? Whom did he work for and what did he accomplish? Does the consultant's field of expertise tie in with the client's needs? Is the consultant's personality such as to permit him to work with the company's people or will he generate negative-productive antagonisms?

The client should check references and previous clients to verify the consultant's claims to success. Any consultant's refusal to cooperate in this background check should in itself raise a red flag of caution. Many consultants come to a client through one referral. Yet the new client's problems may not have the same mixture as the referral client's. Therefore, the former should, where possible, check beyond the one reference.

It has been a constant source of amazement to us how many hard-bitten, tough-minded, normally cynical executives accept at face value the man with whom they are ready to make a generally very expensive commitment—both in terms of fees and potential internal disruption.

2. THE CLIENT DOES NOT SEEK CLARIFICATION OF HOW THE CONSULTANT WILL OPERATE. At the interview stage, a prospective client should have a clear-cut understanding of the approach the consultant intends to use and basically his method of operation.

These are the types of questions that should be asked: Will the consultant simply observe? Will he use a stopwatch? Will he be interviewing executives and/or employees? If so, which ones? How long will the job take? Will the consultant's services be intermittent or continuous until completion? What help will he need from the company? What records will have to be made available to him? Will he provide interim reports? Will he conduct expensive surveys that perhaps the company has already made? How many people will be assigned to the job? What are the potentials for disruption of the company's day-to-day operations? In short, the client should clearly understand what this comparative stranger will be doing around the company during his tenure.

3. THE CLIENT FAILS TO SEEK CLARIFICATION OF WHAT HIS MONEY WILL BUY. Here again, a clear-cut understanding should be reached at the interview stage. What exactly will the consultant do in terms of solving problems? Will he simply submit a report? Will he survey and do nothing more than redefine the problems from his perspective? Will he follow up on his recommendations? Will he provide interim reports, written or oral? Will he hold the client's hand and implement his recommendations? Will the client be doing business with the consultant or the consultant's staff? Does the consultant plan return visits to check on the implementation of his recommendations and adjust them where necessary?

If, for example, he finds a piece of equipment antiquated, will he simply note that fact or will he be specific in terms of suggesting a replacement by brand, cost and anticipated results? How much will this service cost?

If the consultant operates on a per diem basis, how many days should it take? And if the fee includes "expenses," just what do these expenses include?

Obvious? Seemingly so. Yet, surprisingly, many clients engage consultants without ever really knowing what final product they are buying until the very end of the consultant's tenure. By then, it's too late.

4. THE CLIENT FAILS TO ACCURATELY IDENTIFY THE PROBLEM. We have already covered this facet from the point of view of the consultant. Let's look at it now from the client's. A small tool manufacturer found his costs were excessively high—as evidenced by the fact that while his prices were competitive, his competition was making money. High costs, he concluded, could only mean low productivity from equipment and/or personnel. His profit structure had been keeping pace with the rest of the industry up until a year ago. He called in a consulting firm heavily experienced in manufacturing.

After seven weeks of effort, the consulting firm, by revamping assembly lines, reduced manufacturing costs by $3\frac{3}{4}\%$. Within his field of specialty, the consultant apparently did a competent job. The economics of the situation, however, were such that his bill, $11,000, absorbed the first 16 months of savings. The client was not ecstatic over the results, especially since the resultant savings did not really solve his problem.

Four months later, quite by accident, the client discovered that he had been buying a raw material alloy that was 12% higher in cost than what his competition was buying for a slightly different but equally functional material. Somewhere along the line the industry had changed alloys and he hadn't gotten the word. His purchasing department had been exposed to the new material but somehow between purchasing, engineering and manufacturing, this exposure came to a dead end. As his company had a 58% material factor, a switch to the new material added almost 7% to his profits.

Identifying this type of problem is, of course, difficult. If it does elude identification or if there is any possibility that the problem itself lies elsewhere, then the client should enlist the aid of the consultant.

When interviewing the latter, the client should explain his definition of the problem and, if necessary, have the consultant spend a few days verifying it before committing both the client and consultant to a long-term expensive commitment. In the above case, the client should have explained that his profits were about 2% of sales as opposed to about 9% for the rest of the industry. He should then have had the manufacturing consultant determine whether, after an analysis, he (the consultant) saw the possibility of saving enough by altering manufacturing procedure to increase the profitability of the company up to the industry average. And, if so, how?

5. THE CLIENT FAILS TO EXPLAIN ITS RESOURCE LIMITATIONS. At the initial interview or shortly after the consultant has assessed the problem, the client should explain what resources the company has available for solving the problem plus any other limitations not at once apparent. The obvious purpose is to permit the consultant to either tailor his solutions to what is available or to very quickly assess whether he can indeed develop a useful product with these limitations.

For example, a consultant was called in by a medium-sized luggage manufacturer to reorganize its manufacturing plant. The plant was housed in an old building and its equipment reflected the age of the building. The consultant drew up a list of recommendations for the purchase of new equipment. With it, he recommended a new production flow line. "This will result," he reported proudly three weeks later, "in approximately $200,000 in labor savings per year. In addition, using the same space now being used, production output will increase 15-20%."

"How much will it cost?" asked a suspicious company president.

"The major pieces of equipment will run about $850,000 and ancillary equipment perhaps another $75,000."

"Beautiful!" said the president. "If we were General Motors, which we are not. We're up to our neck at the banks as it is. We thought if we went something less than first class, we could make a good start for something like $250,000 and then with the savings from that investment continue a program of modernization."

The consultant submitted his bill for $8,500 and went off into the sunset mumbling something about "Why didn't someone tell me?" The president mumbled also. "That's the trouble with consultants. It's not their money. What do they care how they spend it?"

6. THE CLIENT FAILS TO ADEQUATELY INFORM HIS ORGANIZATION OF THE CONSULTANT'S ROLE AND GOALS. An electric appliance manufacturer projecting a substantial increase in his sales volume decided that his middle and lower levels of management needed to reorganize for this expansion. New responsibilities would have to be assigned; decision making at these levels would now have a greater impact as volume increased.

He called in an organizational specialist. "I've got good people. But I'm not sure we've delegated enough responsibility to make them maximally effective. I can visualize hiring more people as our sales increase but before I do, I want to make sure I'm using the people I've got to the fullest."

The client then passed the word along in memo form: "On Sept. 6th, Mr. —— will, as an outside consultant, work with us in reorganizing our management structure. Your fullest cooperation is requested." Panic hit the ranks. There is a natural inclination to equate "reorganization" with "reductions in force." And an outside consultant is often considered a euphemism for "hatchet man."

Instead of getting cooperation, the consultant got inflated definitions of the responsibilities from the people he interviewed. Knives were sharpened as most of the executives attempted to defend their own jobs. It was every man for himself. The only unity was in mutual distrust of the consultant. The resistance fed on itself and reached the point where the consultant reported that his efforts were coming to nought. "They're pulling in one direction. I'm pulling in another. I can't get a straight story from anyone." The client blamed the consultant. "I can't hold your hand on this. Maybe it's the way you're going about it." The consultant's departure was imminent.

Fortunately, when the dust of recrimination cleared, the president issued a clarifying memo stressing that the reorganization would not result in reductions of force but rather would involve more individual responsibilities with greater personal opportunities through more visible efforts.

Failure to establish a cooperative climate for the consultant by top management is one of the chief reasons for the failure of the client-consultant relationship. It is often not recognized because the latter's natural tendency is to lay the blame for an antagonistic nonproductive climate on the consultant's techniques and personality.

7. THE CLIENT FAILS TO ADEQUATELY TRY TO SOLVE ITS OWN PROBLEMS. A medium-sized food processing company found its sales slipping. It called in a marketing specialist firm.

The consulting firm spent the first six weeks doing market surveys. It developed a very comprehensive picture of the company's marketing position, market potential, product acceptance, etc. Once it felt it had the tools with which to work, it went to work to try to solve the problem. During the course of its efforts, the senior consultant on the job lunched with the assistant sales manager. He posed the question, "What do you think is wrong?"

"I don't think. I know. Our salesmen were put on salary. They should be on commission. Our sales manager, my boss, is a driver. His idea of sales managing is to climb on his salesmen's backs. Their morale is shot and with little possibility of seeing their efforts more tangibly rewarded, their retaliation is to lay down on the job."

"Why haven't you told anyone?"

"I have. My boss. He told me that this is the way he did it with his previous company, not incidentally a food processing company, and this is the way we're going to do it here. I can't go over his head."

The consultant recommended that the salesmen be put on commission and that the sales manager be replaced. His fee for $7\frac{1}{2}$ weeks of work including the surveys came to $38,000—equivalent to slightly less than three years salary for the assistant sales manager. The company had the answer all the time. It just never looked for it; never probed deeply enough within its own organization for the answer. The company, therefore, had, in reality, no need for an outside consultant. When the story came out, it felt bilked. It hadn't been bilked. The consultant simply did what the company could have and should have done itself. This logic, however, has not abated its newfound antipathy toward consultants.

## How Contacts Are Made

We should perhaps say a word about how contacts are made between client and consultant.

1. THE CLIENT LOOKS FOR A CONSULTANT. This occurs when the prospective client recognizes the need for a consultant either to evaluate a course of action before it is taken, to solve a particular problem or to evaluate a potential opportunity. Sources available to a prospective client to help him zero in on a consultant include friends, relatives, business acquaintances, trade associations, mailings from consultants, chance reading of a consultant's writings that touch a nerve, deans of graduate business schools (for moonlighting faculty members with generally very good in-depth skills), consultants' associations, etc. The list is endless. One might even find a consultant by cruising cocktail parties where someone is bound to be a "consultant." *Finding* a consultant is easy. One need, in fact, go no further than the yellow pages. Finding the *right* consultant is not so easy. Of the list above, trade associations, business acquaintances and graduate business school deans probably represent the most reliable sources.

2. THE CONSULTANT LOOKS FOR A CLIENT. Here again we touch on mailings which generally include brochures and the inevitable copies of testimonials, etc. Mailings, however, are not generally productive to the prospective client unless the consultant is a specialist and his specialty hits a bull's eye on a current or incipient problem with which a prospective client might be wrestling.

A second way is for the consultant to make a referral part of his deal with another client. "Mr. Smith, we do expect and hope that after we do a good job for you, you will perhaps call one or two business acquaintances and suggest that it might be useful if they see us." Sometimes they add, "It is this quid pro quo that reduces our selling costs and the savings, of course, are reflected in our fee schedule." This method can be useful if there is some relationship between the problem the referral had and the problem the prospective client has.

The third method is the cold call. This may be to sell a specific service (setting up a computerized bookkeeping system, for example) or a general service ("For a moderate fee, we'll send our people in to survey your business and make appropriate recommendations."). The latter consultant generally has a list of people that may be called for referrals. Unfortunately, the list of less satisfied clients is generally larger, and of course, is tactfully omitted. This type of consultant, incidentally, is the most prone to make recommendations that are not feasible or which do not take into account the peculiarities of a particular business. At best, the prospective client would be taking pot luck.

## Summary

Although most of the examples we've used relate to medium-sized companies, the principles apply also to small and large corporations. We believe the reader will share our conclusion that developing a higher rate of successful client-consultant relationships depends primarily on what safeguards the client takes initially. Despite the fact that the principle of *caveat emptor* applies in full force to this relationship, the company that feels the need for outside help ought not be deterred from seeking it.

A one-time expenditure to organize an on-going operation or a facet of management can be an extremely profitable investment. Nothing in this article should be inferred to discourage such investments. The inference, rather, is an exhortation to make them judiciously with a minimum of risk and a maximum of return. This judicious process starts with a recognition of the potential pitfalls.

# C. Intraorganizational Relationships with the Client

## 8. INTEGRATION AND UTILIZATION OF MANAGEMENT SCIENCE ACTIVITIES IN ORGANIZATIONS

*Michael Radnor, Albert H. Rubenstein
and Alden S. Bean*

---

### Introduction

The integration of the management sciences into U.S. business organizations has been continuing over approximately the last 15 years. The problems engendered by this process of organizational change have been the

Editors' Note: Reprinted with permission from *Operational Research Quarterly*, June 1968, pp. 117–141.

*Table 1: Distribution of companies by industry*

| | | | |
|---|---|---|---|
| Aircraft and aerospace | 5 | Food | 10 |
| Chemical and pharmaceutical | 14 | Materials processing | 6 |
| Electrical | 5 | Oils | 6 |
| Engineered products | 7 | Service | 6 |
| Financial | 4 | Transportation | 3 |

subject of considerable speculation and theorizing in both the professional operational research/management science (OR/MS) and general business literature but of very little empirical research. For the last 6 years we have been gathering data on how this integration has been proceeding and in this paper we report on a partial analysis of a portion of our data. Both the analysis of the present data and the continued collection of new data is still in progress, and the study has recently been extended to include U.S. Federal Civilian Agencies, and to several other countries.

The data which we are presenting at this time have been drawn from 66 major U.S. corporations. The companies are among the biggest in U.S. business, with all but 9 appearing in the 1965 *Fortune* listing of the largest U.S. corporations. We were, therefore, looking at the progress of OR/MS activities in the corporate giants of U.S. business, and we were essentially concerned with corporate rather than divisional activities. Table 1 shows the distribution by industry.

In seeking to establish the probable existence of OR/MS in a company, we asked company members to indicate the location of recognized activities which were performing work utilizing the newer methods of mathematical analyses and/or who were involved in non-routine computer systems activities. These activities were normally described to the firms under such labels as operational research, management science, systems analysis and similar names. We should emphasize at this point that we will be describing U.S. experience. There seems to be little doubt that major differences do exist between the U.S. and U.K. experiences and in the make-up or definition of OR/MS.

### The Changing Spectrum of OR/MS in U.S. Business

Operational research/management science activity in the United States is organizationally very new. Operational research has been on the U.S. industrial scene for little more than 15 years, and for most companies it is far newer than that. Thus our study covers a period in which an innovative function was being introduced into organizations, and it, therefore, understandably reflects the resulting instability engendered by such a change process.

From our data it appears that certain important parameters have emerged from the relative newness of the management science function. A series of introductory and transitional phases in terms of both the personnel in the OR/MS field and in the general environment in which the activities have taken place can be proposed. For example, it appears that since the early 1950's the population of OR/MS practitioners to be found in U.S. industry has gone through, and is continuing to go through, a transformation. Further, there seems to have been a gradual change in the level of awareness and industrial cultural acceptance of the management sciences in U.S. business organizations. Finally, the last 10 years or so have seen the widespread utilization of a new technology that is a major part of and a profound influence on the future of the management sciences—namely, the use of the computer in management information systems. In sum, it seems that we can observe some significant differences in several key parameters between the period of the early 1950's and the early 1960's, and the more recent U.S. experiences, i.e., in the mid-1960's.

## OR/MS Personnel

The behaviour of organizations in their attempts to acquire the new skills that may be necessary to enter a new field is a facet of organizational behaviour that has received relatively scant attention from social scientists. While no adequate theory yet exists in the area, there are indications that might lead us to expect to find changes over time in the populations of personnel who are active in a new organizational function such as OR/MS, and differences in the strategies and success of various organizations in acquiring such new skills.

Let us begin by examining the changes that appear to have occurred in the types of OR/MS personnel being utilized by companies. It appears that at least 5 general categories can be distinguished.

MILITARY TYPES. These were the scientists and mathematicians who have become involved in operational research as a consequence of military operational research activities. These could be further subdivided into: "the pioneers"—those scientists and mathematicians who became involved in operational research during World War II; a small, relatively select group who came into the field under the special conditions of the prevailing war requirements. Our data seem to indicate that a relatively small number of these types are still to be found in general U.S. non-military or non-aerospace business organizations. Thus, in our sample of 66 companies, we were only able to clearly identify 8 such types who have been engaged in such civilian business organizations, with only 3 of these still to be found in 1966. It should be pointed out that more such personnel would undoubtedly have emerged had we conducted major studies with the aerospace and military related firms. There is a second potential population which has received its introduction to and training in OR/MS from the military—namely the post-war military group. Again, in our 66 companies we came across very few such persons.

PROFESSIONAL SCIENTISTS. These are scientists and mathematicians who were brought in to apply operational research techniques, generally during the 1950's. They frequently came from R. and D., engineering, quality control and other engineering staff functions in manufacturing or operations. While this group typically came into the OR/MS picture during the 1950's and the early 1960's we are still able to observe an influx of such types. These new entries are science and mathematics graduates who are entering management science work in their first or near-first jobs.

OR/MS SPECIALISTS. These are practitioners who have received specific training in management science techniques prior to entering their current business careers. They generally have academic qualifications in operations research, computer sciences, applied mathematics and statistics, and systems analysis. These specialists are made up of the relatively few graduates of the early management science programmes in the mid-1950's and the more recently trained practitioners who have graduated from an operational research or modern industrial engineering programme, probably sometime since the early 1960's. These latter personnel are the products of the growing number of U.S. university curricula devoting themselves to operational research as an educational area. Together with this group we are including those people whose training has essentially been in applied mathematics or in electrical engineering and specializing in computer technology.

MANAGEMENT SPECIALISTS. These are the products of some of the more recent, broadly based programmes in industrial engineering, industrial management and business administration which have a significant proportion of their curricula devoted to the quantitative methods, computers and information systems areas. Such practitioners would typically have a B.S. or M.S. in Industrial Engineering or a Masters of Business Administration (M.B.A.).

ORGANIZATION MEN. These are generally production or marketing men or, in some cases, personnel out of the controller's office who have come up through the organization and have moved into OR/MS via computers or through special training. They are sometimes persons who were specifically put into the leadership of OR/MS activities by management in order to infuse some "practicality and/or prestige" into OR/MS. We may speculate that this particular group of people in many cases may represent an interim leadership and that they eventually may be replaced by the OR/MS and

*Part II: Premodeling*

*Table 2: Incidence of OR/MS leader types (major activities)*

| | Military | | Profes-sionals | | OR/MS spe-cialists | | Manage-ment spe-cialists | | Organi-zationals | | Total known |
|---|---|---|---|---|---|---|---|---|---|---|---|
| | No. | % | No. | % | No. | % | No. | % | No. | % | (N) |
| Pre-1950 | 1 | 20 | 0 | — | 2 | 40 | 0 | — | 2 | 40 | 5 |
| 1950-5 | 3 | 12 | 13 | 50 | 3 | 12 | 0 | — | 7 | 27 | 26 |
| 1956-9 | 5 | 10 | 21 | 49 | 4 | 9 | 0 | — | 13 | 30 | 43 |
| 1960-3 | 3 | 7 | 13 | 30 | 9 | 22 | 4 | 10 | 13 | 31 | 42 |
| 1964-6 | 2 | 5 | 8 | 21 | 12 | 28 | 4 | 10 | 16 | 38 | 42* |

*The difference between the N = 42 and the total sample of 66 companies is accounted for by 4 "death" cases where there has been no subsequent rebirth; 22 cases where the leader type data were not available; and minus 2 cases where a company had two major OR/MS activities.

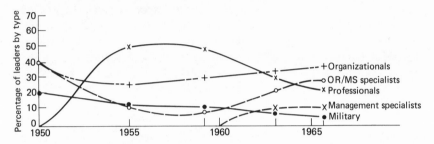

management specialists, particularly the latter, when they have obtained more experience and have themselves become, to some extent, "organization men."

The categorization which we have presented above is closely related to the organization vs. professional orientation dichotomy (or local vs. cosmopolitan).[1]* It also contains the added factors of time, training, age and selection differences. We also recognize that we could expect to find some people who are both highly professionally and highly organizationally oriented.

### Leadership Changes

An examination of the changes in patterns of leadership of OR/MS activities using the above personnel types may help us appreciate the impact of the

[1]A. W. Gouldner, "Cosmopolitans and Locals: Toward an Analysis of Latent Social Roles," *Admve. Sci.* Q2 (1957/8):281.
*We are also indebted to a conversation with Professor John Abrams of the University of Toronto, during which the idea of defining OR/MS personnel in this way was generated in the mind of one of the authors. It is also of interest to note a communication from Professor S. L. Cook in which a similar categorization was suggested.

differences in OR/MS populations. In Table 2 we show the incidence of each of the OR/MS types as leaders of the *"major"* OR/MS activity, at any one time, in each company. We have elected to look at the leadership of only the "major" activities so as to avoid the "noise" which would be generated if one were to admit every activity (including minor ones) in those situations where OR/MS had achieved a measure of organizational "diffusion." The data shown are for those cases where the backgrounds of the leaders were known well enough to enable them to be categorized. As will be seen from the sample sizes, our data were generally fairly complete in this respect. Examination of the patterns of leadership succession by leader types points to a shift toward the management specialists as leaders since 1960. Table 3 groups the leaders according to the organization–professional orientation mentioned earlier.

The various leader types appear to have experienced differences in the type and location of relationship problems in their organizations. Table 4 shows the proportions of each leader type to experience relationship difficulties with "clients," "other non-client staff groups," "top management" and "assorted other departments." It can be seen that the most common source of friction with "clients" came from professional scientist, OR/MS and management specialist groupings, while the organization men seemed

Table 3: Incidence of OR/MS leader types:
professional vs. organizational backgrounds

| At end of period | Professionals | | Organizationals | | Total known (N) |
|---|---|---|---|---|---|
| | No. | % | No. | % | |
| Pre-1950 | 3 | 60 | 2 | 40 | 5 |
| 1950–5 | 19 | 73 | 7 | 27 | 26 |
| 1956–9 | 30 | 70 | 13 | 30 | 43 |
| 1960–3 | 25 | 60 | 17 | 40 | 42 |
| 1964–6 | 22 | 52 | 20 | 48 | 42 |

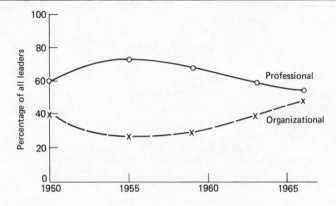

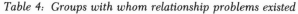

Table 4: Groups with whom relationship problems existed

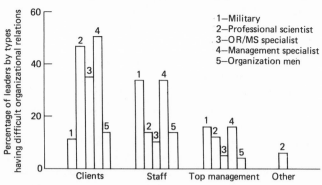

1—Military
2—Professional scientist
3—OR/MS specialist
4—Management specialist
5—Organization men

to have far fewer problems with their clients. The youth of the management specialist group can perhaps help explain their generally poor showing in respect to their relationships with client and staff. Typical of the problems encountered by professional scientist leaders with their clients were complaints of their "inability to communicate" and problems associated with their "difficulties in relation to implementation." By contrast, the professional scientists and to a lesser extent the OR/MS specialists had relatively fewer problems with non-client staff groups, while the organization men seemed to have the same amount of trouble in this respect. This finding that the professional scientist did not get on well with client groups, while the organization man did, and conversely in regard to some of the generally more professionally oriented non-client staff, is readily understandable. It is important to note that in many cases the "clients" were either corporate or divisional "staff" groups, as opposed to "line" groups, with the non-client staff being generally in a service relationship to OR/MS. For example, one highly professionally oriented OR/MS specialist—a leading member of the Operations Research Society of America and the author of a well-known text on OR/MS—had encountered considerable resistance from the manufacturing department but had received excellent cooperation from the head of the economic planning department, a Ph.D. who "understood."

### General Personnel Changes

So far we have been observing the patterns of change in OR/MS leadership. We also have data which indicate that similar changes have been going on among the OR/MS analyst population. These data are not complete since the backgrounds of only a sample of the analyst population were known for most companies. In general the bias was in the direction of our not having data on a larger number of newer inputs to an activity, and on the divisional personnel. So far we see in these data the relatively small and decreasing incidence of the military types, the decline of the professional scientist types since the mid-1950's, and the growth of the OR/MS and management specialists since the early 1960's, particularly the management specialists. The pattern for the organizational type analysts varies from that found with the organizational type leaders. In the case of the analysts we can observe that they represent a far smaller proportion than they did as leaders and that they have failed to grow proportionately. This may be partly due to the absence of data from divisional activities, but it may also reflect a desire to use the organization man as a group leader—to give an activity "prestige, leadership and a practical bent"—but not as an analyst for which he would generally not be technically qualified.

The type of personnel currently being sought to be analysts is of some interest. Five companies indicated that they were looking for OR/MS specialists, 8 for management specialists, and only 1 for a professional scientist. This last was by a professional scientist leader located in a secondary operational research group in a R. and D. department and he was interested in a professional scientist or an OR/MS specialist. In this same company the head of management services, who reported to top management, indicated that he was looking for OR/MS people of the management specialist variety. He said "We will pay $15,000—but don't want a 'math' type." A large processing company with a very successful and well-established OR/MS activity that was currently seeking management specialist types indicated that in 1962 they had had no M.B.A. graduates in their OR/MS activity (which was located in R. and D.), but that this had grown to five M.B.A.'s by 1965. One of their operational research analysts in 1966 commented on these M.B.A.'s by saying "They saw it as a quick way to get into management." It is also of interest to note that none of the companies were looking for military types, or organizational types, and virtually none for professional scientist types.

Similarly, in 1966 the organization man leader of an OR/MS activity in a large food company who was looking for OR/MS and management specialists said that "In the future I won't hire a management science person unless he has at least 2 years' experience"; otherwise he found they were "always looking for cookbook answers" and "they had no common sense." A successful professional scientist, head of management services in a large chemical company, said in 1965 that it was "hard to get people to go beyond numbers. There is need for people who can educate others. It is much easier to find people who are model builders." He indicated that he wanted people "with business school backgrounds, with organization theory and some OR/MS exposure." The personnel manager of a large merchandising house said that they were "having a problem getting the right kind of people" for their OR/MS activity—"Operational research people tend to be 'myopic' in comparison with the experienced organization men" that these latter who "had the 'savvy' [namely organization men] lacked the 'tools'." A number of other companies indicated that they did *not* want any Ph.D.'s. Several firms indicated that they had active internal training programmes in OR/MS techniques for company personnel, and from the text materials supplied to us these would appear to be relatively advanced programmes.

Additional data on company personnel preferences were available from 15 companies (not in the sample of 66) who had placed actual personnel specifications on the job markets. In 7 cases an OR/MS specialist was being sought, in 6 a management specialist, in 1 an OR/MS specialist or a management specialist, and in the final case it was specified that the applicant should not fall into what would, in effect, be the military or OR/MS specialist categories. Thus it would seem that there already have been changes in the make-up of the OR/MS population and that current hiring preferences are in such a direction as to continue the expansion of the OR/MS and management specialists at the expense of the professional scientist types. We would, therefore, expect that these OR/MS and management specialists would become an increasingly larger proportion of OR/MS personnel to be found in the field. There appear, however, to be some significant differences in company preferences between these two categories of personnel.

In summary, the first 15 or so years of OR/MS activities in U.S. business organizations have seen a definite shift in its leadership and technical personnel. We have gone from a leadership in which the professional, scientifically oriented transferee to OR/MS predominated to a period in which both the OR/MS trained specialist and the most broadly trained industrial engineer or business-school-trained personnel types have joined the persistent group of organization men as the most prevalent type of OR/MS leader. At the same time there has been a similar shift in the analyst population, away from the military types and professional scientists to the OR/MS and management specialists. These trends would seem to be continuing with the process probably not yet finding a steady state. Our investigations into these population changes and the career patterns of OR/MS personnel are continuing. We are also hoping to obtain data on the British experience which we suspect may show some rather significant differences from that which we have observed in the U.S. This would seem to be in keeping with Stafford Beer's speculation on the national differences between the American and British operational research situations.[2] In this he would, in our terms, seem to be implying that in British operational research activities, the organizational types have played a larger part than in the U.S., and the professional scientists and OR/MS specialists a much smaller role, with consequent beneficial effects on implementation. This would be congruent with our findings that organization men appeared to have generally better relations with their clients.

[2]C. West Churchman and A. H. Schainblatt, "The Researcher and the Manager: A Dialectic of Implementation," *Mgmt Sci.* (B) 11, No. 4 (February 1965); and *Commentaries* (especially Stafford Beer) 12, No. 2 (October 1965).

## General Changes in the OR/MS Environment

While the above-discussed shift in OR/MS personnel has been taking place there have been a number of changes in the general environment in which OR/MS activities are carried on in companies.

OR/MS EXPOSURE. One of the most frequently discussed requirements for a successful management science activity has been that of giving company managements exposure to and education in the management science area. For example, one phase of the recent discussion in *Management Science* concerning "the dialectic of implementation"[2] was concerned with this question. From our data it appears that relatively few top managers can be said to have had extensive exposure to formal management science programmes, but the degree of such exposure has possibly changed over recent years, and especially so since the widespread utilization of computers in management information systems. In a dozen out of our sample of companies the top managers had recently attended one of the seminars offered by one of the large computer suppliers, had been present at some other type of programme devoted to the applications of either computer and/or management sciences in business decision-making and control, or had attended internal programmes staffed either by their management science personnel and/or by outside consultants or academics, devoted to giving top management some exposure to these ideas. One of the country's largest corporations had kicked off operational research in their company at the divisional level by having all the division managers attend a two-day programme on operational research given by several well-known figures. They were then sent back to their divisions to develop projects with their own staffs that might be amenable to operational research approaches, for presentation to the next general meeting of all top company management. In addition, in a number of cases it was indicated to us that some of the top managers were making it a point to read the more general literature related to this area. It is not uncommon now to find members of top management taking part in conferences and panels where they are representing their company's progress either in the computer systems and/or operational research fields. It was not infrequent in our interviewing of members of top management to have them attempt to probe us on what other companies and their competitors were doing in these fields. There seemed to be a general level of interest in what was happening competitively in OR/MS. While we did not specifically direct questions to this point, in 18 out of the 48 companies recently visited, comments were volunteered concerning what competitors were doing and how their company compared with competition. A top vice-

[2]C. West Churchman and A. H. Schainblatt, "The Researcher and the Manager: A Dialectic of Implementation," *Mgmt Sci.* (B) 11, No. 4 (February 1965); and *Commentaries* (especially Stafford Beer) 12, No. 2 (October 1965).

president in one company said, "If we don't use OR/MS we will be making a serious error. It will put us at a competitive disadvantage to those who do."

THE WIDESPREAD UTILIZATION OF COMPUTERS. Every large company with whom we have been in recent contact was the possessor of a fairly large-size computer system. In 24 out of 42 recent cases, operational research activities, systems design activities and computer operations were in some way, and very often closely, interrelated. Further, in discussing the management science area with members of top management they were often likely, in their discussions, to interrelate the operational research activities with the computer systems design and operations activities. One of the top managers of a large food company, for example, described operational research as "part of the total computer function." This was less often the case for the operational research personnel themselves. In one company in which there was a major push to develop a management information system, the head of the operational research group made the point that operational research was a "larger concept than the computer." This integration by top managers would be in keeping with a concept of the operational research type activities becoming closely tied in with the development of computer systems. In 28 out of 42 companies recently visited there were major computer-oriented programmes going on—generally the design of major management information systems. Further, in 18 cases the operational research activity was either reporting to the manager of the over-all computing and systems activities and/or currently working largely in the information systems area, with 3 to 4 more cases close to this point.

## Location and Mission of OR/MS Activities

While we have been witnessing the above-discussed changes in the population of OR/MS personnel and in its general environment, we have been able also to observe some significant changes in both the location of OR/MS activities in the firm and in their mission.

For the purposes of analysis we have divided up the firm into several spheres of activity, roughly paralleling the normal business functions. These are shown in the form of a stereotype organization chart (Figure 1).

Where and how a company's OR/MS activities are located, and the missions they perform, are clearly dependent upon each other to some degree, and it is, therefore, useful to look at these two variables together. It can be seen from Table 5 that OR/MS activities started in the 1950's to a large extent in R. and D., engineering, manufacturing (or operations), and in the financial area (controllers). During the first few years there was an expansion of the proportion of R. and D. groups, followed since the late 1950's to early 1960's by a period of very substantial relative contraction of OR/MS in R. and D. Engineering and manufacturing generally both failed to estab-

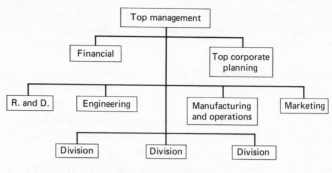

*Figure 1*

*Table 5: Patterns of growth and decline of OR/MS activities throughout 1966 in 66 companies*

| In: | Major OR/MS activities at end of period | | | | | | | | | |
|---|---|---|---|---|---|---|---|---|---|---|
| | Pre-1950 | | 1950–5 | | 1956–9 | | 1960–3 | | 1964–6 | |
| | No. | % | No. | % | No. | % | No. | % | No. | % |
| R. and D. | 1 | 25 | 8 | 29 | 15 | 30 | 9 (6)* | 12 | 3 (5) | 6 |
| Engineering | 1 | 25 | 5 | 18 | 6 | 12 | 4 | 5 | 2 | 4 |
| Manufacturing and operations | 0 | — | 3 (1) | 10 | 5 (1) | 10 | 10 (2) | 13 | 5 (4) | 10 |
| Financial | 2 | 50 | 7 | 25 | 16 | 32 | 22 (2) | 30 | 17 (3) | 34 |
| Top management and planning | 0 | — | 2 | 8 | 6 | 12 | 17 | 23 | 21 | 42 |
| Marketing | 0 | — | 0 | — | 0 | — | 0 | — | 0 (1) | — |
| Divisional | 0 | — | 3 (2) | 10 | 2 (3) | 4 | 1 (8) | 1 | 2 (10) | 4 |
| Total | 4 | 100 | 28 (3) | 100 | 50 (4) | 100 | 73 (18) | 100 | 50 (23) | 100 |
| Diffusions | 0 | — | 2 | — | 1 | — | 8 | — | 14 | — |

*Numbers in parentheses refer to the number of secondary (non-major) activities.

lish themselves as locations of major OR/MS activity. By contrast, the financial area has demonstrated sustained and substantial expansion, to become by the 1960's the major location of OR/MS activities in U.S. business organizations. The possession by the financial function of the vitally important data sources that OR/MS needs to perform, and in many cases the location of the data-processing computer operation in the controller's area have been key elements in this trend.

For example, the demise of one OR/MS activity that had been located in the manufacturing department of a company and its later rebirth under an organizational leader in the controller's department can be directly related to this information problem. Speaking in 1966 of the defunct OR/MS group the controller said:

156

"I opposed the operational research group because they were doing glorified data-processing work. I saw no reason to let them do data processing which is the controller's job." He said that he had been reluctant to permit them to collect data in his office and that "lack of data" had been one of the main reasons for their failure.

Operational research/management science activities in corporate planning and others reporting directly to top management were of relatively minor importance during the first decade, but have grown steadily in proportion to become a significant location in the 1960's. Marketing has been virtually nonexistent as a location for major OR/MS activities until recently, when, as part of a general process of diffusion of OR/MS activity within some firms, marketing OR/MS activities have appeared. The number of divisional activities has in turn grown and contracted over the years, but has recently begun what may turn out to be a period of more sustained development.

The process of "diffusion" of OR/MS activities within the firm is of considerable interest. Such a process might be looked upon as a rationalizing or normalizing of the new management science approaches. We can speculate that we may now be observing in this diffusion, with its implied broader acceptance, the beginnings of a "maturity" phase for OR/MS in U.S. business organizations. The desire of functional and divisional groups to have their own OR/MS would seem to indicate at least some recognition of its value, even though other variables, e.g., desire for control, would also be highly relevant. This might be looked upon as an example of Selznick's co-optation strategy.[3]

Concurrent with these changes in patterns of location have come shifts in the mission or nature of the project portfolios being pursued by the various OR/MS activities. Table 6 shows these changes in overall mission defined in terms of major, mixed or limited project missions. The evaluation of the overall mission was based on both internal company descriptions of the project portfolios at any given period, as well as our own evaluation of their actual project lists. By a major project mission, we are referring to a portfolio which can be generally categorized as devoted to the longer-range, broader-scoped programmes. Included in this grouping would be, for example, efforts devoted to the construction of overall corporate models to be used in planning and in the making of major top management decisions. At the other end of the spectrum we have the limited-project missions devoted to short-run, smaller-scoped problems. Where the programme of an OR/MS activity fell to a major extent towards one or the other of these extremes, then they were so categorized. The others were placed in what we have termed a "mixed" project mission category.

Table 6 shows that approximately 50 per cent of all OR/MS activities in our sample were devoting their efforts to limited-mission portfolios. The

[3]P. Selznick, *TVA and the Grass Roots* (Berkeley: University of California Press, 1949).

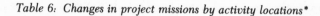

Table 6: Changes in project missions by activity locations*

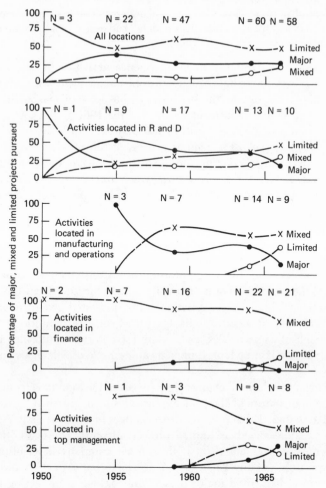

*Individual figures omitted for activities located in engineering and planning (see text).

mixed portfolio was being followed by a growing segment, reaching approximately 30 per cent of the total by the 1964–6 period; this at the expense of emphasis to major project missions, which has fallen steadily as a percentage since about 1950 from over 40 per cent down to 20 per cent of the total. If we examine the portfolio trends through each period we can observe the on-going activities tending to move away from the long-range major portfolios. This comes about by a combination of mission change and by a net reduction in the number of new activities coming in with long-range missions (net of activities ceasing operation). This consolidated picture, however, combines several contrary trends which can be observed in the various organizational areas.

The drop in emphasis given to major projects by activities located in R. and D. is sharply visible, with the limited-project portfolios becoming quite prevalent. In fact, what we are observing is not only a de-emphasis of the major model-building-type activities but also in some cases a withdrawal of R. and D. activities from corporate decision-making programmes and a concentration on design of experiments and on R. and D. project selection activities. This can be seen for both the long-standing activities and for those coming in more recently. A good example of this type of change in emphasis occurred in a large oil company:

> In 1966 a member of top management commented that the OR/MS group, which in 1960 had been located in R. and D., had been focusing their efforts on marketing requirements and that "they didn't do so well. *They took a 'total systems approach.'* It was so all-encompassing that had they stuck to it, *it would still have been ten years before we had had anything in operation.* They were spending many man-years in problem definition and discussions. *I made them retreat and take a more restrictive view* and they have since gotten some applications that have been quite profitable. I have a healthy scepticism on the costs of building and maintaining corporate models." This activity was subsequently transferred to the controller's department in the financial area of the company in late 1960.

The mission spectrum of OR/MS activities in manufacturing and operations shows, as one might expect, a tendency to emphasize the limited type of projects, with a steady decline in major programmes. There were 3 activities started in 1950–5 which are exceptions to this trend. Of the 3, one "died" shortly after its formation, a second was transferred to planning in 1963 and the last transferred to top management in 1964.

This emphasis on the short-term, limited portfolio was particularly evident in the case of OR/MS activities located in financial departments. We did, however, note a slight tendency for the newer entries to de-emphasize this type of work. Contrary to what we might have expected, activities reporting to top management have also in the past devoted themselves to limited activities although we found that this has been changing, with the newer OR/MS entries emphasizing the longer-range and mixed missions. Although we have not illustrated the case of groups located in planning departments, they have as would be expected emphasized the major programmes, although even there some shorter-term work has been pursued.

In summary, and perhaps contrary to much of the discussion one tends to hear in OR/MS circles as to where the "real" pay-offs from OR/MS work lie (namely the long-range major programmes), it would appear that the trends in actual portfolio emphasis had been for OR/MS activities to begin to move toward the major programmes up through the middle 1950's, possibly influenced by the then-current operational research philosophies, but then to move steadily away from this "grand optimization" type concept, over the next few years, with this trend only beginning to be reversed with the advent of OR/MS activities in corporate planning groups in the late

1950's to early 1960's. Also relevant to this recent shift has been the entry of the large computer set-ups.

At this point it would seem reasonable to tie together the location of OR/MS activities in R. and D. under the leadership of a professional scientist or an OR/MS specialist and the activity's engagement in long-range major model-building activities with resulting problems with clients and management. Similarly, at least in the short run, an OR/MS activity in finance lead by an organizational type, and working on short-range service programmes, might be expected to encounter fewer client and management problems. Examination of the relationships between the organizational location of OR/MS, its leadership type and the incidence of relationship problems with clients helps illustrate these remarks in terms of the incidence of deaths, declines and pattern of transfers of major corporate and divisional OR/MS activities. By decline we refer to the situation where the major OR/MS activity in a company ceases to fulfil that role, with this generally being taken over in some other area. The heaviest attrition rates from these causes occurred when OR/MS activities were located in R. and D., engineering and in manufacturing. In more recent years we have observed several transfers out of the financial area but with most of these going up to top management, and one to planning. Most of the transfers from R. and D. were to finance, which provided 50 per cent of its transferee intake. Top management OR/MS activities have emerged primarily as a result of transfers in, with 10 out of 16 total starts, and 50 per cent of these coming from finance. It would also be noted that 34 per cent of the 125 major corporate activities that were identified in the 66 sample companies had either been transferred or died during the last 15 years, a good reflection of the degree of ferment engendered by the introduction of this new organizational function.

It is also interesting to note the timing of these declines, deaths and transfers. Up until 1960 there were very few such changes for major activities in that only 3 "deaths," 3 declines and 4 transfers occurred among the 89 known activities in our sample. However, in 1960–3, 8 "deaths" occurred, along with 6 declines and 14 transfers. The "deaths" occurred in groups located in engineering (2), manufacturing and operations (1), top management (1), planning (1), marketing (1) and divisions (2). The declines occurred in R. and D. (5) and divisions (1). The transfers came out of R. and D. (5), manufacturing and operations (3), finance (2), top management (1), planning (1), marketing (1) and divisions (1). Thus this period might be seen as one in which there was considerable movement out of the R. and D. area (5 declines, 5 transfers) with some indications of tendencies to change elsewhere among the 95 known major activities operating in that period in our sample of companies.

In the 1964–6 period, there were 3 "deaths," 2 declines and 10 transfers among the 69 major activities involved. The 3 "deaths" occurred in R. and D., manufacturing and operations, and finance. The declines were in manufacturing and operations and a division. The transfers were out of R. and D. (1), manufacturing and operations (2), finance (4), top management (2) and planning (1). Thus the period might be characterized as one in which activities located in manufacturing and operations and finance were having major problems, the previous poor experiences with R. and D. locations being apparently reduced, and problems in other locations continuing at about the same levels.

What of the leaders of the activities in each of these organizational areas? In 1959, 88 per cent of OR/MS activities in R. and D. were being led by professional scientist types. Similarly, engineering groups were led by military types and professional scientists. In manufacturing, half of the activities were headed by organization men. The leadership in finance was in the hands of the professional scientists (47 per cent), OR/MS specialists (20 per cent) and organization men (27 per cent). Professional scientists headed most of the top management groups and OR/MS specialists and professional scientists headed the planning groups. By 1966, with R. and D. and engineering largely out of the picture, leadership in the manufacturing groups had shifted to the professional scientists and OR/MS specialists, and in finance we saw a drop in the proportion of professional scientist leaders and an expansion in the OR/MS specialists and organization men, and the entry of the management specialist leaders. The OR/MS specialists and organization men are now largely responsible for the management of the top management and corporate planning OR/MS activities. Further, out of 27 cases of activities being transferred, 15 (55 per cent) were activities led by professional scientists; 5 (19 per cent) by OR/MS specialists; and 4 (15 per cent) by organization men. Of the 15 professional scientist leaders, 7 (47 per cent) failed to survive the transfer, 3 of the 5 OR/MS specialists (60 per cent) and 1 of the 4 organization men (25 per cent) failed to survive; 2 military types and a management specialist who were also involved in transfers did survive the shifts.

These findings confirm that there have indeed been the previously indicated shifts in leadership, namely the decline in the military types and professional scientists leading R. and D. and engineering groups and the expansion of OR/MS specialists, management specialists and organization men leading financial, top management and planning activities. The heavy attrition rates that affect the professional scientist leader types in transfers has helped to increase the relative prominence of the management specialists and organization men as leaders of OR/MS activities.

Earlier, from Table 4 we saw that the professional and OR/MS specialist leaders tended to experience more friction with clients than the organization men. Another aspect of this finding can be seen by noting the organizational location of the activities experiencing such problems with clients. From our data it can be seen that having problems with clients was not only a function of leader type but also of location. Thus professional scientists had more trouble with clients than any other groups, and they had in general more trouble when they were located in R. and D. than when they were in other areas, as did virtually every other group. Even the organization men had more trouble with clients when working out of R. and D. than from other locations. The fewest problems would appear to arise with clients, naturally enough, when an activity was located in a division. We will return later to the nature of the OR/MS—client relationship, but these comments complete for us the tie-in between location, leadership, mission (and client relationships), and birth, decline and death patterns of OR/MS activities.

The implication of these findings would seem to suggest that OR/MS is best removed from R. and D. or engineering as a central location, possibly to the financial areas and then on to top management or to planning. However, certain problems seem to arise for the OR/MS activity in the financial area. One difficulty may be the problem of attracting the OR/MS specialist types, who may see the environment of the controller's office as being too restrictive to their aspirations. Another may be this very limitation in perspective which may define away key opportunities for OR/MS. In a large primary materials processing company, an OR/MS specialist spoke of his experience in reporting to the controller:

> The OR/MS activity was run in the controller's department like any other business activity. Very little attention was ever given to it. It was very frustrating to have to rely on the accounting means of evaluation which were imposed upon us. Problems were not solved on this basis. It forced the selection of projects into only the area of tangible dollar return programmes. As a result, we carried out process optimization projects for which tangible and immediate returns could be demonstrated.

This anecdote brings out another point, namely that the conditions and direction which will satisfy OR/MS professionals and make a company an attractive work location may not necessarily conform with pragmatic local company needs. Research and development departments are frequently faced with this dilemma.

## Top Management Relations

The level of top managerial support has, as we noted earlier, been stated as being one of the key variables affecting the likelihood that an OR/MS activity will be successful. In discussing this question, however, with both members of OR/MS activities and members of top managements, it seemed evident that the level of awareness and interest concerning OR/MS at the very highest levels of the large companies in our sample (i.e., presidents and chairmen) was generally rather slight. In 10 out of 13 companies in which we discussed this point, it was indicated to us that top management's level of interest and awareness in OR/MS was generally small, although it was frequently said to be more than it had been in 1960, for example. Rather, it was more generally at the vice-presidential levels that the interest and sponsorship of OR/MS activities had been occurring, even though there are a few outstanding examples of presidents who have been major sponsors. For example, the president of one multi-national company has been a major supporter of operational research since the earliest days and has insisted on all his companies supporting operational research activities. In another giant corporation, operational research was "kicked off" on a divisional basis by a presidential letter to all division managers telling them, in effect, that operational research was a "good thing" and he wanted every division to "get some." In a number of other cases OR/MS sponsors have, in recent years, risen to the very top levels of companies and have carried their interests and support of OR/MS with them.

An examination of the results of, and changes in, sponsorship of OR/MS activities shows that there is a strong relation between the fortunes of the sponsors and their OR/MS groups. Examination of the effects of either the loss or retention of a sponsor for activities in each of the organizational areas indicates that loss of a sponsor carries with it a high risk that the group will not maintain its position. In 5 cases where a sponsor was lost there resulted 1 "death," 1 decline plus transfer from R. and D. to finance, 2 other transfers to finance—one of which went through several subsequent transfers, with the final group going over from manufacturing to top management and then back to manufacturing where it operated at a reduced level.

By contrast, 12 activities which had retained their sponsors were generally much more stable and apparently successful. In 4 cases the activity followed the sponsor in his promotions, either up to top management or to planning, and 6 of the groups that started in either R. and D., manufacturing or finance finished up in top management or planning—which could be viewed as a "promotion" for the activity. There was only 1 "death" and 1 "demotion" from top management to finance. Also interesting would appear to be the greater likelihood of losing one's sponsor when located in R. and D. Two of the sponsors lost in this area were vice-presidents of R. and D., a notably high turnover group.

The following case materials are illustrative of the relationships between OR/MS and top management:

> In a military-oriented company in the mid-1960's the OR/MS military-type leader resigned and the activity "died" following a major clash with the president, of whom the leader had said, "He hates OR/MS type activities." Communications between the OR/MS leader and members of top management had been very sparse and poor for some years.
>
> The president of a transportation company had supported a very large budget for a major operational research project in the mid-1950's over the strong objections of other members of his top management team and outside

counsel. The project succeeded and the operational research group has been highly successful since then.

## Client Relations

Earlier in this paper we discussed relationships between OR/MS leader types, organizational location and client relations problems. Some factors mentioned by interviewees which may contribute to poor receptivity of the group and/or a poor general reputation are:

1. Poor project results
2. Use of highly technical terminology
3. Unsatisfactory experience with outside operational research consultants
4. Unorthodox or unbusinesslike appearance of operational research personnel
5. Identification with a highly specialized functional area
6. Inability to demonstrate cost effectiveness
7. Method of allocating project costs
8. Differences in planning horizons

In an earlier paper[4] we have described the client's receptivity in terms of his willingness to allow projects to be selected, data to be gathered and projects to be implemented in his area. Thus we asked the interviewees to discuss these indicators of client receptivity. We received 108 comments with respect to 79 of the activities known to exist in 51 different companies over the period from 1950 to 1966; 69 of the 108 comments reported poor general client receptivity at some time during the period.

When we asked the interviewees to specifically identify the clients to whom their comments referred, the difficult clients shown in Table 7 were mentioned. These comments reflect a pattern which is not too surprising if one considers the traditional relationships of the functions in question. For example, groups located in R. and D. might be expected to have problems with clients in highly customer-oriented areas such as marketing and production. Likewise, a corporate staff function might be expected to have difficulty with decentralized divisions, and a group located in finance or accounting might be expected to have difficulties with production people, divisional people and clients in general in view of their traditional role as auditors and perhaps as cost accountants. This raises the question of whether the OR/MS groups are being responded to as stereotypes according to location within the organization. Further data are being gathered and

[4]A. H. Rubenstein, M. Radnor, N. R. Baker, D. R. Heiman and J. B. McColly, "Some Organizational Factors Related to the Effectiveness of Management Science Groups in Industry," *Mgmt Sci.* 13 (1967):B508.

*Part II: Premodeling*

Table 7: Incidence of client receptivity problems

| OR/MS location | Client location | | | | | | Totals | |
|---|---|---|---|---|---|---|---|---|
| | Market-ing and sales | R. and D. and engineer-ing | Manu-facturing and operations | Other staff | Division | Clients in general | No. | % |
| R. and D. | 5 | 0 | 3 | 0 | 6 | 1 | 15 | 71* |
| Engineering | 0 | 1 | 1 | 0 | 1 | 1 | 4 | 80 |
| Manufacturing | 2 | 0 | 1 | 1 | 4 | 5 | 13 | 76 |
| Finance | 1 | 1 | 7 | 0 | 6 | 4 | 19 | 56 |
| Top management | 0 | 1 | 1 | 1 | 4 | 3 | 10 | 56 |
| Planning | 0 | 0 | 1 | 1 | 5 | 1 | 8 | 62 |
| Totals | | | | | | | | |
| No. | 8 | 3 | 14 | 3 | 26 | 15 | 69 | 64 |
| Per cent | 80** | 75 | 70 | 50 | 72 | 47 | — | — |

*Per cent of OR/MS activities, by location, reporting client receptivity problems.
**Per cent of all OR/MS groups reporting client receptivity problems, by particular clients.

analysed to help determine whether these general comments reflect actual behaviour with respect to specific projects.

While the above analysis of comments gives one perspective on client relations, a slightly different view results if we count the number of companies in which the comments occurred. We have analysed the comments from 51 different companies regarding client relations with OR/MS activities in various locations and points in time, in the areas of project selection, data collection and implementation. We found that 30 (59 per cent) of the companies experienced one or more of these problems, while only 7 (14 per cent) indicated having no problems with clients. The other 14 companies had mentioned having client problems without specifying the details. Eight companies referred to difficulties with clients in selecting projects. It was noticeable that the R. and D. groups again tended to encounter their poor relations in regard to project selection with marketing clients. While data collection problems have represented a general problem over-all, as we will see when we analyse staff relations, only 12 companies specifically mentioned clients as a source of this problem. Implementation, on the other hand, was the most commonly mentioned problem appearing in 22 of the companies.

Of the frequently mentioned means of dealing with implementation problems, one has been the establishment of a liaison function either in the form of a formal liaison group or by using other staff personnel for liaison purposes. Another has been the formulation of a policy to be followed relative to coordinating client–operational research project activity. We have analysed the changes in company implementation problems over time com-

| | Pre-1950 | | 1950-5 | | 1956-9 | | 1960-3 | | 1964-6 | |
|---|---|---|---|---|---|---|---|---|---|---|
| | No. | %* | No. | % | No. | % | No. | % | No. | % |
| Activities mentioning having implementation problems | 1 | 25 | 3 | 11 | 12 | 24 | 19 | 24 | 11 | 22 |
| Activities mentioning using a liaison group and/ or a co-ordination policy | 0 | | 3 | 11 | 7 | 14 | 17 | 22 | 25 | 50 |
| Total known major activities | 4 | | 28 | | 50 | | 73 | | 50 | |

*Per cent of all known major activities.

pared with the number of companies using such a policy and/or liaison approach. Table 8 illustrates our findings.

Thus it appears that implementation problems have plagued OR/MS rather constantly over the past 10 years, while the attention given to liaison and co-ordination has increased. Whether the liaison and co-ordination effort has been carried through to the implementation stage on individual projects is a question which requires further study.

One of the most frequently mentioned problems was related to the general centralization–decentralization dilemma. The prevalence of these decentralization-based client problems (72 per cent out of a total of 69 comments on difficulties with clients were related to this) leads us to view the problems that corporate OR/MS activities have had with many clients as being, in fact, a manifestation of the difficulties that virtually all corporate staff activities encounter with divisional clients. We have noted the same effects in our studies of the relationships between corporate research and divisions.[5,6]

If, as would seem to be the case in a number of instances, OR/MS performs essentially as a corporate research function, then the need for a developmental liaison and implementation function could be crucial to the success of the activity. In several companies the industrial engineer seemed to be beginning to take on such a role vis-à-vis manufacturing and operations clients. In one company an extensive operational research education programme was in progress specifically aimed at the upgrading of its large number of industrial engineers for this very purpose. It goes without saying

[5]M. Radnor, "Control of R. and D. by Top Managers in 48 Very Large Companies," in Operational Research and the Social Sciences, edited by J. R. Lawrence (Tavistock, London, 1966).

[6]A. H. Rubenstein and M. Radnor, "Top Management's Role in Research Planning in Large Decentralized Companies" (1966). In Proceedings of the Third International Conference of Operational Research Societies, Oslo, 1963, pp. 505–519, Dunod, Paris.

*Part II: Premodeling*

that the difficulties of OR/MS personnel in communicating with clients was seen as a major problem in a number of companies, with professional scientist leaders predominating as a focus of such complaints.

How do OR/MS activities attempt to respond to the types of difficulties noted above? A sample of these responses and an indication of the frequency of use is indicated by the following cases:

| Company No. | Perceived problem | Response |
|---|---|---|
| 46 | 1. Project selection: client has a big project but wants fast solution | 1. Break the big problem up into meaningful small ones and feed the short-run solutions to the client until the whole job is done |
| 8, 11, 40 | 2. Lack of project, data, and implementation | 2. Use the industrial engineers to help find projects, gather data and implement |
| 23, 32, 41, 43, 61, 62 | 3. Impatience and lack of understanding of operational research by the client | 3. Bring the client into the project as a team leader or at least as a team member |
| 21 | 4. "Spotty" reception in the divisions | 4. Find a highly receptive divisional client and publicize the successful results of his projects |
| 20, 46 | 5. Corporate operational research group not able to get meaningful projects or implement in the divisions | 5. Form a project evaluation team made up of divisional controllers and place operational research liaison men in the divisions |

In addition to the above specific reactions to problem situations, several other strategies have been put to use by the OR/MS activities in our sample. Among these are widespread educational programmes for top management people down to clerical people; requiring the client to match the OR/MS effort in financing and manning; and rotation of operational research trained people into line positions. Two companies mentioned a special kind of a problem which would seem to be symptomatic of central, corporate, operational research in its dealings with divisions. We are indebted to one of our interviewees who aptly dubbed it the "weaning-off" problem: How should the corporate activity handle the updating of the ever-increasing number of operational projects which are used repeatedly by the divisions?

In order that we may illustrate some of the dynamic aspects of the integration of OR/MS, several short and partial case studies are related below.

These cases generally deal with facets of client relations as we have mentioned them above, with the emphasis on implementation.

One basic materials producer has its corporate operational research group located in the R. and D. department. The professional scientist head of the group said that "the test of OR/MS is the ability to implement in the operating groups" and that "the operational research group had had a handful of projects which were technical successes but implemental failures." The groups which were hardest to get along with were the marketing groups and the raw materials production units. The "marketing people take a less analytical approach to problems and are more emotional." The producing groups, primarily raw material mining people, find quantitative methods "distasteful."

One critical problem was an investment planning project undertaken in the early 1960's. The project was a "technical success" but the operating division for which it was done was reluctant to use the device because it represented *control by a central power*. The project was never used. The division in question still resists operational research help from the corporate staff.

This company is one of those which has gone to the academic world for help in educating line management to the benefits of management sciences. It has recently created a *corporate operations research co-ordinating function* whose job is to make sure that a project which may develop in one division gets proper exposure and consideration in all relevant parts of the corporation.

In a major transportation company, the former head of the operational research group indicated that a divisional director of planning who was a Ph.D. in sociology had resisted implementation in his area.

He was not outwardly opposed to having projects selected in his area or to having data collected, but he would not make a firm commitment on the values assigned to the decision variables. On initial contact he would tentatively accept certain propositions about relevant variables and expectations. The operational research group would formulate the problem and develop solutions on that basis, but when they tried to implement he would disparage the whole thing on the grounds that the underlying assumptions were not reliable.

The controller of the company singled out this same individual as being *very highly opposed* to operational research. He said "he constantly changes parameters and specifications on problems," but he "does it in a very nice way—he's a smooth operator."

A large service company formed an operational research group in the late 1950's under the financial vice-president's sponsorship. The group was headed by a military type, a scientist who had learned operational research as a member of an early World War II group. He was formal leader of the corporate operational research group but continued to devote part time to his duties as a scientist.

After a few small-scale successes, the group undertook a large-scale problem in the early 1960's—an overall corporate planning and budgeting system. After 15 man-years of effort the project was not even partially implemented, although parts of it were ready for implementation. A former member of the group said that the marketing departments in the divisional offices were not receptive to the project in the beginning because they had to spend their own time gathering data for the operational research group. It also appeared that they would have to change their office procedures to accommodate the new system. As the project continued, it was given wide publicity in the organization, and eventually reached "monster" proportions in the eyes of top general management.

At a crucial point in the project's development, an important management change occurred and the controller became president of the company. He instituted a general cost-cutting campaign which resulted not only in the "death" of this project but of the whole operational research group. The financial vice-president who had sponsored the group was transferred out of the corporate office and given a position in a division. The scientist who had headed the group returned to his former position and has been passed over in subsequent promotions. He feels that he probably did not handle this particular project as well as he could have, but that in the final analysis, "politics really killed operational research here."

## Staff Relations

We have already noted that OR/MS activities, at least its leaders, have tended to have less severe *major* problems in their relationships with non-client staff groups than with clients. If, however, we include *all* staff groups, non-client and client, a somewhat different picture emerges. The staff areas which appeared to provide the most difficulty for OR/MS were in finance, marketing and the divisional staffs. The problems with marketing and the divisional groups have already been alluded to, but the relationships with the financial area, specifically the controller's department, are of some interest.

While data collection problems were not a major consideration in general client relations, they represent a higher percentage of the staff relationship problems, especially among controllers. For example, one controller admitted perceiving the operational research group as a glorified data processing group which threatened to infringe on his area of responsibility, so he refused to give them the cost data they needed to solve specific problems. The original operational research group "died" in 1965 and the controller began studying the feasibility of incorporating an OR/MS capability in his own area as a part of a new management information system.

In 10 cases where strained relations were reported between OR/MS and controllers' areas, and where the causes were specified, we found that 8 had to do with the general question of the role and function of the controller's department *vis-à-vis* OR/MS. Thus we had such cases as: "OR/MS was seen by the controller's department to be 'encroaching on their prerogatives'" or "the controller was battling to take over control of OR/MS." In a number of cases the general environment and approach of a traditional accounting department was at issue.

We may speculate that an important element in the future of OR/MS in U.S. business will be the way in which the controller's function develops. If, as is sometimes suggested, the controller can make the transition to something akin to the management and information scientist, this could have major implications for OR/MS as a central organizational function. Again, the ownership of the computer and systems design capabilities are important aspects of this question. It was of interest to note that in the several cases where computer and systems design operations had been set up outside the financial area, the controllers were said to have generally "traditional accounting outlooks."

## Personality Difficulties

While our study was not specifically designed to collect data on personality conflicts, it is interesting to note the relative frequency of remarks and comments about OR/MS relations with clients and staff which had reference to personality characteristics. The kinds of comments we received varied from a polite "the operational research leader had a communications problem" to a flat "the operational research leader thinks the R. and D. manager is a bastard." Of 75 negative comments about OR/MS–staff relations, 18 made reference to personality conflicts. Of 52 negative comments about OR/MS–client relations, 9 concerned personality differences. Thus 24 per cent of staff relations problems were said to relate to personality, as opposed to 17 per cent of the client relations problems. Thus while personality is undoubtedly a factor in all interpersonal relations in organizations, these remarks suggest the proposition that personality factors may be more important in some types of OR/MS relationships than in others.

## Conclusion

We have reviewed some of the experiences of 66 major U.S. corporations in their attempts to utilize OR/MS methods over the past 15 years. Several major parameters which may influence the success of OR/MS activities have been identified and discussed. We hope that this analysis will stimulate further discussion and will lead to the generation of more propositions which can be tested in the field. Additional work is being done in this area by the authors and other members of the Research Management Group, Department of Industrial Engineering and Management Sciences, Northwestern University.

# 9. THE RELATION BETWEEN FORMAL PROCEDURES FOR PURSUING OR/MS ACTIVITIES AND OR/MS GROUP SUCCESS

*Rodney D. Neal and Michael Radnor*

During the past ten years Northwestern University has been engaged in numerous programs studying various organizational issues pertaining to OR/MS activities in large commercial/industrial firms and the federal government. Some of the areas that have been investigated are the growth and development of OR/MS in large organizations,[19, 25] project selection,[4, 22] the liaison function between the OR/MS group and clients[15, 23] and project implementation.[20] This paper reports on another aspect of the long-term study by examining the extent to which formalized procedures for pursuing OR/MS activities advocated in the literature are being utilized in the field and some of the consequences of their usage. The data and resulting conclusions are based on personal interviews with 178 OR/MS managers, practitioners, and clients in 108 large business firms. The relation between proceduralization and the success of OR/MS activities is tested and found to be significant overall, but varying under different organizational circumstances. The implications these findings have for the management of OR/MS groups are summarized and discussed.

## Study Objectives

Over the years there have been many proponents of OR/MS techniques who have made recommendations for improving the success of OR/MS activities. Many of these recommendations, which will be discussed in the sections on charters and project procedures, have been primarily structured approaches to problem solving while others have also included guidelines for selecting, evaluating, implementing, and monitoring OR/MS-induced programs.

This study was undertaken to determine what procedures were actually being applied in the field and to what extent procedural elaboration appeared to affect the level of success of an OR/MS group. An accompanying objective was to identify any intervening variables that might affect any possible relation between proceduralization and success.

Data were obtained during personal interviews with leaders of OR/MS activities in 108 business organizations. The interview averaged approxi-

Editors' Note: Reprinted with permission from *Operations Research*, March-April 1973, pp. 451–474.

mately two hours and was concerned with several aspects of each activity's operation, history, and environment. The key subjects were these:

1. Independent variables.
   a. Whether the group had an operating charter or not.
   b. The level of procedural elaboration used in pursuing an OR/MS project.
2. Dependent variables.
   a. The project-implementation rate.
   b. The level of success of the group determined on the basis of several indicators other than the implementation rate.
3. Intervening variables.
   a. Whether the OR/MS leader had a professional or organizational orientation.
   b. The extent to which top management was interested and involved in OR/MS endeavors.
   c. Various environmental factors that might conceivably affect the relations between proceduralization and success; three were perceived as affecting the principal relation:
      (1) The age of the OR/MS group.
      (2) The relative size of the OR/MS group.
      (3) The degree of diffusion of OR/MS talent throughout the organization.

Chi-square tests were then used to determine the relation between:

1. Proceduralization and success, overall.
2. The orientation of the OR/MS leader and the group's levels of proceduralization and success, respectively.
3. The extent of top management interest and involvement and the group's levels of proceduralization and success.
4. Proceduralization and success within these OR/MS group classifications:
   a. Age.
   b. Relative size.
   c. Degree of OR/MS diffusion.

## Data Sources

One hundred and eight companies, selected on the basis of having OR/MS activities, agreed to participate in the study. In these 108 companies data were obtained from 109 supervisors of OR/MS activities, 32 other OR/MS practitioners, and 37 liaison and client personnel. The main source of information in each company was the respective OR/MS manager. In 25 per cent of the companies an effort was made to verify information received from the principal respondent by interviewing one or more OR/MS practitioners and one or more clients. Comparing answers from various sources within companies showed some occasional, but generally insignificant, differences. For the most part, the answers from all sources were consistent.

The investigation was conducted during 1970 and concentrated on large firms. All but 16 of the organizations visited were contained in the 1970 *Fortune* listing of the largest US corporations. Eleven of the 16 companies were large enough to have qualified for listing, but were currently divisions within larger firms. Only three companies in the sample had annual revenues of less than $200 million. An attempt was also made to obtain data from OR/MS activities in a variety of industrial sectors, as Table I shows.

## OR/MS Charters

The presence of an OR/MS-group charter was used as an indicator that the group operated under some form of overall long-range policy that served to integrate it effectively within the organization. In a few cases it appeared that the groups without charters were better established within their respective organizations than many groups with charters, but these groups were still included among those without charters. A review of the literature using an OR/MS topical bibliography prepared by Milan and Radnor[16] as a reference guide revealed only one article, written by E. O. Boshell[5] touching on the subject of charters. The paucity of discussion concerned with establishing the purpose and fit of OR/MS groups within their respective organizations is congruent to the fact that only about half (or 46 of the 108)

*Table I: Distribution of companies by industry*

| Sector | Frequency |
|---|---|
| Automotive/transportation equipment | 10 |
| Engineering products | 10 |
| Chemical/pharmaceutical | 4 |
| Chemical/synthetics | 8 |
| Electrical | 10 |
| Finance | 10 |
| Food processing | 10 |
| Materials processing | 5 |
| Merchandising | 10 |
| Utilities | 11 |
| Petroleum | 10 |
| Transportation | 10 |
| Total | 108 |

OR/MS groups visited had some form of charter. Thirteen did have job descriptions, while the remaining 49 had nothing.

Vandenborre et al., in a recent study of Benelux OR/MS groups, also noted an absence of OR/MS charters.[28] They argued that "the failure to specify goals leads to the conclusion that managements have no clear rationale for the introduction of QR [quantitative research] methods, and that they are uncertain about its potentialities and the benefits it would bring." (Their definition of "quantitative research" makes it similar to OR/MS in the US and UK.) They go on to state: "Introducing the QR group without a specific charter may have serious consequences for the survival and development of QR in the firm. Without a well defined set of responsibilities, a definite program, and the rules by which the group's performance will be measured, it is difficult to see how the necessary active and concrete support can be attained from top management to fully utilize QR's potential."

The charters that were available did vary considerably in content and emphasis. Most of the managers felt that the charters served a useful purpose in their respective organizations, if only to establish the legitimacy of the group and contribute to a sense of permanence by just being in the same organizational manual as the older, more established functions.

It was apparent that company charters had greater or lesser significance for different people in different organizations. One of the purposes of this study is to determine how having a charter may significantly relate to the level of success enjoyed by an OR/MS group.

## Project Procedures

Unlike charters, a great deal seems to have been written about procedural guidelines for understanding and implementing OR/MS programs. Table II is a composite of several steps advocated in the literature with interpretative indications of the procedures recommended by each of ten writers on the subject. A common characteristic of the ten guidelines is that they all seem to be concerned with only one particular program and its solution at a time, with the exception of Malcolm,[14] who has discussed in some detail the importance of project selection. In an actual situation, an OR/MS group is very often faced with several, possibly a great many, potential projects. Initially the most crucial problem, and thus possibly first procedural step, might really be that of selecting the best set of projects on which the group should work. The intent would be three-fold: (1) to build organizational confidence in the group, based on projects with a high probability of success, (2) to establish a solid, relevant need for OR/MS techniques based on a varied mix of projects that involve a relatively wide multilevel cross section of the organization, (3) to ensure a logical and efficient ordering of projects so that they would build into one another and the results of previous programs would not be obliterated by those immediately following.[25, 28]

*Table II: Procedural steps for pursuing OR/MS activities and their advocates*

| | Ackoff [2, 3] | Church-man [7, 8] | Cook [9] | Drucker [10, 11] | Enrick [12] | Hertz [13] | Mal-colm [14] | Quade [17] | Ruben-stein [24] | Schellen-berger [26] |
|---|---|---|---|---|---|---|---|---|---|---|
| Preliminary analysis | X | X | X | X | | X | | | X | X |
| Problem formulation | X | X | X | X | X | X | | X | X | |
| Statement of objectives | X | X | | X | X | X | X | X | | |
| Feasibility criteria, cost/benefit | X | | | X | X | X | X | X | X | X |
| Resources/constraints | X | | | X | X | X | | X | X | |
| Alternatives | X | X | | X | X | X | X | X | X | |
| Model design | X | X | X | | X | X | X | X | X | X |
| Collect data | | | X | X | | | | X | | |
| Derive solution | | X | X | X | X | | X | | | X |
| Test | | X | X | | X | X | | X | | X |
| Present results and evaluation | | | X | | X | X | X | X | | |
| Prepare for implementation | | X | | | | | X | | | |
| Documentation, procedural manual | | X | X | | | X | | | | |
| Training | | | | X | | X | | | | |
| Determine effectiveness | | | | | | | X | X | | |
| Modifications | | | | | | X | X | | | |
| Schedule for implementation | | | | | | | X | | | |
| Implementation | | X | X | X | X | | X | X | | |
| Post audit | | | | | | | X | | | |
| Update and maintain | | | | | | X | X | | | |

Malcolm outlines the following steps for selecting a project set:

1. Establish criteria for evaluation and selection of OR/MS projects.
2. Survey problems amenable to OR by questioning operating and staff personnel, looking at problems defined by management, and investigating what others are doing.
3. Develop a preliminary approach for each problem, defining objectives, models, uses, study steps, economics, data requirements, and interest.
4. Apply criteria for the selection of appropriate projects.
5. Rank projects, considering resources.
6. Develop proper mix of long- and short-range projects, with a suitable variety.
7. Select projects and schedule.

The ten sets of procedures, along with Malcolm's discussion of project selection, have been combined into this idealized procedure:

1. Project-proposal phase (preliminary selection).
   a. Development of intermediate- and long-range plans with associated problems and needs.
   b. Listing of relevant OR/MS projects.
   c. Preliminary rating of projects in terms of risk, need, and timing.
   d. Preliminary selection of OR/MS projects.
2. Project-initiating phase (formalization of initiating requests, justification).
   a. Problem formulated in terms of objectives and criteria for measuring the accomplishment of objectives.
   b. Feasibility considered in terms of technical, operational, and behavioral factors.
   c. Cost/benefit analysis with respect to the overall organization.
      (1) Development costs—one shot.
      (2) Operation costs—repetitive.
      (3) Benefits.
3. Project-approval phase (final selection).
   a. Review of project requests by committee of concerned individuals, such as OR/MS practitioners, potential clients, and representatives of other staff functions.
   b. Resolve conflicts, negotiate priorities, work out project schedules.
   c. Make recommendations to top management.
   d. Obtain top-management approval.
4. Project-development phase.
   a. Plan/schedule events (including review points) and resources.
   b. Establish a project team that includes the ultimate users.
      (1) Establish responsibilities.
      (2) Establish lines of communication.

c. Collect data.

d. Develop model/solution (may have more than one).

e. Test model/solution (with hypothetical or actual data).

f. Evaluate test results and modify as necessary.

5. Project-review phase.

a. Review results in accordance with expectations (describe unforeseen difficulties, costs, gains).

b. Make recommendations.

c. Obtain top-management approval.

6. Project implementation phase.

a. Project indoctrination.

b. Schedule events (including review points) and resources.

c. Prepare user manual (outline control mechanics).

d. Train personnel.

e. Monitor progress and correct problems that occur.

7. Project routinization phase.

a. Evaluate project to determine degree of success, problems, improvements, and future extensions.

b. Write final report and circulate as desirable.

This normative procedure was used as a guide for determining the degree of procedural elaboration followed by each OR/MS group. After completing the study, the criteria listed in Table III were selected as being used with sufficient frequency to allow for comparative analysis. The criteria that were excluded from the list in Table III were either rarely used or not easily identified and classified for comparison. Four of the 108 companies were excluded because of incomplete or questionable data. Table IV shows the frequency distribution of the number of these criteria used in each com-

Table III: Criteria used to establish procedural elaboration levels and frequency of use among the 104 companies in the comparative sample

| Criteria | Frequency |
| --- | --- |
| Formal selection committee | 36 |
| Long-range planning | 46 |
| Formal initiation request | 52 |
| Cost/benefit analysis | 62 |
| Task force | 34 |
| Permanent liaison | 34 |
| Schedule of events | 82 |
| Schedule of resources | 78 |
| Monitor progress | 77 |
| Formal post audit | 34 |
| Reports/documentation | 66 |

pany; the median number of procedures is six, the mean is 5.76, and the standard deviation is 2.74.

A chi-square test was performed to determine the extent of the relation between having a charter and the degree of proceduralization. Class divisions were made as close to the median values as possible. The results of Table V indicate a relation significant at the 0.0005 level with one degree of freedom.

Although the relation was strong, both indicators of proceduralization were still used to specify an overall level of proceduralization.

## Success Indicators

Measuring the success of an OR/MS group is occasionally proposed, but appears to be rarely or haphazardly done.[28] There seem to be several reasons for this, identifiable both in the literature and in the field. Often, the situa-

*Table IV: Frequency distribution of the number of criteria used to establish the procedural elaboration found in each company*

| No. of criteria used | Frequency |
|:---:|:---:|
| 0 | 9 |
| 1 | 0 |
| 2 | 3 |
| 3 | 12 |
| 4 | 9 |
| 5 | 10 |
| 6 | 12 |
| 7 | 20 |
| 8 | 13 |
| 9 | 10 |
| 10 | 4 |
| 11 | 2 |
| Total | 104 |

*Table V: Relation between charters and project proceduralization*

| | Companies with | |
|:---|:---:|:---:|
| | Five or less procedures | Six or more procedures |
| No charter | 29 | 14 |
| Charter | 10 | 37 |

$Chi^2$ = 14.22; Yates correction for contingency was applied.

tion surrounding an OR/MS activity is such that it is difficult not only to establish accurate, valid measurements in terms of dollars, but also to acquire the needed data.[1,6,29]

One approach has been to use the percentage of OR/MS projects completed and used as a measure of success.[20,27] The approach taken by this study was to have the OR/MS manager fill in the matrix shown in Table VI.

Table VI: Average of all company percentages of work completed or not and/or used or not

|  |  | Percentage of jobs | |
|  |  | Not completed | Completed |
| Percentage | Not used | 8 | 14 |
| of jobs | Used | 6 | 72 |

Table VII: Distribution of companies indicating percentages of OR/MS jobs used

| Percentage of jobs used | Frequency of occurrence |
| --- | --- |
| 0–10 | 3 |
| 11–20 | 0 |
| 21–30 | 3 |
| 31–40 | 5 |
| 41–50 | 13 |
| 51–60 | 9 |
| 61–70 | 6 |
| 71–80 | 25 |
| 81–90 | 22 |
| 91–100 | 18 |
| Total | 104 |

Table VIII: Frequency distribution of success of OR/MS groups as perceived by their OR/MS managers

| Level of success | Frequency | Scoring factor |
| --- | --- | --- |
| Low | 2 | 0 |
| Low to fair | 3 | 1 |
| Fair | 30 | 2 |
| Fair to high | 14 | 3 |
| High | 59 | 4 |
| Total | 108 | |

The percentages in our table are an average of all the responses. The total percentage of projects that served a useful purpose, in this case 78 per cent, was then taken as an equivalent to the implementation rate. The distribution of company rates for 104 of the companies for which the data was complete is shown in Table VII.

Five other indicators of success were used to establish an additional group success score, as shown in Tables VIII to XII. The tables also include the scoring factors attributed to each answer.

A chi-square test was performed between each of these criteria and the rate used to determine to what extent each could be represented by the implementation rate alone. The tests indicated significant relations between the implementation rate and the first four criteria and an insignificant association between implementation and the percentage of the projects gener-

*Table IX: Frequency distribution of top-management support of OR/MS groups as perceived by the OR/MS manager*

| Level of success | Frequency | Scoring factor |
|---|---|---|
| Low | 18 | 0 |
| Fair | 32 | 1 |
| Fair to high | 3 | 2 |
| High | 55 | 4 |
| Total | 108 | |

*Table X: Frequency distribution of client receptivity*

| Level of receptivity | Frequency | Scoring factor |
|---|---|---|
| Low | 3 | 0 |
| Low to fair | 3 | 1 |
| Fair | 29 | 2 |
| Fair to high | 23 | 3 |
| High | 50 | 4 |
| Total | 108 | |

*Table XI: Frequency distribution by degree of project backlog*

| Degree of backlog | Frequency | Scoring factor |
|---|---|---|
| Service exceeds demand | 18 | 0 |
| Service equals demand | 16 | 1 |
| Demand exceeds service | 73 | 2 |
| Total | 107 | |

ated by non-OR/MS personnel. However, the correlation coefficients were all under 0.3, and therefore the used rate was not accepted alone as a representative measure of success. For this reason, two separate dimensions were used to measure success and test the relation between proceduralization and group success. The first was the project's used rate and the second was a total score developed from the individual scores assigned to each of the five criteria of Tables VIII–XII.

An additional point must be stressed. A number of the indicators of success used were dependent on the perceptions of OR/MS managers of their own "success." We are well aware from our work that such perceptions

*Table XII: Frequency distribution by percentage of OR/MS projects generated by non-OR/MS personnel*

| Percentage of projects generated | Frequency | Percentage range | Scoring factor |
|---|---|---|---|
| 0–10 | 6 | 0 | 0 |
| 11–20 | 5 | | |
| 21–30 | 6 | 1–25 | 1 |
| 31–40 | 7 | | |
| 41–50 | 16 | 26–50 | 2 |
| 51–60 | 10 | | |
| 61–70 | 9 | | |
| 71–80 | 17 | 51–75 | 3 |
| 81–90 | 13 | | |
| 91–100 | 16 | 76–100 | 4 |
| Total | 105 | | |

*Table XIII: Relation between having a charter and project use rate (UR)*

| | UR $\leq$ 79% | UR > 79% |
|---|---|---|
| No charter | 27 | 16 |
| Charter | 15 | 32 |

Chi$^2$ = 7.3.

*Table XIV: Relation between project procedural elaboration and project use rate*

| | UR $\leq$ 79% | UR > 79% |
|---|---|---|
| 0–6 procedures | 33 | 22 |
| 7–11 procedures | 17 | 32 |

Chi$^2$ = 5.8.

become more and more congruent with those of top managers and presumably with some realistic standard. We did nevertheless feel that it was important also to use measures tied to hard data, and hence less liable to distortion, such as "project backlog" and "percentage of projects generated by non-OR/MS personnel." Finally, we should note that some consistent and systematic overoptimism, even if accepted on the perceptual measures, would not tend to distort importantly the relations being examined in this study.

## Preliminary Tests and Results

The tests between proceduralization and group success were arranged in series, each test incorporating a greater number of the procedural and success indicators discussed in the previous sections. All divisions were made as close to their median values as possible.

As Table XIII shows, the relation between having a charter and the project use rate is significant at the 0.01 level with one degree of freedom. Apparently, having a charter was significantly associated with the OR/MS group's project use rate.

*Table XV: Relation between charter and procedural elaboration versus project use rate (UR) and success score (SS)*

|  | SS $\leq$ 14 UR $\leq$ 79% | SS > 14 UR > 79% |
|---|---|---|
| No charter, 0–6 procedures | 21 | 3 |
| Charter, 7–11 procedures | 2 | 22 |

Chi$^2$ = 27.1.

*Table XVI: Simplified comparison of relation between policy and procedures and success*

|  | Low | Medium | High |
|---|---|---|---|
|  | SS $\leq$ 14, UR $\leq$79 | SS $\leq$ 14 and UR > 79; or SS > 14 and UR $\leq$ 79 | SS > 14, UR > 79 |
| No charter, 0–6 procedures | 21 | 16 | 3 |
| No charter, 7–11 procedures; charter, 0–6 procedures | 10 | 14 | 6 |
| Charter, 7–11 procedures | 2 | 10 | 32 |

Chi$^2$ = 35.4.

Table XIV shows that, at the 0.02 level with one degree of freedom, there is also a significant relation between project proceduralization and an organization's project use rate.

Table XV shows the relation between organizations with little proceduralization, i.e., no charter and 0–6 procedures; and organizations with considerable structure, i.e., a charter and 7–11 procedures, with respect to low or high levels of success. A low level of success is indicated by a use rate equal to or less than 79 per cent and a success score equal to or less than 14; the reverse characterizes a high success level. Only the extreme conditions were considered in this test. The relation was significant at the 0.0005 level with one degree of freedom.

The next tests considered 104 companies for which complete data were available. Normally, this would be a four-by-four test, but because some of the expected cell values were less than five, the minimum required, the relation was collapsed into a three-by-three table, as shown in Table XVI. The overall relation was significant at the 0.005 level with four degrees of freedom.

The preceding series of tests supported in a consistent and increasingly significant manner the classically based argument of those in favor of greater proceduralization for OR/MS activities. That is, "there exists a significantly positive relation between the establishment of overall policy and procedural guidelines and the success of the OR/MS group."

The tests also indicated that, while the ability to implement projects was an important sign of success, it was not the only indication. The success of an OR/MS group appeared also to be dependent on the impact of a series of projects on the total organization as well as the project use rate. Small, relatively certain projects developed and implemented in a friendly environment might provide a high implementation percentage without establishing the full potential worth of the OR/MS group or developing the interest and support of the greater organization. This leads to a variety of possible situations. A new OR/MS group may purposely follow a policy of small jobs that can be accomplished quickly with little risk of failure. It would be expected that its implementation rate would be high, but its overall success score would be low. An established OR/MS group would possibly be more willing to take chances in risky areas that, if successfully handled, would yield much greater rewards; thus, such a group would have a lower percentage of successful implementations, but their impact on the organization might be considerably greater, with a correspondingly higher success score.

Although these tests demonstrated the relation between success and procedures, and might indicate that the latter were determined by the former, there could still exist some exceptions. The next four sections will investigate four possible intervening factors that could cause variations in the relation.

However, before going on to these tests, a note of caution must be sounded. The relations being developed in this study are correlations between indicators of formalization and success. It may well be, indeed, that having a charter and formalized procedures helps promote success. It may be just as true that groups achieving success then go on to develop such processes and, hence, that the formalization is more an indicator than a determinant of success. We suspect that both may be true, and reinforcing, to some degree. We are planning further research to study these relations. However, the correlations, whether demonstrating causation or correspondence, seem important enough, in their very description, to be worth reporting on at this time.

### Effect of Leadership

It seems quite possible that proceduralization and the success of an OR/MS group could very well both be dependent variables relative to some third factor, and, from a behavioral standpoint, this third variable might be the leadership of the group. To investigate this possibility, two groups of leaders were selected for study: the OR/MS managers, and the organizations' top managements. Data were obtained relative to several characteristics of the OR/MS manager such as age, education, experience, and aspirations. However, only two questions were asked about top management: First, what was the number of people the OR/MS manager perceived as being in top management? And then, what was the number of these top managers who showed an interest and were inclined to become involved in OR/MS projects affecting their operations?

OR/MS managers were separated into two categories: Those with what appeared to be a professional orientation, and those with an organizational orientation—a classification established by previous Northwestern studies.[19] The professional tended to have a theoretical background, limited primarily to experiences in OR/MS work, was less inclined to remain with any particular company, and more often indicated a preference to stay in an OR/MS capacity. The organizational usually had a practical or functional background, had a wider range of past experiences, had remained longer with the current firm, and tended to view the OR/MS manager job as a step to a more responsible position. Thirty-three of the OR/MS managers were characterized as professionals, while 71 were assigned to the organizational category.

There appeared to be no significant relation between being either a professional or organizational and having a charter or not, or having a high level of procedural elaboration for pursuing individual projects or not. On the other hand, there was a significant relation at the 0.05 level with two degrees of freedom between having a manager with an organizational orientation and the success of the OR/MS group, as Table XVII shows.

Table XVIII shows the frequency distribution of top managers interested and involved in OR/MS activities out of the total number of top managers

*Table XVII: Professional/organizational orientation versus success*

|  | Low | Medium | High |
|---|---|---|---|
|  | SS $\leq$ 14, UR $\leq$ 79% | SS $\leq$ 14 and UR > 79; or SS > 14 and UR $\leq$ 79 | SS > 14, UR > 79% |
| Professional | 16 | 12 | 5 |
| Organizational | 17 | 28 | 26 |

Chi$^2$ = 7.7.

*Table XVIII: Frequency distribution of the percentage of top managers interested and involved in OR/MS activities in each organization*

| Percentage of top managers interested and involved | Frequency |
|---|---|
| 0–10 | 16 |
| 11–20 | 24 |
| 21–30 | 11 |
| 31–40 | 7 |
| 41–50 | 12 |
| 51–60 | 1 |
| 61–70 | 4 |
| 71–80 | 7 |
| 81–90 | 5 |
| 91–100 | 3 |
| Total | 90 |

in each organization, as perceived by the respective OR/MS managers. The median was 25 per cent.

There was no significant relation between having high or low top-management interest and involvement and having a charter or not, or having high proceduralization or not. However, there was a significant relation between interest and involvement and success, as indicated by Table XIX. The level of significance was 0.01 with two degrees of freedom.

The results of the tests were such that the possibility of an autocorrelation between both proceduralization and success with respect to either the OR/MS managers' orientation or degree of top-management interest and involvement could be eliminated. At the same time, it did appear that an organizational orientation and top-management involvement also contributed positively to the OR/MS groups' success rate.

Table XIX: *Top-management involvement versus success*

|  | Low | Medium | High |
|---|---|---|---|
| Percentage of top management involvement | SS $\leq$ 14, UR $\leq$ 79% | SS $\leq$ 14 and UR > 79; or SS > 14 and UR $\leq$ 79 | SS > 14, UR > 79% |
| 0–25 | 20 | 17 | 10 |
| 26–100 | 5 | 18 | 20 |

Chi$^2$ = 12.2.

### Effect of Age of OR/MS Group

The age of an OR/MS group was established on the basis of the year when it became a recognized, distinct practicing entity within the organization. Table XX shows the distribution of originating years. The average age was seven years, the median age was six years. The groups were divided into three categories for comparative purposes: Those initiated during 1954 through 1959 were classified as old, those starting between 1960 through 1965 were middle-aged, while those established between 1966 and 1969 were considered young.

The historical development of each group varied somewhat; for example, some groups died and were reborn with or without members of the original groups. Table XXI provides data on the numbers of transfers and what were apparently deaths at the time of this study.

No attempt was made to determine the effects of transfer, diffusion, or death relative to organizational exposure and development of OR/MS activities based on age. Obviously there would be some effect, but this study proceeded with the assumption that the perceived presence of an OR/MS group would be reasonably continuous in its development from birth to the present, and thus the organization's awareness of the OR/MS group could be viewed in terms of age alone.

Table XXII shows the means and, where available, median values of the different variables previously considered in this paper. Table XXIII indicates the level of significance of the differences between factor means within each age classification.

The tendency for OR/MS groups five to ten years old to peak in the indicators of charter, procedural elaboration, project-use rating, and success score could be due to several causes. In the case of procedural elaboration and charters, new groups usually started out with relatively little. Problems occurred and procedures were instituted to correct them. The results could lead to some over-reacting that might impose too much structure on the OR/MS process increasing to a peak during the middle years of a group's

*Part II: Premodeling*

*Table XX: Frequency distribution of OR/MS groups by birth years*

| Year of birth | Frequency | Year of birth | Frequency |
|---|---|---|---|
| 1954 | 2 | 1962 | 6 |
| 1955 | 8 | 1963 | 3 |
| 1956 | 0 | 1964 | 8 |
| 1957 | 5 | 1965 | 16 |
| 1958 | 2 | 1966 | 4 |
| 1959 | 6 | 1967 | 11 |
| 1960 | 9 | 1968 | 11 |
| 1961 | 6 | 1969 | 7 |

Total: 104 groups.

*Table XXI: Frequency of transfers and deaths of OR/MS groups sampled in this study*

| Frequency of transfer | No. of OR/MS groups |
|---|---|
| 0 | 33 |
| 1 | 33 |
| 2 | 11 |
| 3 | 2 |
| 4 | 1 |
| Death | 5 |
| Total | 104 |

*Table XXII: Factor means and medians relative to OR/MS group age*

| Factors | Years Group Established | | | | | |
| | 1954–1959 | | 1960–1965 | | 1966–1969 | |
| | Mean | Median | Mean | Median | Mean | Median |
|---|---|---|---|---|---|---|
| Charter | 44% | — | 52% | — | 33% | — |
| Project procedures | 5.9 | 6.0 | 6.5 | 7.0 | 4.5 | 5.0 |
| Organizational orientation | 61% | — | 67% | — | 79% | — |
| Top mgmt. support | 33% | 25% | — | 25% | — | 25% |
| Use rate | 66% | 70% | 73% | 80% | 71% | 75% |
| Success score | 12.6 | 12.0 | 13.6 | 15.0 | 13.7 | 14.0 |
| Size of OR/MS group | 1.2 | 0.9 | 1.5 | 1.4 | 1.1 | 1.0 |
| Diffusion of OR/MS | 1.7 | 1.9 | 1.5 | 1.4 | 1.3 | 1.2 |
| Class frequency | 23 | | 48 | | 33 | |

history, and then discarded thereafter. As the group would become older, better established, and recognized in the organization, it was likely that it would be able to operate along less formal lines. Therefore, some of the previous methods or rules no longer served an apparently useful purpose, and were abandoned.

There was also some possibility that newer groups learned to an extent from apparent weaknesses in older groups. Personnel coming from older groups to a newer group might be more inclined to introduce formal procedures in the new organization that they perceived as missing in the older activities.

The study indicated, somewhat weakly, three possible reasons for the

Table XXIII: Levels of significance between factors within age classifications
of OR/MS groups
(Insignificant differences of over 20 are indicated by an I.)

| Factors | Old to middle-aged | Old to new | Middle-aged to new |
|---|---|---|---|
| Charter | I | I | 0.05 |
| Project procedures | 0.16 | 0.04 | 0.0001 |
| Organizational orientation | I | 0.06 | 0.12 |
| Top-mgmt. support | I | I | I |
| Use rate | 0.12 | I | I |
| Success score | −0.14 | −0.10 | I |
| Size of OR/MS group | I | I | −0.16 |
| Diffusion of OR/MS | −0.16 | −0.02 | −0.05 |
| Class frequencies | 23–48 | 23–33 | 48–33 |

Table XXIV: Frequency distribution of ratios of OR/MS practitioners
to company revenue in $100 million

| OR/MS practitioners/$100 million | Frequency |
|---|---|
| 0.13–0.90 | 19 |
| 0.91–0.80 | 15 |
| 0.81–1.20 | 18 |
| 1.21–1.60 | 15 |
| 1.61–2.00 | 10 |
| 2.01–2.40 | 5 |
| 2.41–2.80 | 9 |
| 2.81–3.20 | 2 |
| 3.21–4.00 | 5 |
| 4.01–10.00 | 6 |
| Total | 104 |

*Table XXV: Factor means and medians with respect to the relative size of the OR/MS group, ratio of practitioners to $100 million in revenue*

| Factors | Ratio | | | | | |
| --- | --- | --- | --- | --- | --- | --- |
| | Less than one | | One or less than two | | More than two | |
| | Mean | Median | Mean | Median | Mean | Median |
| Charter | 35% | — | 52% | — | 49% | — |
| Project procedures | 4.7 | 5.0 | 5.9 | 7.0 | 7.0 | 7.0 |
| Organizational orientation | 60% | — | 73% | — | 69% | — |
| Top mgmt. support | 26% | 20% | 36% | 25% | 49% | 43% |
| Use rate | 71% | 75% | 70% | 75% | 79% | 80% |
| Success score | 12.2 | 12.0 | 14.0 | 14.0 | 14.4 | 15.0 |
| Diffusion of OR/MS | 1.4 | 1.0 | 1.3 | 1.2 | 1.9 | 1.9 |
| Size of firm ($mil./yr.) | 1980 | 1300 | 900 | 600 | 910 | 700 |
| Class frequency | 40 | | 35 | | 29 | |

higher implementation rate for young and middle-aged groups with respect to the older. The first is that young groups seem often to concentrate on fairly easy projects with a high likelihood of being successfully used. Middle-aged groups apparently continue this practice, but also venture into more sophisticated programs that offer higher returns with a greater over-all impact. Many of the older groups have been in their organizations suffi-ciently long to "skim off the cream" of projects certain of success. They also are more likely to be well established, with a reservoir of good will and esteem, and can afford to take chances with the less certain undertakings available.

The lower success scores for older groups are not, at first glance, consis-tent with this explanation. It may well be that older groups tend to be less of a factor as a change agent within their respective organizations, or the lower score could be due to relative perceptions about the present situation and how it used to be in terms of impact on the organization. Ritti and Goldner [21] suggest that, "as older areas become more predictable, they become less powerful." They add: "Groups handling newer areas are seen as possessing brighter . . . individuals who make up the potential for future leadership. The newer and emerging specialty with a relatively undefined role is often viewed by top management as more uncertain, as more prob-lematic, and as needing greater attention and support."

Another possibility for the lower success score in the older OR/MS groups could arise from the fact that these older groups tend to be in larger organi-zations. They may find it more difficult to reach top management or bring about changes having a total organizational impact.

*Table XXVI: Levels of significance between factors within different relative sizes of OR/MS groups*

| Factors | Small to medium | Small to large | Medium to large |
|---|---|---|---|
| Charter | 0.08 | 0.13 | I |
| Project procedures | 0.04 | 0.001 | 0.05 |
| Organizational orientation | 0.12 | I | I |
| Top mgmt. support | 0.01 | 0.001 | 0.05 |
| Use rate | I | 0.08 | 0.05 |
| Success score | 0.02 | 0.005 | I |
| Diffusion of OR/MS | I | 0.05 | 0.001 |
| Size of firm ($mil./yr.) | 0.005 | 0.01 | I |
| Class frequencies | 40–35 | 40–29 | 35–29 |

*Table XXVII: Total number of OR/MS practitioners in the organization/OR/MS core group size: frequency of occurrence*

| Total no./core no. | Frequency of occurrence |
|---|---|
| 1.00–1.40 | 51 |
| 1.40–1.80 | 11 |
| 1.81–2.20 | 12 |
| 2.21–2.60 | 6 |
| 2.61–3.00 | 2 |
| 3.01–3.40 | 9 |
| 3.41–3.80 | 2 |
| 3.81–4.20 | 2 |
| 4.21–15.00 | 9 |
| Total | 104 |

### Effect of Relative Size of OR/MS Group

The relative size of an OR/MS group was indicated by the number of practitioners in the group with respect to the revenue of the firm in $100 million. Table XXIV shows the size distribution. The average OR/MS-group-to-revenue ratio was 1.64 practitioners to every $100 million in revenue. The median was 1.21. Capital funds were substituted for revenues when calculating the size/revenue ratio for financial institutions. The relative size of an OR/MS group was related to the size of its respective organization. This factor was also included in the comparative table of class means, to provide some idea of the relation. Table XXV shows the factor means and medians.

There were several strong and consistent relations between the various factors contributing to and indicating the success of an OR/MS group across the relative size classes of OR/MS activity. The larger the relative size of the OR/MS effort, the more likely there was a charter, greater procedural elaboration, top-management support, and a corresponding higher implementation rate and success score. It appeared that the larger the OR/MS group's relative size, the greater was the extent of OR/MS diffusion. It also seemed that the relative size of the group decreased with respect to the size of the organization.

It appeared that all of the factors contributing to success as well as the level of success tend to vary positively with the size of the OR/MS group. There were some slight indications that some of these factors might peak near an average ratio of two practitioners to $100 million of annual revenue. However, it would be expected that any optimum ratio would change with respect to any of several other possible variables, such as company size and OR/MS diffusion.

## Effect of OR/MS Diffusion

The extent of diffusion of OR/MS talent was based on a ratio between the total number of OR/MS practitioners estimated to be in the company by the OR/MS manager and the number in the core OR/MS group. Table XXVII shows the distribution of these ratios. The average ratio of total practitioners to core practitioners was 1.50; the median was 1.41. The groups were divided into three classes: those with no diffusion, a ratio of 1.0; those with medium diffusion, a ratio of over 1.0 to 2.0; and those with considerable or much diffusion, over one external practitioner for every core practitioner. Tables XXVIII and XXIX show the factor means and medians, and the significance levels.

*Table XXVIII: Factor means and medians relative to the diffusion of OR/MS*

| Factors | Ratio of core group to total number of practitioners in the organization | | | | | |
| | 1.0 | | Over 1.0 to 2.0 | | Over 2.0 | |
| | Mean | Median | Mean | Median | Mean | Median |
|---|---|---|---|---|---|---|
| Charter | 24% | — | 36% | — | 36% | — |
| Project procedures | 5.1 | 5.0 | 6.2 | 7.0 | 5.1 | 6.0 |
| Organizational orientation | 54% | — | 53% | — | 61% | — |
| Top mgmt. support | 28% | 25% | 43% | 33% | 38% | 25% |
| Use rate | 70% | 80% | 70% | 75% | 73% | 76% |
| Success score | 12.5 | 12.0 | 14.7 | 14.0 | 13.5 | 14.0 |
| Size of OR/MS group | 0.9 | 0.7 | 2.1 | 2.0 | 1.8 | 1.4 |
| Size of firm ($mil./yr.) | 820 | 600 | 900 | 700 | 2320 | 1600 |
| Class frequencies | 37 | | 36 | | 31 | |

In this series of tests there appeared to be significant peaks in the relation between the level of OR/MS diffusion and the degree of procedural elaboration, success scores, and top-management support, the peaks occurring in the companies with a medium amount of OR/MS diffusion. OR/MS groups with medium diffusion were more likely to be small in size. There was a weak relation between larger diffusion ratios and having a charter, being relatively larger in size, and having an OR/MS leader with an organizational orientation.

These results suggest that little diffusion might inhibit the implementation and use of OR/MS programs. On the other hand, considerable diffusion could reduce the role and significance of the core group with respect to the organization's OR/MS effort. It was not clear whether the overall use of OR/MS in the firm was affected or not.

*Table XXIX: Levels of significance between factors within different class levels of OR/MS diffusion*

| Factors | None to medium | None to much | Medium to much |
|---|---|---|---|
| Charter | 0.14 | 0.16 | I |
| Project procedures | 0.05 | I | 0.05 |
| Organizational orientation | I | I | I |
| Top mgmt. support | 0.0005 | 0.05 | 0.07 |
| Implementation rate | I | I | I |
| Success score | 0.005 | 0.14 | 0.05 |
| Size of OR/MS group | 0.001 | 0.20 | 0.04 |
| Size of firm | I | 0.015 | 0.02 |
| Class frequencies | 37–36 | 37–31 | 36–31 |

*Table XXX: Relation between overall policy and procedures versus success*

| Tests | Level of significance/diff. |
|---|---|
| Total within total sample ($N = 104$) | 0.005/4 |
| *Tests within the classes* | |
| Age of group: Old ($n = 23$) | I/1 |
| Middle ($n = 48$) | 0.005/1 |
| Young ($n = 33$) | 0.10/1 |
| Size of group: Small ($n = 40$) | 0.05/1 |
| Medium ($n = 35$) | 0.10/1 |
| Large ($n = 29$) | 0.02/1 |
| Diffusion: Little ($n = 37$) | 0.10/1 |
| Medium ($n = 36$) | 0.01/1 |
| Much ($n = 31$) | I/1 |

# Environmental Test Results

Chi-square tests were performed within each of the classes to determine the extent that the principal relation remained significant. Table XXX shows the results.

With the exception of the old-age category and the much-diffusion category, the tests in this section showed a sufficiently significant relation between procedures and success to uphold the principal argument, even with the reduction in test sizes.

# Conclusion

PRINCIPAL ARGUMENT. The principal argument of this study, that procedural elaboration and the success of an OR/MS group are positively related, proved to be significant at the 0.05 level with four degrees of freedom. The correlation of attributes was 0.41, which indicated that there still existed other factors that also exerted, individually and/or jointly, a considerable influence on the success of an OR/MS activity.

The question at this point was: Could the two variables of the principal argument be positively related to some third, and therefore autocorrelating variable? Because of this possibility, the study then attempted to identify other factors, first behavioral and second environmental, that might affect, jointly, procedural structure and group success. Once these factors were identified, the principal argument was tested within factor classes representing various categories or levels of these attributes to determine if the principal argument still remained significant even with the loss of power associated with the reduced number of observations in each test.

BEHAVIORAL CONSIDERATIONS. Two factors were selected as being representative of important behavioral influences on OR/MS proceduralizations and success. One was associated with the orientation of the OR/MS manager, either professional or organizational. The other was top-management knowledge, interest, and involvement in OR/MS. Tests showed that there were significant relations between each of these variables and group success, but not with the elaboration of procedural guidelines. This indicated that the variables of the principal argument were not jointly correlating with respect to either of the two behavioral factors.

Tests were still performed on the principal argument within the following class categories of the behavioral factors: OR/MS manager's orientation: professional or organizational; and top-management knowledge, interest, and involvement: low or high. The principal relation proved significant in the last three categories, but not in the first.

While there was no direct relation between proceduralization and the two behavioral factors, the results of these tests were such as to suggest that the interactions between procedural elaboration and an organizational orientation, and procedural elaboration and high top-management involvement might contribute to the success of an OR/MS group, and more so in situations where the OR/MS managers had a professional orientation and/or where management involvement was low.

ENVIRONMENTAL CONSIDERATIONS. Of the several environmental factors that were considered, three proved to have similar associations with both procedural elaboration and group success: the age of the group, its relative size, and the diffusion of OR/MS within the organization. Tests were performed on the principal relation within levels of these factors, and, with two exceptions, the relation between procedures and success remained significant.

In these cases there was apparently some autocorrelation between the two principal variables and each of the three environmental factors, but it was not sufficient to nullify effectively the proceduralization-success relation. It also appeared that there was some positive interaction effect on OR/MS success between proceduralization and the following class levels: middle-aged groups, relatively large groups, and organizations with medium diffusion.

Although it would appear, based on the results of this study, that the proceduralization of OR/MS activities does have a positive effect on the success of an OR/MS group, the authors feel that further research is needed to confirm the direction of the relation. There is still the very likely possibility that proceduralization, rather than causing success, may be an indicator of a successful group.

### Some Final Comments

This second of our current two-paper series[18] elaborates on one of the issues identified in the general study of the progress of OR/MS in the large US industrial organizations, namely, the apparently growing trend towards formalization of OR/MS. This process poses a classical organizational dilemma. We have demonstrated the relation between proceduralization and success. And yet, might not this very success contain the seeds of eventual failure? We have seen other innovative, change-oriented, management technologies stultify and degenerate into routine maintenance technologies. And yet, if OR/MS is to become a mature and stable element in the organizational scene, then it may have to develop the institutional dimensions that proceduralization, as we have defined it, indicates. In this sense, our paper has two important messages. The first is to demonstrate the relation between proceduralization and success. The second purpose is normative: We could not help describing current practice in some detail, without also postulating an all-encompassing set of such formal procedures. Some of our readers may find the latter as helpful as the former.

## REFERENCES

1. Ackoff, Russell L. "Unsuccessful Case Studies and Why." *Opns. Res.* 8 (1960): 259–263.
2. ———. "Some Unsolved Problems in Problem Solving." *Opnal. Res. Quart.* 13 (1962): 1–11.
3. ———. "Management Misinformation Systems." In *Managing Computer-Based Information Systems*, edited by J. Dearden, F. McFarlan and W. Zani. Homewood, Ill.: Richard D. Irwin, 1971.
4. Bean, Alden S. and Tansik, David A. "The Evaluation of OR/MS Project Recommendations: Some Notes from a Field Study." Unpublished paper, Northwestern University, July 1968.
5. Boshell, E. O. "Operations Research, Top Management Tool." *Dunn's Review and Modern Industry* 65, No. 3 (1957): 49–51.
6. Caminer, John J. and Andlinger, Gerhard R. "Operations Research Roundup." *Harvard Business Review* 32, No. 6 (1954): 132–136.
7. Churchman, C. West. "OR as a Profession." *Management Sci.* 17 (1970): B37–B53.
8. ———; Ackoff, Russell L., and Arnoff, Leonard W. *Introduction of Operations Research.* New York: John Wiley, 1957.
9. Cook, E. V. "Discussion of Implementation and Its Assessment for OR Projects, Together with Four Implementation Case Histories." Imperial College of Science and Technology, Univ. of London, London, September 1969.
10. Drucker, Peter F. *The Practice of Management.* New York: Harper and Row, 1954.
11. ———. "Management Science and the Manager." *Management Sci.* 1 (1955): 115–126.
12. Enrick, Norbert L. *Management Operations Research.* New York: Holt, Rinehart, and Winston, 1965.
13. Hertz, David B. "Mobilizing Management-Science Resources." *Management Sci.* 11 (1965): 361–367.
14. Malcolm, D. G. "On the Need for Improvement in Implementation of OR." *Management Sci.* 11 (1965): B54–B57.
15. Mills, Robert C., III. "Liaison Activities at R & D Interfaces: A Model, Some Empirical Results and Design Considerations for Further Study." Northwestern Master's Thesis, June 1967.
16. Mylan, David and Radnor, Michael. "The Adoption and Diffusion of OR/MS Activities in Business and Government: US and Overseas-Annotated Bibliography." Northwestern University, July 1963.
17. Quade, Edward S. "Progress and Problems in Systems Analysis." In *Management Behavior and Organization of Demands*, edited by Robert T. Golembiewski and Frank Gibson. Chicago: Rand McNally, 1962.
18. Radnor, Michael and Neal, Rodney D. "The Progress of Management Science Activities in Large U.S. Industrial Corporations." *Opns. Res.* 21 (1973): 427–450.
19. ———; Rubenstein, Albert H., and Bean, Alden S. "Integration and Organization of Management Science Activities in Organizations." *Opnal. Res. Quart.* 19 (1968): 117–141.
20. ———; ———, and Tansik, David A. "Implementation in Operations Research

and R&D in Government and Business Organizations." *Opns. Res.* 18 (1970): 967–991.

21. Ritti, R. R. and Goldner, Fred H. "Professional Pluralism in an Industrial Organization." *Management Sci.* 16 (1969): B233–B246.

22. Rubenstein, Albert H. "Shades of Project-Selection Behavior in Industry." In *Operations Research in Research and Development*, edited by Burton V. Dean. New York: John Wiley, 1963.

23. ——. "Studies of Liaison, Interface, and Technical Transfer in R & D." Excerpts from a Northwestern University proposal, April 1968.

24. ——. "Notes from Lectures in Seminar on Organizational Design." Northwestern University, Winter 1970.

25. ——; Radnor, Michael; Baker, Norman R.; Heiman, David R., and McColly, John B. "Some Organizational Factors Related to the Effectiveness of Management Science Groups in Industry." *Management Sci.* 13 (1967): B508–B518.

26. Schellenberger, Robert E. *Management Analysis.* Homewood, Ill.: Richard D. Irwin, 1969.

27. Turban, Efraim. "A Sample Survey of Operations-Research Activities at the Corporate Level." *Opns. Res.* 20 (1962): 708–721.

28. Vanderborre, R.; Vangenbulcke, J., and Vanwynsberghe, D. *The Process of Introduction and Diffusion of Quantitative Research Methods in Benelux Firms.* Univ. of Louvain, 15 November 1969.

29. Weinberg, Robert S. "Multiple-Factor Break-Even Analysis: The Application of OR Technology to a Basic Problem of Management Planning and Control." *Opns. Res.* 4 (1956): 152–186.

# D. *Communication and Premodeling*

## 10. IMPROVING MODELER-USER INTERACTION

*Thad B. Green*

The operational researcher is no longer simply a modeler. Perhaps the successful ones always have been more. In any case, the necessity for a broadened role is becoming more apparent. First, there appears to be an increase in dissatisfaction among the current users of quantitative techniques.[1] Secondly, and following closely in this shadow of discontent, there is evidence supporting the operational researcher's increasing fear of a decreasing usage of the techniques.[2] The pervasiveness of these two concerns is uncertain. The justification is unmeasured. Yet the handwriting is on the wall. Man cannot live by models alone.

Editors' Note: Reprinted with permission from *Operational Research Quarterly*, 1977, pp. 527–537.

Constructing models and deriving mathematical solutions is not synonymous with solving problems. Success depends on people as well as process. Models that affect people should not be constructed independently from them. Not only does the operational researcher identify problems, define them, and gather relevant data for constructing and testing models, he must identify resistance and resistors, gain acceptance of proposed solutions, develop implementation strategies, and elicit cooperation to implement them. In order to accomplish these tasks successfully, it is a practical necessity for the operational researcher to interact successfully with numerous people.

This interaction is highlighted in an empirical study by Amspoker et al.[3] They determined the level of effectiveness of fourteen operational research project groups which functioned during 1967-72 in a billion dollar, diversified, industrial corporation. Each project team consisted of OR analysts, representatives from the user group, and representatives from the management information unit in the organization. It was concluded that "the most effective project groups directed a significantly higher average number of internal communication hours toward representatives from the user corporate area than did the less effective groups." They further point out that "these internal communication characteristics, both individually and collectively, are felt to have resulted in the high feeling of trust and cooperation which existed in the most effective groups." This conclusion is consistent with the empirical study by Radnor et al.[4] which also documented the importance of the relationship between the client and the OR analyst. The purpose of this interaction is best summarized perhaps by the statement "models are for managers, not mathematicians."[5]

The people-dependent nature of successfully implementing operational research techniques extends beyond the user per se. It includes a variety of others who are either directly or indirectly affected. For example, Rubenstein et al.[6] state that a necessary condition in order to carry out an OR project is for the user to give the analyst freedom to gather data. However, it is intuitively obvious by implication that this freedom is not necessarily forthcoming simply because the analyst was given "authorization" to gather the data. The analyst often finds it necessary to develop a cooperative spirit from a variety of persons subordinate to the user. But willingness to do so alone may not be sufficient. This has been illustrated by Stillson[7] who reported a study which focused on determining the optimum maintenance policy for service station equipment. The person in the study who was required to gather the data not only lacked the incentive to record it accurately and completely, but the normal time demands of his job precluded his effectiveness in doing so. The point is that if someone had asked if his current job requirements would allow him to collect the data rather than ordering him to do so, the problem probably could have been averted.

The importance of interaction with a variety of people is further illustrated by the Amspoker *et al.* study which analyzed the communications of the project team with persons external to the team. They concluded that the external communication "probably increased the chance of successful project implementation."[3] In another study, Harvey[8] analyzed thirty-one OR projects. He concluded that one alternative for being more successful in applying quantitative techniques would be to "identify the human and organization problems in advance." To do this effectively, of course, requires interaction with, and inputs from, a wide range of people in the organization. A final point of interest comes from Stillson's analysis of the development and implementation of the equipment replacement model previously mentioned. He concluded:

> One of the basic problems in implementing this study was the failure to anticipate and characterize the nature of change that was required by the company. This indicates a lack of understanding of the day-to-day operations and the personnel involved in them. What might have been the course of implementation had the team discussed their results with the operating personnel *prior* to the presentation to management? This would have extended the time to complete the study phase but may have saved the over-all effort. Estimates of cost and time for implementation would have been more realistic and recommendations made on a sounder basis. One general conclusion, then, is that the operations researcher get closer to the operation he is studying.[7]

This illustration, like those previously cited, points to the necessity for interaction between the OR analysts and others in addition to interaction among the analysts themselves.

## Problems of Going Beyond

Much of the needed interaction can and should be in a group setting. But the operational researcher, not unlike other group leaders, falls prey to the shortcomings inherent in the traditional group interaction format. The participants may go off on a tangent unrelated to the intended purpose of the session. Or they may fall into a rut, overemphasizing some specific point at the expense of underdiscussing more important issues. Another tendency is for one or more group members to dominate the discussion. Supportive evidence of this last disadvantage comes from the Amspoker *et al.* study. They conclude that the "perceived group leaders in the least effective (OR) groups appeared to monopolize internal group communication."[3] In addition to the problem of dominance, one or more of the group members may utilize a considerable amount of the group's time to persuade others to accept their personal views. Not only does the dominance and persuasion contribute to tangents and ruts, other group members may well be precluded from voicing valuable thoughts.

Another group interaction problem involves personality differences among members which may result in conflict situations. This further deters the effectiveness of the group's purpose. Radnor *et al.* empirically verified the significance of personality difficulties in the segment of their study which focused on both problems among the quantitative analysts and their staff members, and problems between the quantitative analysts and their clients. The data gathered in their study show that "24% of staff relations problems were said to relate to personality, as opposed to 17% of the client relations problems."[4] And even if personality conflicts are absent, differences in opinion may give rise to disruptive discourse.

For these and other reasons, group participants often are prevented from effectively contributing during a group session. Skillful, well-trained, long-experienced group leaders no doubt can minimize these difficulties. But most persons who find themselves leading a group are not gifted in this way. Operational researchers, like many other people, often have not been provided the extensive training necessary to become a highly effective group leader.

### Introducing Nominal Grouping

Rather than using the traditional group format, one alternative the operational researcher may wish to consider is nominal grouping. It is "a method in which several assembled individuals (usually five to ten) follow a highly structured, non-interacting format to achieve an assigned goal."[9] A nominal grouping session begins with a *listing phase* in which each person is asked to generate silently a written list of ideas in response to a specific question, such as "Would you please list as many problems as you possibly can which you think may arise when implementing the mathematically derived solution described to you a few minutes ago?" After the listing phase, a *recording phase* follows in which each person, in round-robin fashion, reads aloud one item from his list in order for the group leader to write it on a large sheet of paper in front of the room in full view of all group members. When all items have been recorded in this way, a *voting phase* allows each group member to cast votes to express opinions regarding the priority of importance of the items in the total information set. Open discussion among group members is not allowed during any of these three phases. Discussion after the voting phase is optional.

The acceptance of nominal grouping among practitioners speaks well for its simplicity and intuitive soundness. Since the nominal grouping technique was first described in 1970,[10] it has been used in a variety of organizations including the U.S. Department of Agriculture, the U.S. Department of Housing and Urban Development, the U.S. Department of Labor, Mississippi Medical Center, Wachovia Bank, CECO Corporation, and on college campuses such as Mississippi State University, the University of Georgia and the University of Wisconsin.[9] The literature indicates that nominal grouping has been applied specifically for program planning,[10,11] organization development,[12] problem identification,[9,13] and subjective probability estimation.[14] In addition, nominal grouping has been used by the author and his colleagues in numerous organizations, particularly in governmental agencies. These applications have included many of the typical operational researcher activities—identifying existing problems which need to be overcome, gathering information to facilitate accurate and comprehensive definition and structuring of problems, identifying planning dimensions, generating ideas for developing models and solution approaches, determining key features to build into implementation strategies, identifying barriers to implementation success (including both financial and people-related barriers) and gaining acceptance and support of key individuals. The author has repeatedly seen nominal grouping successfully applied in these ways in both large and small organizations in industry and government. It is within this experienced-based frame of reference that nominal grouping is recommended to the operational researcher. However, it should be noted that although this article is based on more than the conceptual soundness of using nominal grouping for operational research purposes, it is not based on an abundance of vigorous experimental research because only three empirical studies on nominal grouping have been published and none focus directly on OR applications.[13,14,15] Therefore, the discussion that follows is principally the result of numerous applications of nominal grouping in a variety of organizations by the author and his colleagues, both those in academia and those in the real world.

## Group Composition and Size

When using nominal grouping, the initial decisions to be made by the operational researcher involve group composition and size. Whether or not group members should be homogenous or heterogenous in position, knowledge, experience, etc., generally depends upon the objective of the session. For example, suppose the task to be given the group is to "Identify the scheduling problems which the foremen currently experience." It may be possible to obtain partial information from the foremen's superior and subordinates. But if you really want to know the kinds of scheduling problems the foremen face, ask the foremen. A homogenous group—all foremen—is called for. However, a different group objective may suggest a heterogenous group. For example, the group task may be to "Identify the dimensions which should be incorporated in the production scheduling model." In this case, a heterogenous group including persons from production, sales, shipping, purchasing, and cost accounting, perhaps should be involved. In all situations, however, experience in using nominal grouping indicates that each group should be homogenous in terms of *authority* because subordinates and their superiors may be inhibited in the presence of each other. For this same reason, the author has found that care must be taken to choose a group leader whose presence will not inhibit group performance. This may well mean that the operational researcher himself should not conduct the session, even though the tendency is for him to prefer to be present. Yet his absence may be the only way to be certain he does not inhibit others from communicating information crucial to his success.

The group size can vary from two or three up to eleven or twelve persons, although six to ten is more typical. Time is a principal limiting factor on group size because as size increases more time is required, primarily in the recording phase. Experience with nominal grouping suggests that the approximate time duration for completing a session is as shown in Table 1. This is only an approximation because the time required is a function of the group task as well as group size. With the group size at six to ten, the author's experience has been that as many as 40-60 different ideas can be generated in a 10-15 minute listing phase.

## The Listing Phase

After group composition and size have been determined, the group members can be assembled for conducting the nominal grouping session. When each group member has taken a seat around the table, the grouper (this is the name usually given to the group leader in a nominal group) begins this session by discussing the purpose of the meeting. Generally speaking, the group should not have prior knowledge of the specific purpose of the session. The importance of this was recognized from early experiences in applying nominal grouping. First, when group members had prior knowledge, they tended to come to the meeting with preconceived notions that prohibit the kind of free, uninhibited thinking desired. Second, there was some evidence that pre-meeting persuasion and political maneuvering took place in a way that distorted the group results. With this in mind, the listing phase begins with the grouper indicating for the first time the purpose of the meeting. In addition, particular emphasis is directed to making the group aware of the importance of the session and encouraging them

*Table 1: Expected time requirements for varying group sizes*

| Size of the Nominal Group | 2-5 | 6-10 | 11-15 |
|---|---|---|---|
| Approximate Time Duration | About 1 Hour | About $1^1/_2$ Hours | About 2 Hours |

to be open and honest as they contribute ideas. Next, the grouper describes the nominal grouping approach to be used by explaining the listing-recording-voting phases.

The specific instructions for the listing phase begin by distributing to each member a sheet of paper with the group task typed at the top. These several statements should thoroughly and concisely state the task on which the group is to focus. The grouper reads the task aloud as everyone follows on their handout. Then he allows time for questions and discussion if clarification is needed to facilitate understanding of the task. The importance of stating the group task cannot be overemphasized. It is this statement that defines the mental set which channels the thinking process of each participant. Needless to say, stating the task is always a potential pitfall. This problem has caused many nominal grouping applications to end with less than desired results.

As the beginning of the listing phase draws near, the grouper provides several specific instructions to the group. The participants are asked to list, in writing, as many ideas as possible in response to the assigned task. Creativity is encouraged, and they are asked to list any and all ideas, even those that may seem trivial or insignificant. The grouper asks them to use short phrases of key words rather than using long sentences when making their list. Brevity is important here otherwise a time problem will occur during the recording phase. The importance of conciseness should be reiterated to the group because experience indicates a tendency for group members to use lengthy sentences even though they have been encouraged not to do so. The final instruction emphasizes that there is to be no discussion during the listing phase, but rather each person is to silently think, generate and list ideas. After these instructions have been given to the group, the grouper may want to allow time for any questions from the group about the task or technique to be used. The grouper then indicates how much time they have for listing, and allows them to begin. Fifteen minutes is usually adequate, but experience again has taught us an important lesson. The time needed varies principally with the nature of the task. The time required generally varies inversely with the specificity of the task, with the broad, general, comprehensive questions having a greater variety of responses thus requiring more time than the specific, narrow questions. In addition, the time requirements vary directly with the competence and willingness of each participant to contribute.

## The Recording Phase

When the time allocated for the listing phase expires (a time extension is permissible if needed), the grouper prepares for recording. With large sheets of paper (newsprint is good) taped to the wall prior to the beginning of the session, all that remains is to provide the group with several additional instructions. The grouper would say, for example, that to begin the recording he will call on the person to his left to read the first of several items he has on his list. After recording this on one of the large sheets, the grouper will ask anyone else who has the same item on their list to raise their hand so he can indicate beside the recorded item the number of other people who also had the item listed. To enable the group to make this decision, the grouper first will ask if anyone needs clarification from the person who read the item. This may be needed to help someone decide whether their item is the same. However, during the clarification only the person who read the item is allowed to comment, and only briefly. Group members should be encouraged not to consider one of their ideas as identical to one just recorded if even the slightest difference exists. If group members are liberal in judging *similar* ideas as *identical* ones, many valuable thoughts may be lost unnecessarily. The grouper should stress this potential problem during the recording phase as well as when giving instructions.

Except for clarification, discussion among group members is not allowed during the recording phase. This prevents the problem of persuasive and/or evaluative comments being made prior to the voting phase. However, experience indicates that at least one member in almost every group invariably will have a strong desire to express opinions during the recording phase. In fact, even though they have been instructed not to discuss the ideas being recorded, they will take advantage of every opportunity to do so. Consequently, perhaps the most problematic task for the grouper during the entire process is to tactfully prevent discussion at this point. The grouper precludes discussion best by strictly adhering to the recommended process. First he asks one person to read an item from his list to be recorded. Then he asks if anyone needs clarification and if so to raise their hand. If clarification is needed, call on the reader to briefly clarify. Next the grouper asks for a show of hands of those who also have the same item listed, and he so indicates by placing one check mark per person by the item on the recording sheets. The group should be reminded that if they indicate that one of their items is identical to one just recorded, they need not read it from their list at a later time. The process continues with the grouper calling on the next person to read the first item from his list. After recording it, the grouper asks if anyone needs clarification, and then if anyone else has it listed. When he gets back to the first person called on, the grouper asks him to read the second item from his list. Calling on group members in this round-robin fashion continues until each person has read all listed items.

One final instruction to the group is appropriate prior to recording. If other ideas come to participants' minds during the recording phase which are not already listed, group members should feel free to add them to their list. This is especially likely to happen because an idea read by one person for recording often stimulates other ideas. Allowing listing during the recording phase takes advantage of the benefits of this hitch-hiking effect. However, group members should not be told prior to the listing phase that they will be allowed to list during the recording phase. If they know this in advance, the time pressure during the listing may not have the productive effect that theoretically exists.

When recording actually begins, the grouper should write down ideas verbatim, unless the item is too long. This often is a problem because experience with nominal grouping indicates that groupers have a tendency to record ideas in their own words rather than those of the group members. This is especially true when a participant reads an excessively long item. When length is a problem, the person who had the item listed should be asked to condense it. The grouper should not condense it for him, and should not allow other group members to help either because the original thought may in some way be changed. Finally, when recording ideas, they should be numbered sequentially on the large sheets to facilitate the voting phase to follow.

### The Voting Phase

After the recording phase has been completed, the grouper should point out that the purpose of the voting phase is to increase further the value of the total information set by establishing a priority to items generated by the group. Each person will be asked to vote by identifying the five (or some other appropriate number) most important ideas recorded. The top five items are to be identified in order of priority simply by indicating (using the sequence number of the recorded item) the item considered most important, then the second in importance, etc., as follows:

1st No. _____
2nd No. _____
3rd No. _____
4th No. _____
5th No. _____

The grouper can allow whatever time is necessary for the voting, although experience indicates that about five minutes typically is adequate. Again, as in the previous two phases, discussion is not allowed. This permits the voting results to represent the opinions of each individual without the usual influence of persuasive and talkative members of the group. For various reasons, the group may be allowed time after the voting to discuss the ideas recorded. It has been the author's experience that, in some cases, group members will leave the session frustrated and discontent if they are not given an opportunity to express their opinions. Allowing for open discussion after the voting phase can avert this potential problem as well as provide a more accurate sense of the group's feelings than can be detected from the objectivity inherent in the nominal grouping process. It may even be desirable to have a second voting phase after the group discussion in order to determine the impact that verbalization has had on the group's thinking and the previously established order of priority of the ideas generated.

In concluding the voting phase, the grouper asks each group member to pass in his anonymous ballot for tabulation. One approach for counting the votes is to assign weights of 5, 4, 3, 2, and 1 to items receiving first, second, third, fourth, and fifth place votes, respectively. To illustrate, assume that only a modest number of items, such as ten, were recorded. The tally sheet would simply list the numbers one through ten in column one. Column two would be used to indicate the points for ballot No. 1. If the first ballot was as follows,

| 1st No. | 4 |
|---------|-----|
| 2nd No. | 10 |
| 3rd No. | 1 |
| 4th No. | 7 |
| 5th No. | 6 |

the tally sheet would include the points shown below. The voting from each ballot would be indicated in the same manner. Then, the points (weights) for each idea would be summed. The item with the largest total points is the first priority item, and so on. These voting results serve as a general indication of the group's assessment of the relative importance of each idea.

| Ideas | Points from Ballot No. 1 | Points from Ballot No. 2 | Total Points |
|-------|--------------------------|--------------------------|--------------|
| 1 | 3 | + | |
| 2 | | | |
| 3 | | | |
| 4 | 5 | + | |
| 5 | | | |
| 6 | 1 | + | |
| 7 | 2 | + | |
| 8 | | | |
| 9 | | | |
| 10 | 4 | + | |

The voting results may or may not be provided to the group. This depends upon the involvement they are to have beyond the session, and upon the degree of commitment that the operational researcher wants to demonstrate to the group. In any case, the session should terminate with a very sincere word of appreciation for their time and effort, and with some indication of what will happen now that they have made their contribution.

## Summary

When nominal grouping is evaluated within the context of the role of the operational researcher, it is concluded that the technique holds considerable promise for practical application in gathering information and generating ideas in each of the premodeling, modeling, and implementation stages. The operational researcher may find, as others have, that nominal grouping can be a highly effective format to use when working with groups. This may be especially true when either the group composition and/or the controversial nature of the topic in question is such that a discussion group recognizably will not be productive. Additionally, the structured, controllable format of the nominal group allows a rather substantial number of persons to effectively contribute and participate in the change process being directed by the operational researcher. The contributions by the participants may indeed result in better models and implementation strategies, and the fact that those who are to be affected by the change have been given the opportunity to participate in it may well serve as a much needed facilitating impact on the change process.

### REFERENCES

1. Grayson, C. Jackson, Jr. (1973) "Management Science and Business Practice." *Harvard Business Review* 51:41–48.
2. Green, Thad B. and S. Roland Jones. (1973) "Decision Science Applications: A Synthesis of Recent Research." Manfred W. Hopfe, editor, *Advancing, Applying, and Teaching the Decision Sciences.* American Institute for Decision Sciences, Atlanta, 308.
3. Amspoker, Robert D., J. Randall Brown, Robert D. Smith, and Robert H. Culhan. (1973) "Organizational Factors Related to Operations Research Project Group Effectiveness." Manfred W. Hopfe, editor, *Advancing, Applying, and Teaching the Decision Sciences.* American Institute for Decision Sciences, Atlanta, 102–105.
4. Radnor, Michael, Albert H. Rubenstein, and Alden S. Bean. (1968) "Integration and Utilization of Management Science Activities in Organizations." *Operational Research Quarterly* 19:117–141.
5. Konczal, Edward F. (1975) "Models Are for Managers, Not Mathematicians." *Journal of Systems Management* 26:12.
6. Rubenstein, Albert H., Michael Radnor, Norman R. Baker, David R. Heiman, and John B. McColly. (1967) "Some Organizational Factors Related to the

Effectiveness of Management Science Groups in Industry." *Management Science* 13:B508–B518.

7. Stillson, Paul. (1963) "Implementation of Problems in O.R." *Operations Research* 10:140–147.

8. Harvey, Allan. (1970) "Factors Making for Implementation Success and Failure." *Management Science* 16:B312–B321.

9. Green, Thad B. and Paul H. Pietri. (1974) "Using Nominal Grouping to Improve Upward Communication." *MSU Business Topics* 22:37–43.

10. Delbecq, Andre L. and Andy Van de Ven. (1970) "Nominal Group Techniques for Involving Clients and Resource Experts in Program Planning." T. J. Atchison and J. V. Ghorpade, editors, *Academy of Management Proceedings*. The Academy of Management, San Diego, 208:227.

11. Delbecq, Andre L. and Andrew H. Van de Ven. (1971) "A Group Process Model for Problem Identification and Program Planning." *The Journal of Applied Behavioral Science* 7:466–492.

12. Mosley, Donald C. and Thad B. Green. (1974) "Nominal Grouping As an Organization Development Intervention Technique." *Training and Development Journal* 28:30–37.

13. Green, Thad B. (1975) "An Empirical Analysis of Nominal and Interacting Groups." *Academy of Management Journal* 18:63–73.

14. Gustafson, David H., Ramesh K. Shukla, Andre Delbecq, and G. William Walster. (1973) "A Comparative Study of Differences in Subjective Likelihood Estimates Made by Individuals, Interacting Groups, Delphi Groups, and Nominal Groups." *Organizational Behavior and Human Performance* 9:280–291.

15. Van de Ven, Andrew and Andre L. Delbecq. (1974) "The Effectiveness of Nominal, Delphi, and Interacting Group Decision Making Processes." *Academy of Management Journal* 17:605–621.

# Part III: Modeling

# A. Modeling for Managers

## 1. MODELS ARE FOR MANAGERS, NOT MATHEMATICIANS

*Edward F. Konczal*

---

Applications of computer business models have met with both success and failure. Some of the failures can be traced to lack of management involvement in the modeling process. This may be due to the fact that many managers feel uncomfortable with the scientific aura of these computer models. Indeed many modeling efforts in econometrics and business research are cast in terms of advanced mathematics and statistics. However, what many managers do not realize is that the application of a

Editors' Note: Reprinted with permission from *Journal of Systems Management*, January 1975, pp. 12–15.

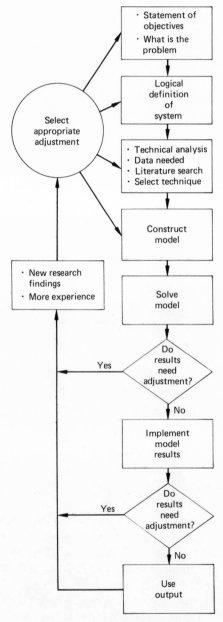

*Figure 1: The model building process*

quantitative technique to a business problem is, in many ways, an art form that should include managers as co-artists along with the technical staff. It may be useful, therefore, to look at some of the not-so-quantitative aspects of model building and to indicate how managers may become more involved in model construction and how they may contribute more to successful implementation of computer models.

The diagram in Figure 1 outlines the flow of activities in model construction. Managerial guidance and knowledge is important throughout model construction and implementation. For example, in the very early stages, it is management who should determine what to model and, based on cost and benefit estimates, management must also determine if a modeling approach is worthwhile. From there on, management should become involved in every model building stage.

Once the decision to use a model is made, the detailed planning and technical analysis can begin. At the end of the analytical stages we should have a model. After we shake down the model for inconsistencies, and apply validation tests, we should have a *useful tool*. But the work does not end here. If the model is to remain a decision making aid, model research *should* continue.

The initial model will be changed in light of new checks, new research insights, and more experience (for both managers and specialists). Furthermore, the iterative process, depicted in Figure 1, should include evaluation both of the model itself and the original objectives and purpose. Reformulation of the model will reflect both these considerations. Continuous management involvement in this evaluation process will go a long way to insure successful application of computer models.

While managerial input is important in all model building activities, managerial guidance is most important in (1) formulating the philosophy of model construction, (2) providing judgment that will temper the objectiveness of model methodology, (3) insuring that the model is an accurate model, (4) providing an efficient administrative structure for model work. This article will focus on these aspects of model building where management input will have the largest payoffs.

## Model Construction-Philosophy

It is most important to realize at the beginning of any modeling effort, that the sole purpose of computer models, within the corporate realm, is to help managers manage better. Therefore, business models should increase productivity by helping managers to:

Minimize the effects of surprise happenings.

Cope with increased complexity.

Minimize the impact of bad decisions.

*1. Models Are for Managers, not Mathematicians*                    213

Capitalize on the value of the systems approach.

Keep up with rapid change.

Avoid the limitation of intuitive reasoning. [1]

To achieve this aim, the business computer model must build upon the subconscious, informal and non-rigorous "mental models" that managers have been building for many years. Andrew Carnegie, for example, counted active smokestacks to help him make decisions. Today the business-environmental system is more complex to allow such a simple approach to business modeling. Computer models will help to assess this increasingly complex business environment. But, the guidance, judgment and intuition of managers will always be important ingredients both in formulating decisions and in building models to make better decisions.

To facilitate the interaction of management philosophy and experience with the technical skill of the specialist, the ultimate purpose of model construction should be clear to everyone involved in model construction; business models should help managers make decisions that will enhance company profitability. Therefore, model builders should become committed to company profitability and not solely to the elegance of technique.

## Methodology

Quantitative management techniques have been sufficiently documented. [2] It would be redundant to cover these techniques here. In addition, it is common knowledge that the basic characteristic of quantitative business modeling is to define the business system, under study, in terms of mathematical language. Mathematics is used to express relationships that exist in the real system. But the truth is in the actual phenomena and not in the math. Furthermore, since the model is really a skeletal abstraction, we should not expect the mathematics to capture all characteristics of the real system. Many intangible factors have to be analyzed on the basis of

*Figure 2*

| Model Activity | Preferred Level of Managerial Involvement |
| --- | --- |
| Stating Objectives | High |
| Logical Definition of System | High |
| Data Analysis, Technique Selection | High-Medium |
| Construct Model | Medium |
| Solve Model | Low |
| Select Adjustment | High |
| Implement Results | High |
| Use Output | High |

judgment, experience and intuition. This is where management input is most important. Managers involved in model activity should always be ready to provide suggestions to adjust the model due to:[3]

1. *Internal information*—knowledge about past runs of the model.
2. *External information*—knowledge about exogenous factors not covered by the model or not compatible with model parameters.
3. *Analysis of output*—predicted or simulated items may be out of line with past patterns; output of model seems unreasonable.

Judgmental adjustment should be made both during model construction and after the model is run. Furthermore, managerial input in the adjustment process can be valuable in almost every model activity. This is indicated in Figure 2, since it is only in the model solution activity where managerial involvement will be low.

These adjustments seem to indicate a paradox in using quantitative models; *first* computer models are built using the rigid discipline of mathematics, but then I say that the model should be flexible to include management judgment. Why then is it valid to alter the model? The answer lies in the fact that a model is not a substitute for judgment but highlights factors that need subjective interpretation. Therefore, it is valid to temper the objective discipline with judgment when the model does not capture a relevant and sensitive aspect of the real system. This helps to insure that the model will be internally consistent and that it will mirror past observed behavior.

### Model Validation

Management input, so important during model construction, is also vital in model validation: the certification process that gauges whether or not the model captures enough of the real world to be a reliable decision making aid. Certification is really a two stage process: (1) *Verification*—Determine if the model behaves the way its builder intends; is the model logically correct. (2) *Validation*—Test if the model agrees with the real system.

Verification is usually handled solely by the technical specialists and is usually accomplished by a systematic number of computer runs that should highlight defects in the logical construction of the model. These tests insure that all parts of the model hang together and that there are no programming errors. Test runs may include:

1. Running parts of a complicated model and verify the results.
2. Taking random parts out of a probabilistic type model and running them as if they were deterministic models.
3. Setting up simple test situations that will test many combinations of circumstances.[4]

Managers probably cannot contribute much during this process, since many detailed quantitative measures are employed. However, if a good rapport exists between model specialists and model users, managers should feel comfortable that proper logical tests will be employed.

The second stage of the validation process, that is, certifying that the model is a good abstraction of the real system, can be split into two categories: (1) *Parametric evaluation*—Formal statistical tests employed both during model construction and after a number of runs are made. (2) *Non-parametric evaluation*—These are descriptive, less sophisticated tests that yield insights into the performance and reliability of the model.[5]

Managers can make significant contributions in the second category. Now experience and judgment are very important in determining if the model captures the important items of the real system. Up to the validation stage model building activity is mostly a pure research activity. After the model is "certified" it may find its way into influencing decisions. Therefore, managers who are going to use the model must be satisfied that it is an accurate representation of the real system in which they live and work.

## Managing and Documenting

Once model research becomes a sustained activity administrative functions become important. Managers should insure that model building effort is carried on efficiently. This means that the model manager must coordinate a wide variety of activities and disciplines (economics, statistics, operations research). He must see that model work will flow smoothly. To do this he must be skilled not only in technical areas but also in planning operations and preparing budgets.[6] In addition, he must be an effective personnel administrator. This may be the most difficult job since model builders are usually creative people whose work motivations may be complex.

The model manager's job is crucial and difficult since it functions as the vital link between the technical specialist and the manager, both of whom may view model construction in a different light. The specialist is many times more interested in profitable use of models and not in the technique itself. The model manager has to speak the language of both groups and has to keep both satisfied.

In the past the model manager's job was not easily staffed since there weren't many management oriented people who possessed more than a passing knowledge of modeling techniques. Fortunately, this condition has changed. Many new managers have been exposed to quantitative techniques in college. In addition, many experienced managers are now familiar both with the quantitative techniques and how they may be profitably employed. This should help to increase the productivity of future model building efforts.

Administration of model work should also include seeing to it that good documentation of model activity is kept current. Files and records kept during model construction should help to develop and improve the model. Furthermore, good documentation will help to indoctrinate new analysts and speed up their contributions to model work.

An adequate documentation system should have a minimum of the following files:[7]

1. *Literature File*—books, journals, articles related to model activities.
2. *Model File*—how the model was developed and reformulated.
3. *Data File*—what data was used in the model, data estimates, revisions, accuracy, etc.
4. *Statistical Reference File*—statistical tests and estimation of parameters, problems, objectives and methods of statistical operations.
5. *Forecasting File*—past forecast errors, analyses of errors, data assumptions used to compute forecasts; comparisons with other models.
6. *Simulation Experiment File*—analysis of the "what if" conditions; runs made to analyze operating characteristics of the model—important for appraising if model should be reformulated.
7. *Computer Program File*—documentation is always important in programming; this file will describe all programs used and how they are employed in the model runs.
8. *Budget and Planning File*—monetary activities and overall objectives; aids in scheduling, program reporting and keeping within financial constraints. This file helps improve efficiency of model work.

## Conclusion

The business environment is sure to become increasingly complex in the future. The potential value of computerized business models will, therefore, also increase. However, successful applications of these models will be insured only if the decision making users of these models become actively involved in model building activities. As successful applications become widespread and as managers gain more knowledge in modeling techniques we should see computerized business models becoming an indispensable aid in many business functions.

### REFERENCES

1. Robert K. Mueller, "The Managementality Gap," *IEEE Transactions on Systems Science and Cybernetics*, January 1969. This article is good discussion of both model philosophy and the application of quantitative methods in management.

2. A few of the many articles covering quantitative business techniques are listed here:
   William G. Browne, "Techniques of Operations Research," *Journal of Systems Management*, September 1972, pp. 8–13. *Business Week*, "The 'New Management' Finally Take Over," August 23, 1969, pp. 58–62.
   P. H. Butterfield, H. J. Loue, "Operations Research as a Tool for Decision Making," paper presented to American Institute of Chemical Engineers, August 27, 1969. IBM Corp., *Management Science at Work*, (IBM, 1971).
3. A. A. Hirsche, "The BEA Quarterly Model as a Forecasting Instrument," *Survey of CURRENT Business*, August 1973.
4. R. C. Meier, W. T. Newell, H. L. Pazer, *Simulation in Business and Economics* (New York: Prentice-Hall, 1969, pp. 294–96).
5. D. J. Dhrymes (et al.), "Criteria for Evaluation of Econometric Models," *Annals of Economic and Social Measurement*, 1/3/1972, pp. 291–324. An excellent discussion of model verification and validation methods.
6. H. R. Hamilton (et al.), *Systems Simulation for Regional Analysis* (Cambridge: MIT Press, 1969), Appendix A, a good source of information on managing a model building effort.
7. A. Zellner, "The Care and Feeding of Econometric Models," *Selected Paper* No. 35, Graduate School of Business, University of Chicago. Many pragmatic insights into model buildings are covered in this excellent paper.

# 2. MODELS AND MANAGERS:
# THE CONCEPT OF A DECISION CALCULUS

*John D. C. Little*

---

## 1. Introduction

The big problem with management science models is that managers practically never use them. There have been a few applications, of course, but the practice is a pallid picture of the promise. Much of the difficulty lies in implementation and an especially critical aspect of this is the meeting between manager and model. I believe that communication across this interface today is almost nil and that the situation stands as a major impediment to successful use of models by managers. Furthermore, I want to suggest that the requirements of the interface have implications for the design of the model itself.

As an area to illustrate the ideas presented, we shall use marketing. This

Editors' Note: Reprinted with permission from *Management Science*, April 1970, pp. B466–B485, published by The Institute of Management Sciences.

field well demonstrates the problems and opportunities at hand. Marketing has high managerial content in the sense that decisions are often non-routine and usually require a bringing together of people ideas, data, and judgments from diverse sources. Although something is known about underlying processes, much uncertainty remains to confront the manager. Data is prolific but usually poorly digested, often irrelevant, and some key issues entirely lack the illumination of measurement. At the same time, marketing is of interest for its own sake. This is not only because of its key and sometimes controversial role in the society but also because fundamental knowledge in marketing has application beyond business into the marketing-like activities of governments, universities, hospitals, and other organizations.

The terms "manager" and "decision" will be used frequently. Let it be noted now that a "manager" is frequently a fuzzy, shifting mix of people and a "decision" is usually a murky event, identifiable only in retrospect.

The paper is organized under the following headings: (1) Introduction, (2) What's wrong? (3) How do managers use models? (4) What might be right? (5) An example from marketing, (6) What happened to science? and (7) Conclusions.

## 2. What's Wrong?

Some of the reasons that models are not used more widely by managers appear to be:

(1) *Good models are hard to find.* Convincing models that include the manager's control variables and so contain direct implications for action are relatively difficult to build, particularly in the areas that are of greatest concern. Some progress, however, is certainly being made. In marketing, for example, see Montgomery and Urban [6].

(2) *Good parameterization is even harder.* Measurements and data are needed. They require high quality work at the design stage and are often expensive to carry out.

(3) *Managers don't understand the models.* People tend to reject what they do not understand. The manager carries responsibility for outcomes. We should not be surprised if he prefers a simple analysis that he can grasp, even though it may have a qualitative structure, broad assumptions, and only a little relevant data, to a complex model whose assumptions may be partially hidden or couched in jargon and whose parameters may be the result of obscure statistical manipulations.

Typically, the manager is willing and eager to accept flawless work that delivers the future to him with certainty. Unfortunately, as he digs into any study performed by human researchers in an ordinary OR group, he finds assumptions that seem questionable, terminology that is confusing, and a certain tendency to ignore a variety of qualitative issues the manager feels are important. The manager feels that to get deep into the model and find out what is really going on is totally out of the question because he lacks the time and background. The solution to this predicament is often for him to pick on some seeming flaw in the model, usually a consideration left out, and make that the basis for postponing use into the indefinite future.

In this situation the operations researcher's response is often to conclude that his model is not complete enough. Therefore, he goes back to work to make things more complicated and probably harder to understand. Meanwhile, the manager continues to use intuitive models that are much simpler than the one rejected.

I might point out the professional OR/management science fraternity also escalates the model builder into complexity. A favorite pastime in the trade is to tell a model builder, "You left such and such out."

Some people have asked why it is necessary for a manager to understand the models he uses. After all, most of us drive cars and few of us understand the details of an internal combustion engine. An $R$ and $D$ manager is not expected to follow the technical niceties of the work being done in his labs. However, I would argue that the kind of understanding that is required is defined relative to the job. As drivers we had better understand what will happen when we turn the steering wheel even though we do not need to know how to repair the brakes. The $R$ and $D$ manager had better be able to tell effective teams from ineffective ones, but this will not usually require him to be a specialist in laboratory technique. The marketing manager should understand a marketing model in the sense of knowing very well what to expect from it but need not know the details of its computer program.

(4) *Most models are incomplete.* Having complained about complexity as a bar to understanding, I now decry incompleteness. This means that I hope we can invent simple models that have the capacity to include quite a few phenomena.

Incompleteness is a serious danger if a model is used for optimization. Optimization can drive control variables to absurd values if critical phenomena are omitted. One popular answer to this difficulty is not to optimize. Sometimes this is the right thing to do—we should say out loud the model provides only part of the decision making information and that the rest must come from elsewhere. However, in most cases we want to be able to evaluate and compare. This is embryonic optimization and incompleteness can be a pitfall.

The above list of obstacles of implementation could be extended but should suffice to ward off complacency.

### 3. How Do Managers Use Models?

Here is an impression, albeit anecdotal, of how managers actually use models.

*Part III: Modeling*

The OR group of a major oil company recently did a survey on the use of mathematical programming in production scheduling at their refineries. Refinery scheduling was a pioneer application of mathematical programming and has been an active research area for 10–15 years. At one refinery the dialog between the interviewer and the local OR analyst went somewhat as follows:

INTERVIEWER: "Do you make regular mathematical programming runs for scheduling the refinery?"

ANALYST: "Oh yes."

INTERVIEWER: "Do you implement the results?"

ANALYST: "Oh no!"

INTERVIEWER: "Well, that seems odd. If you don't implement the results, perhaps you should stop making the runs?"

ANALYST: "No. No. We wouldn't want to do that!"

INTERVIEWER: "Why not?"

ANALYST: "Well, what happens is something like this: I make several computer runs and take them to the plant manager. He is responsible for this whole multi-million dollar plumber's paradise.

"The plant manager looks at the runs, thinks about them for a while and then sends me back to make a few more with conditions changed in various ways. I do this and bring them in. He looks at them and probably sends me back to more runs. And so forth."

INTERVIEWER: "How long does this keep up?"

ANALYST: "I would say it continues until, finally, the plant manager screws up enough courage to make a decision."

What is the plant manager doing here? Before speculating on this, let me recount some experiences with people using MEDIAC, a media planning model developed by L. M. Lodish and myself [4]. The first step in using the model is preparing the input data. This requires a fair amount of reflection about the problem at hand, a certain effort spent digging out numbers, and usually subjective estimates of several quantities. Thereafter, the model is run and a schedule is generated.

The user looks at the schedule and immediately starts to consider whether it makes sense to him or not. Is it about what he expected? Sometimes it is and, if so, usually that is that. Oftentimes, however, the schedule does not quite agree with his intuition. It may even differ substantially. Then he wants to know why. A process starts of finding out what it was about the inputs that made the outputs come out as they did. This usually can be discovered without too much difficulty by a combination of inspection, consideration of how the model works, and various sensitivity analyses.

Having done this, the user decides whether he is willing to go along with the results as they came out. If not, he can, for example, change the problem formulation in various ways or possibly change his subjective estimates. Sometimes he finds outright errors in the input data. Most of the time, however, if he has been careful in his data preparation, he will agree with the reasons for the answers coming out as they did and he has, in fact, learned something new about his problem. The whole process might be described as an updating of his intuition. The model has served the function of interrelating a number of factors and, in this case, not all the implications of the interrelations were evident to him when he started.

Notice, incidentally, that he has by no means turned over his decision making to the computer. He remains the boss and demands explanations from his electronic helper.

I believe the same type of process is going on with the plant manager in the earlier example. He is involved in an analysis-education-decision process built around man-model-machine interaction in which the man does not lose responsibility or control and instead of understanding less understands more.

Such an interaction should, I believe, be the goal for much of our normative model building.

Further advice to scientists about managers has been reported by Mathes [5]. He asserts that managers and scientists have different approaches to problem solving and that this fact hinders communication between them. Managerial people analyze problems on the basis of differences or changes in situations. Scientific people look for similarities or common elements.

Certainly the model builder by the nature of his role is seeking generalizations that fit many problems. And certainly the manager looks at differences: this year vs. last year, his organization vs. the competition, forecast vs. actual, etc. Pounds [7] has observed that such mechanisms form one of the manager's principal means of problem finding. The same idea is supported by control theory: action in control systems is usually triggered by a discrepancy between observed and desired results.

The model builder can take advantage of the idea of working with differences by having his model give and receive much of its information in these terms.

The following quotes from Mathes may (or may not) be helpful to any group of managers and management scientists working together to apply models:

The difference (managerial) people know only two degrees of probability, zero and one, and the similarity (scientific) people recognize every degree of probability except zero and one.

The difference people tend to act before they think, if they ever think; whereas the similarity people think before they act, if they ever act.

## 4. What Might Be Right?

If we want a manager to use a model, we should make it his, an extension of his ability to think about and analyze his operation. This puts special requirements on design and will often produce something rather different from what a management scientist might otherwise build. I propose a name to describe the result. A *decision calculus* will be defined as a model-based set of procedures for processing data and judgments to assist a manager in his decision making.

From experience gained so far, it is suggested that a decision calculus should be:

(1) *Simple.* Simplicity promotes ease of understanding. Important phenomena should be put in the model and unimportant ones left out. Strong pressure often builds up to put more and more detail into a model. This should be resisted, until the users demonstrate they are ready to assimilate it.

(2) *Robust.* Here I mean that a user should find it difficult to make the model give bad answers. This can be done by a structure that inherently constrains answers to a meaningful range of values.

(3) *Easy to control.* A user should be able to make the model behave the way he wants it to. For example, he should know how to set inputs to get almost any outputs. This seems to suggest that the user could have a preconceived set of answers and simply fudge the inputs until he gets them. That sounds bad. Should not the model represent objective truth?

Wherever objective accuracy is attainable, I feel confident that the vast majority of managers will seize it eagerly. Where it is not, which is most of the time, the view here is that the manager should be left in control. Thus, the goal of parameterization is to represent the operation as the manager sees it. I rather suspect that if the manager cannot control the model he will not use it for fear it will coerce him into actions he does not believe in. However, I do not expect the manager to abuse the capability because he is honestly looking for help.

(4) *Adaptive.* The model should be capable of being updated as new information becomes available. This is especially true of the parameters but to some extent of structure too.

(5) *Complete on important issues.* Completeness is in conflict with simplicity. Structures must be found that can handle many phenomena without bogging down. An important aid to completeness is the incorporation of subjective judgments. People have a way of making better decisions than their data seem to warrant. It is clear that they are able to process a variety of inputs and come up with aggregate judgments about them. So, if you can't lick 'em, join 'em. I say this without taking away from the value of measurement. Many, if not most, of the big advances in scientific

knowledge come from measurement. Nevertheless, at any given point in time, subjective estimates will be valuable for quantities that are currently difficult to measure or which cannot be measured in the time available before a decision must be made.

One problem posed by the use of subjective inputs is that they personalize the model to the individual or group that makes the judgments. This makes the model, at least superficially, more fragile and less to be trusted by others than, say a totally empirical model. However, the model with subjective estimates may often be a good deal tougher because it is more complete and conforms more realistically to the world.

(6) *Easy to communicate with.* The manager should be able to change inputs easily and obtain outputs quickly. On-line, conversational I/O and time-shared computing make this possible.

Every effort should be made to express input requests in operational terms. The internal parameterization of the model can be anything, but the requests to the user for data should be in his language. Thus, coefficients and constants without clear operational interpretation are to be discouraged. Let them be inferred by the computer from inputs that are easier for the user to work with. Expressing inputs and outputs as differences from reference values often helps.

On-line systems come through as being very effective in bringing the model to the manager. Some writers, for example Dearden [2], have belittled the importance of immediate response. They argue that decisions made once a year or even once a month hardly require systems that deliver the answers in seconds. Anyone who has used a conversational system perceives that this argument misses the point. Practically no decision is made on a single computer run. A person develops his understanding of a problem and its solution as he works on it. The critical time is not that of the decision deadline but of the next step in the user's thinking process.

Perhaps equally as important as the operational convenience of conversational programs is their contribution to learning. Good on-line models are user-instructing and introduce a person to the issues of the problem and the model much faster than would otherwise be possible. A person can rapidly get a feel for how the model works through direct experience. This is in sharp contrast to batch processing with its long time lags and imposing tribal rituals of punched cards, systems programmers and computer operators.

In summary, we are learning techniques of model design and implementation that bring the model to the manager and make it more a part of him. We are calling such a model a decision calculus.

## 5. An Example from Marketing

An on-line marketing-mix model for use by product managers is currently being developed. The present version emphasizes advertising budget decisions. It will be described below in an inductive, narrative way. Its mathematical specification is given in Appendix 1.

The product or brand manager is an ideal customer for a decision calculus. He has substantial responsibility for all of the marketing control variables for a brand. He is busy and will not use a model unless it does something for him. He is at ease making judgments and, being a single person accountable for results, he can gather inputs and make judgments without the elaborate coordination required in many other complex decision processes.

The work is being done in cooperation with three different product managers at two different companies. The variety in companies and managers has been helpful for getting perspective on the man-model interface and in keeping the model structure general. The development has proceeded in evolutionary steps. First a very simple advertising budgeting model was brought up and used to demonstrate concepts. Then a more complex model for advertising budgeting, one with sufficient detail to be of practical value, was brought up. This version will be described here. Experience with it is influencing the design of a more elaborate model.

5.1 MODEL STRUCTURE. We seek a simple, robust, easy to control model of sales response to advertising. As a first step brand sales is partitioned into product class sales and brand market share. That is, we separately model what is happening to the whole industry or product class of which the brand is a part and what is happening to the brand's share within the class. Such a breakdown has a number of advantages, not the least of which is that marketing people usually think this way. Consider a given time period. We suppose:

1. If advertising is cut to zero, brand share will decrease, but there is a floor, *min*, on how much share will fall from its initial value by the end of one time period.
2. If advertising is increased a great deal, say to something that could be called saturation, brand share will increase but there is a ceiling, *max*, on how much can be achieved by the end of one time period.
3. There is some advertising rate that will maintain initial share.
4. An estimate can be made by data analysis or managerial judgment of the effect on share by the end of one period of a 50% increase in advertising over the maintenance rate.

Figure 1 gives a pictorial representation of this information. The same data can also be represented as four points on a share response to advertising curve, as in Figure 2. A smooth curve can then be put through the points; for example, the function

(1) $$\text{share} = min + (max - min)(\text{adv})^{\gamma}/[\delta + (\text{adv})^{\gamma}]$$

The constants *min*, *max*, $\delta$ and $\gamma$ are implicitly determined by the input data.

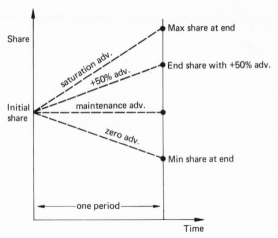

Figure 1: Input data for fitting
a sale response to advertising function

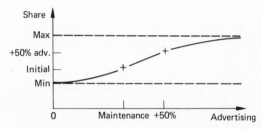

Figure 2: A smooth curve of share vs. advertising
put through the data of form shown in Figure 1

Equation (1) represents a versatile but nevertheless restricted set of response relations. Actually, I am willing to use anything. The curve could go down or up or loop the loop for all I care. It should be changed when and if a product manager wants it changed. Meanwhile, he can give four numbers, each of which has operational meaning to him and which together will specify a curve. It is doubtful that, as of today, we could specify a sales response curve in any greater detail than represented by a smooth curve through four appropriately chosen points.

I now claim that the above structure is robust. Suppose we do a two-level spending test and run a regression that is linear in advertising in order to estimate response. Such a regression might make reasonable statistical sense but by itself would have absurd normative implications (advertising = 0 or ∞); it would not be robust. However, if the regression results are used to estimate the +50% point and a reasonable *max* and *min* are chosen we can expect reasonable answers. This would be difficult to prove

*Part III: Modeling*

in general, but with a specific manager and product it can usually be demonstrated satisfactorily by sensitivity analysis.

To be sure, more sophisticated models and data analyses can easily be suggested. A quadratic term could be put in the regression, for example, but its coefficient would almost certainly be unstable and normatively alarming. A Bayesian analysis or an adaptive control model like that of [3] might restore order, but the intellectual cost of such complications is high. Even if more sophisticated studies are done, they could probably be translated into a set of operational terms like the above. In any case we should start simply.

A person might well ask: Is the structure too robust? Conceivably, a model could be so constrained that output would be almost decoupled from input. This is hardly the case here. The value specified for the share increase with +50% advertising is certain to be an important determinant of advertising rate. The values of *max* and *min* play the role of keeping changes in a meaningful range.

Incidentally, the sketch in Figure 2 shows an S-shaped curve. This is not required by (1). If $\gamma > 1$, the curve will be S-shaped, for $0 < \gamma \leq 1$, a concave function. The particular $\gamma$ will depend on the input data.

A major omission in the description so far is consideration of time delays. To take these into account, the model assumes:

1. In the absence of advertising, share would eventually decay to some long run minimum value (possibly zero).
2. The decay in one time period will be a constant fraction of the gap between current share and the long run minimum, i.e., decay is exponential.
3. The decay determines *min* for the time period.
4. The advertising affectable share, (*max – min*) stays constant.

Let *long run min* denote the long run minimum and *persistence* denote the fraction of the difference between share and long run minimum that is retained after decay. Under the above assumptions:

$$\text{persistence} = (\text{min} - \text{long run min})/(\text{initial share} - \text{long run min})$$
$$(2) \; \text{share} \, (t) - \text{long run min} = (\text{persistence})[\text{share} \, (t-1) - \text{long run min}]$$
$$+ \; (\text{max} - \text{min})[\text{adv} \, (t)]^{\gamma}/(\delta + [\text{adv} \, (t)]^{\gamma})$$

This is a simple dynamic model. It is explainable and it behaves reasonably. It could be further generalized by permitting some of the constants to change with time, but that does not seem desirable at the moment.

But now what is meant by advertising? Dollars? Exposures? A product manager worries about spending rates, media, and copy. Let us construct two time varying indices: (1) a media efficiency index, and (2) a copy effectiveness index. Both will be assumed to have reference values of 1.0. The model then hypothesizes that the delivered advertising, i.e., the adv (t) that goes into the response function is given by

(3) adv $(t)$ = [media efficiency $(t)$] [copy effectiveness $(t)$] [adv dollars $(t)$]

The media efficiency and copy effectiveness indices can be determined subjectively, but better alternatives exist. Copy testing is helpful and data on media cost, exposures by market segment, and relative value of market segments can be used to develop a media index.

So far we have taken up share response to advertising, media efficiency, copy effectiveness, and share dynamics. Consider next product class sales. Two important phenomena here are seasonality and trend. These and any similar effects can be combined into a product class index that varies with time. Thus

product class sales $(t)$ =
[reference product class sales][product class sales index $(t)$]

In addition, there may be a product class response to brand advertising and corresponding time lags. The treatment of this is analogous to that for share. Details are given in Appendix 1.

A variety of other factors affect share and therefore indirectly or directly can affect the product manager's thinking about the advertising budget. Some of these factors are: promotions, competition, distribution, price, product changes, and package changes. These factors are all treated in a simple way, not unlike the way a product manager might handle them without a model.

Upon examining the factors, we find that the product manager has a definite idea about what various changes are likely to do for him. If he plans a promotion he does so with the expectation that something will happen to his sales and share. The same holds for a product change or price change. Therefore we ask him to construct an index of how he believes these factors will affect brand share in each period. The process can be formalized by filling in a table such as Table 1, listing all factors deemed by the product manager to be relevant. The composite index of non-advertising effects is simply the product of the numbers in each column. Brand share will then be the product of the nonadvertising effect index and the share developed from the advertising response relation. For clarity the latter will be called the unadjusted share:

brand share $(t)$ = [non adv effects index $(t)$] [unadj share $(t)$]

People often ask how product managers can make judgments like the above. The answer is that managers make such judgments all the time but in a less formal and less numerical way. Whenever they take an action they form some belief about what will happen. As a result, it has not proven difficult for them to make estimates which they feel reasonably comfortable with.

Essentially, the model is now specified. However, as we have added time varying effects such as media efficiency and the nonadvertising

| Index of Effect on Share | Period | | | |
|---|---|---|---|---|
| | 1 | 2 | 3 | 4 |
| Promotions | 1.00 | 1.10 | .98 | 1.00 |
| Price | 1.00 | 1.00 | 1.00 | 1.00 |
| Package | 1.00 | 1.05 | 1.05 | 1.05 |
| Competitive action | 1.00 | .98 | .95 | 1.00 |
| Other | 1.00 | 1.00 | 1.00 | 1.00 |
| Composite | 1.000 | 1.132 | .978 | 1.050 |

phenomena, we have created a problem for the inputs that determine share response to advertising. What values of the time-varying effects are assumed in the share response inputs? To deal with this question we introduce the concept of a reference case. The reference case is a standard set of values against which changes can be measured. The reference case includes a reference time period. This is not one of the numbered time periods of the calculation but one set apart to serve as a standard. It can be patterned after a real period or can be constructed as a "typical" period. In any case each time varying effect is assigned a value in the reference period. From this data the sales response parameters *min, max*, $\gamma$ and $\delta$ are then inferred.

To summarize the model:

1. *Share*

   brand share $(t)$ = [non adv effect index $(t)$][unadj share $(t)$]

   unadj share $(t)$ = long run min + [persistence][unadj share $(t-1)$ – long run min] + (max – min) [wtd adv $(t)$]$^\gamma$/ $\{\delta + [\text{wtd adv } (t)]^\gamma\}$

   wtd adv $(t)$ = [media efficiency $(t)$][copy effectiveness $(t)$][adv dollars $(t)$]/[reference value of numerator]

2. *Brand Sales*

   brand sales $(t)$ = [reference product class sales][product class sales index $(t)$][brand share $(t)$]

3. *Profits*

   contribution to profit after adv $(t)$ = [contribution per sales unit $(t)$][brand sales $(t)$] – adv dollars $(t)$

The units situation has not been developed in detail here and we have omitted the effect of brand advertising on product class sales. These details are treated in the Appendix.

The basic equations defining the model are really quite few. Nevertheless, the structure permits consideration of share response to advertising, copy effectiveness, media efficiency, product class seasonality and trends, share dynamics, product class response to advertising, and a variety of non-advertising effects such as promotion, distribution, and price. I feel that the structure meets the criteria of simplicity, robustness, and ease of control.

5.2 CONVERSATIONAL I/O. We have said that the model should be easy to use. It must be easy to put data into the computer, easy to find out what is in there, easy to change it, easy to make output runs, easy to search over control variables and make sensitivity analyses. Clerical errors should be quickly correctable. The mechanical operating details should require as little training as possible.

The best way to show how these issues are being approached would be by demonstration at a computer terminal. Short of this we can provide an example. Table 2 shows the trace generated by a person putting in data for "Groovy," a struggling brand in the treacle market. Table 3 shows an input summary printed back by the computer. Table 4 shows an output run.

Some of the options open to the user are: saving data in the computer for later use, changing individual data items, and printing selected items of input or output. He can choose between long descriptive questions or terse questions that type quickly. An important facility is the search option: Any variable or parameter of the model can vary from an arbitrary minimum to an arbitrary maximum in any number of steps. At each step a set of user specified output items is calculated and printed. Thus a search might be made over a control variable to look for improved profit. Or a search might be made over an input parameter to find that value which conforms best to manager's feeling about the parameter's effect on sales.

The traces of Tables 2–4 are largely self-explanatory, except that the item SLOPE in Table 4 needs clarification. This item is intended to answer the question that a user is most likely to ask: Which way should I change advertising to increase profit? But we must ask: What profit? Profit in that period or, since sales changes persist into the future, profit over several periods? We have chosen to anticipate the answer to be "cumulative contribution after advertising" in the last period of the calculation. But which advertising? We expect the question might be asked about advertising in any period. Thus we calculate

SLOPE (t) = the change in cumulative contribution after advertising in the last period, per unit change in adv dollars in t

A positive SLOPE indicates that advertising increases will be profitable (in the above sense); negative, unprofitable; and zero, indifference.

5.3 APPLYING THE MODEL. One might think that ways to apply the model

GO /ADBUDG/

ADBUDG II — A MULTIPERIOD ADVERTISING BUDGETING MODEL

1 COMPUTER ASKS QUESTIONS IN STANDARD FORM

2 COMPUTER ASKS QUESTIONS IN SHORT FORM

ANS = (1)

1 ENTER NEW DATA

2 USE SAVED DATA

ANS = (1)

BRAND NAME: (GROOVY)

NO. OF TIME PERIODS (MAX = 8):(4)

LENGTH OF PERIOD: (QUARTER)

NAME OF FIRST PERIOD: (1 ST Q 70)

GEOGRAPHIC AREA: (US)

    BRAND DATA FOR REFERENCE PERIOD.

    SEASONALITY, TREND, OR OTHER NON-ADV.

    EFFECT REMOVED.

MARKET SHARE AT START OF PERIOD (% OF UNITS): (1.86)

ADVERTISING THAT WILL MAINTAIN SHARE (DOLLARS/PERIOD): (486900)

MARKET SHARE AT END OF PERIOD
IF ADV REDUCED TO ZERO: (1.77)

MARKET SHARE AT END OF PERIOD
IF ADV INCREASED TO SATURATION: (2.25)

MARKET SHARE AT END OF PERIOD IF ADV INCREASED
50% OVER MAINTENANCE RATE: (1.95)

MARKET SHARE IN LONG RUN IF ADV REDUCED TO ZERO:(0)
INDEX OF MEDIA EFFICIENCY (E.G., AVERAGE EFFICIENCY = 1.0): (1.0)

INDEX OF COPY EFFECTIVENESS (E.G., AVERAGE COPY = 1.0): (1.0)

UNITS IN WHICH SALES ARE TO BE MEASURED
(TO BE USED FOR BOTH BRAND AND PRODUCT CLASS.
E.G., POUNDS, GALLONS, CASES, THOUSANDS OF DOLLARS, ETC.): (HOGSHEADS)

CONTRIBUTION PROFIT (BEFORE ADV EXPENSE)

EXPRESSED IN DOLLARS/SALES UNIT: (.68)

AVERAGE BRAND PRICE (DOLLARS/SALES UNIT): (1.812)

    OTHER BRAND DATA

MARKET SHARE IN PERIOD PREVIOUS TO PERIOD 1: (1.86)

    PRODUCT CLASS DATA FOR REFERENCE PERIOD.

    SEASONALITY, TREND AND OTHER NON-ADV

    EFFECTS REMOVED

## Table 2—*Continued*

NAME OF PRODUCT CLASS: (TREACLE)

PRODUCT CLASS SALES RATE AT START OF PERIOD
(UNITS/PERIOD): (290000000)

CONSIDER RESPONSE TO PRODUCT CLASS ADV? (NO)

AVERAGE PRICE FOR PRODUCT CLASS (DOLLARS/SALES UNIT): (1.88)

    TIME VARYING DATA. IF TIME VARIATION NOT SPECIFIED,
    REFERENCE DATA WILL BE COPIED INTO ALL PERIODS.

PRODUCT CLASS SALES RATE HAS SEASONAL OR OTHER NON-ADV
TIME EFFECT ? (YES)

INDEX OF PRODUCT CLASS SALES (REFERENCE CASE = 1.00) FOR PERIOD:

1: .943
2: 1.012
3: 1.065
4: .959

BRAND SHARE HAS A NON-ADV TIME EFFECT ? (YES)

INDEX OF NON-ADV EFFECTS (REFERENCE CASE = 1.00) FOR PERIOD

1: 1.0
2: 1.05
3: .98
4: 1.0

MEDIA EFFICIENCY VARIES ? (NO)

COPY EFFECTIVENESS VARIES ? (NO)

CONTRIBUTION VARIES ? (NO)

AVERAGE BRAND PRICE VARIES ? (NO)

AVERAGE PRICE FOR PRODUCT VARIES ? (NO)

BRAND ADV RATE VARIES ? (YES)

BRAND ADV (DOLLARS/UNIT) IN PERIOD

1: 486000
2: 606000
3: 876000
4: 414000

1 SAVE DATA
2 PRINT DATA
3 CHANGE DATA
4 OUTPUT
5 RESTART
ANS = (1)

DATA FILE NAME: (GROOVY-70)

*Table 3: Summary of input data for GROOVY brand.
It has been stored in a file named /GROOVY-70/. The
letter M stands for millions.*

1 SAVE DATA

2 PRINT DATA

3 CHANGE DATA

4 OUTPUT

5 RESTART

ANS = ②

1 STANDARD PRINT

2 ONLY SPECIFIED LINES

ANS = ①

/GROOVY-70/

1 BRAND NAME: GROOVY

2 NO. PERIODS: 4.000

3 PER. LENGTH: QUARTER

4 FIRST PER.: 1ST Q 70

5 AREA: US

    REFERENCE PER.—BRAND

7 INIT. SHARE (% OF UNITS): 1.860

8 MAINT. ADV (DOL./PER.): .486M

9 MIN SHARE AT END: 1.770

10 MAX SHARE AT END: 2.250

11 END SHARE WITH + 50% ADV: 1.950

12 LONG RUN MIN SHARE: .000

14 MEDIA EFFCY: 1.000

15 COPY EFFECT: 1.000

16 SALES UNIT: HOGSHEADS

17 CONTRIBUTION (DOL./UNIT): .680

18 BRAND PRICE (DOL/UNIT): 1.812

    OTHER BRAND DATA

19 STARTING SHARE: 1.860

    REFERENCE PER.—PROD. CLASS

21 PROD. CLASS NAME: TREACLE

22 INIT. CLASS SALES RATE (UNITS/PER.): 290M

29 CLASS PRICE (DOL/UNIT): 1.880

    TIME VARIATIONS

| PERIOD | 1 | 2 | 3 | 4 |
|---|---|---|---|---|
| 30 CLASS SALES INDEX: | | | | |
| | .943 | 1.012 | 1.065 | .959 |
| 31 NON-ADV EFFECT INDEX: | | | | |
| | 1.000 | 1.050 | .980 | 1.000 |
| 32 MEDIA EFFCY: | | | | |
| | 1.000 | 1.000 | 1.000 | 1.000 |
| 33 COPY EFFECT: | | | | |
| | 1.000 | 1.000 | 1.000 | 1.000 |

*Table 3: Continued*

| 34 CONTRIBUTION (DOL/UNIT): | | | | |
|---|---|---|---|---|
| | .650 | .680 | .680 | .680 |
| 35 BRAND PRICE (DOL/UNIT): | | | | |
| | 1.812 | 1.812 | 1.812 | 1.812 |
| 36 CLASS PRICE (DOL/UNIT): | | | | |
| | 1.880 | 1.880 | 1.880 | 1.880 |
| 37 BRAND ADV (DOL./PER.): | | | | |
| | .486M | .606M | .876M | .414M |

would be obvious. Not really. The model has to be worked into the user's system. There are a number of ways in which this can and should be done. I shall describe one which we have just been through: The model was used to assist in the quarterly review of a brand plan.

The usual pattern of operations with a consumer product is to construct a brand plan. This is done once a year. The plan lays out the whole marketing program in considerable detail. However, as the year progresses and various parts of the program are carried out, changes get made: new opportunities arise, actual results come in and are not quite as expected, and generally a variety of unforeseen circumstances occur. Consequently, a series of review and replanning points are scheduled, usually quarterly. This does not preclude actions at other times, which in fact take place, but it does at least schedule times in which changes are definitely considered or, if already made, are consolidated in a revised forecast of results.

Our goals in applying the model were to start from a "brand plan" view of the market, modify it to accommodate the new information contained in year-to-date results, then evaluate new strategies and repredict future outcomes. Here is what we did:

*Step 1. Setting up the model according to the annual brand plan.* A set of input data was developed which would reproduce as model output the results found in the original brand plan. (If the brand plan had been constructed using the model, this step would not have been necessary.) The product class was identified. The seasonality and trends in product class were worked out. The input data for sales response to advertising was estimated by a combination of judgment and the examination of past time series of advertising and sales data. (In this case there were no spending levels test data but one of the side consequences of our study is that the company is seriously considering such tests for the future.) A promotion was planned for the second quarter and estimated to have a certain effect on share. A copy test, using two different areas of the country, was under way. The brand plan proposed that the test be continued for the year and so the copy index was held constant at 1.0. Similarly, no substantial media changes were anticipated and the media efficiency was held at 1.0. A certain

*Part III: Modeling*

1 SAVE DATA
2 PRINT DATA
3 CHANGE DATA
4 OUTPUT
5 RESTART

ANS = (4)

1 STANDARD OUTPUT
2 EXCLUDE SPECIFIED LINES
3 INCLUDE SPECIFIED LINES ONLY

ANS = (1)

1 CALCULATE CURRENT CASE
2 SEARCH
3 FINISHED

ANS = (1)

| | | 1 | 2 | 3 | 4 |
|---|---|---|---|---|---|
| 1 OUTPUT FOR | GROOVY | | | | |
| 2 PERIOD LENGTH: | QUARTER | | | | |
| 3 STARTING PERIOD: 1ST Q 70 | | | | | |
| 4 AREA: | US | | | | |
| 5 SALES UNIT: | HOGSHEADS | | | | |
| 6 DATA FROM FILE: /GROOVY-70/ | | | | | |
| 8 PERIOD | | 1 | 2 | 3 | 4 |
| 9 MARKET SHARE: (% OF UNITS) | | 1.868 | 1.999 | 2.002 | 2.009 |
| 10 PROD. CLASS SALES (UNITS/PER) | | 237M | 293M | 309M | 278M |
| 11 PROD. CLASS SALES (DOL/PER) | | 514M | 552M | 581M | 523M |
| 12 BRAND SALES (UNITS/PER) | | 5.89M | 5.87M | 6.18M | 5.59M |
| 13 BRAND SALES (DOL/PER) | | 9.22M | 10.6M | 11.2M | 10.1M |
| 14 CONTRIBUTION (DOL/PER) | | 3.46M | 3.99M | 4.20M | 3.80M |
| 15 BRAND ADV (DOL/PER) | | .486M | .606M | .876M | .414M |
| 16 CONT. AFTER ADV (DOL/PER) | | 2.97M | 3.38M | 3.33M | 3.39M |
| 17 CUMULATIVE CONT. AFTER ADV | | 2.97M | 6.36M | 9.69M | 13.1M |
| 23 SLOPE | | 1.634 | 1.169 | .228 | -.379 |

set of spending rates for advertising was envisaged and they were put into the model. A package and price change was under consideration but it had not gone into the plan.

The assembled data was put into the model and fine adjustments were made in the parameters until the model predicted the brand plan results exactly. We then took the model as a reasonable indication of the product manager's feelings about how the market worked as of the time the brand plan was written.

*Step 2. Updating the model on the basis of year-to-date results.* Our analysis was done after the first quarter data were in. Two principal events had occurred. First of all, sales were off from their forecast value. Second, media expenditures had been lower than originally planned. The first question to be asked was whether the lower sales could be attributed to the decreased media expenditures. Therefore, we ran the model with the new first quarter's advertising level. According to the model, the change would account for some but not all of the sales differences. The question then arose whether the advertising had a greater effect on sales than we originally thought or whether some other factors were causing sales to be off. The product manager's opinion was that other factors were probably responsible. The next question was whether the factors would continue to operate and he felt that there was no reason to believe otherwise.

Consequently, we adjusted the nonadvertising effects index to account for the loss in sales observed in the first quarter and not otherwise attributed to the advertising decrease. The same adjustment was then continued through the year.

At this point it was possible to rerun the brand plan with new parameters. It put forth a rather pessimistic view of the year.

*Step 3. Evaluation of new strategies.* In the meantime, a number of new strategies had been proposed. First of all, because of the lower sales in the first quarter and the implied poorer profit position, the advertising levels for the rest of the year had been reduced. Secondly, the package and price change under consideration had been decided upon and was scheduled to begin in the third quarter. In support of that, the trade promotion was changed from the second quarter to the third quarter. Finally, more results were available on the copy test and a sufficient difference had shown up between the two areas that it was planned to implement the better one nationally in the fourth quarter. An estimate of the effect of the new copy on the copy index was made using the results of the test.

All these changes were made to the input. Furthermore, a rough brand plan for the following year was put into the analysis. Then the new plan was run. This suggested there would be a substantial improvement in sales and profit compared to the previous case. It also showed that certain reallocations of advertising spending during the year and certain changes in the budget might well be warranted.

*Step 4. Predictions of Future Results.* After the above runs were made a few further adjustments to strategy were decided upon. Thus the whole plan was run again. This run then became part of the quarterly review.

The above application illustrates the general way we expect the model to enter into the product manager's operation. However, each application is somewhat different. The previous one was very much of a team operation with the product manager being supported by specialists with marketing research and operations research skills. Although this is usually to be expected, in another case the product manager has run the model and made his recommendations almost single-handed. He found that it took two or three concentrated exposures to the model to become comfortable with it. In between he was pulled away by the press of other activities for a month or so at a time. Finally, however, he was confronted by a specific budgeting problem and sat down to work with the model intensively. Out of this effort came a report and a specific set of budget recommendations. His particular concern was the conflict between a strategy of budget cutting, short-range profit taking, and possible erosion of market position and a strategy of maintaining or increasing budgets to try to protect or build share. He worked out sets of assumptions about market behavior and alternative company actions and, using the model, traced out their projected consequences. Finally he wrote it up with his recommendations.

The following conversation then took place between himself and his boss, the group product manager. They went over the report at length and finally the group manager said, "All right, I understand what the model says, but what do you *really* think?"

This is a good question because it uncovers certain important issues. First, has product manager lost control, i.e., does the model really reflect his view of the market? Second, the question may contain some implications that product manager is using the model in a partisan way to make a case for a particular position. Third, has the next level of management lost any control when the product manager's case is buttressed by this new tool?

The product manager was a little surprised by the question but his answer was: "*This* is what I really think. I've spent a lot of time considering the assumptions and results and feel they express my view of the market." As for the issue of whether the report might be partisan, it must be remembered that the product manager system is an advocate system, i.e., each man is supposed to look out for his own brand. It appears, however, the use of models may temper this partisanship because assumptions and data are explicit and subject to examination and relatively easy consideration of alternatives. For the same reason, although the next and higher levels of management need to understand the basic model ideas, once this is accomplished, the explicitness of the model and its inputs can actually make communications between levels more effective.

# 6. What Happened to Science?

Science is concerned with describing nature with fidelity and economy. We have proposed that the managers describe the world as they see it. Can we really afford to pass over issues like: How does the world really work? What is the best way to describe it in a model? How accurate is a given model? How do we measure accuracy?

Clearly these are important issues, although there is a fairly tenable position that says we can gain value from models, even if they do not contain real world measurements. One can argue that a quantitative model can be used as a qualitative device to aid qualitative thinking. In this role there is no need for a one-to-one correspondence between real world quantities and quantities in the model.

However, that is not the intention here. We aspire that the model represent the world well. The standard of comparison, however, will not be perfection but rather what the manager has available to him now. If you look at his present situation you find that he has practically no predictive models beyond simple extrapolation of the past, so that complex models and detailed fidelity are not yet required. Nevertheless, let us hope that careful research will lead us through a series of increasingly accurate and useful models which at the same time are able to be understood and controlled by the user.

Most of the models we are proposing here tend, at least initially, to be over parameterized with respect to the available data. That is, we tend to put in more phenomena than we know how to measure, but do so anyway because we believe they are important. As a result, by suitably picking parameters we can often fit past data fairly easily. Therefore, it may be difficult to develop a good a priori measure of the accuracy of the model.

We should, however, evaluate the model by tracking performance, if this is at all applicable. As decisions are made, we usually forecast the future with the model. We should see whether actual performance differs from the forecast. Ordinarily it will. Then the task is to determine why and correct the model parameters and sometimes the model structure. This process will be greatly facilitated if the model contains a variety of touch points with the real world, i.e., contains quantities which are observable in the real world. The process will also be aided if we design and implement special measurement programs. One of the most obvious side benefits of model use is the pinpointing of critical measurements that should be made.

The task of parameterizing the model is, of course, difficult and important. A good methodology for this is the one used by Armstrong for forecasting [1]. After he had specified what he hoped was a satisfactory structure, he proceeded as follows: First, all the parameters were set by judgment. Then, he tried to estimate each through data analysis. He used as many independent data sets and approaches to analysis as he could invent and separately appraised the accuracy of each. Then he combined the results up to that point by formal methods. Using the now parameterized model, he made forecasts and devised various means of evaluating their quality. One way was to make forecasts from new data. Having done this, he readjusted his parameters to use the information from the new data. The same sequence of initial parameterization, model use, new data collection, and updating the parameters is an adaptive procedure appropriate for most applications of models to ongoing operations.

## 7. Conclusions

In many respects, the biggest bottleneck in the managerial use of models is not their development but getting them used. I claim that the model builder should try to design his models to be given away. In other words, as much as possible, the models should become the property of the manager, not the technical people. I suggest that, to be used by a manager, a model should be simple, robust, easy to control, adaptive, as complete as possible, and easy to communicate with. Such a model, consisting of a set of numerical procedures for processing data and judgments to assist decision making, has been called a decision calculus.

The model is meant to be a vehicle through which a manager can express his views about the operations under his control. Although the results of using a model may sometimes be personal to the manager because of judgmental inputs, the researcher still has the responsibilities of a scientist in that he should offer the manager the best information he can for making the model conform to reality in structure, parameterization, and behavior.

Although it is really too early to tell, I would like to predict how such a model will enter these companies and how the companies will organize to make use of it. First of all, the managers have to learn how to use the model. This requires technical assistance and a teaching program. Technical assistance is required for problem formulation and data analysis. As for a teaching program, our experience suggests that the best approach is to lead the potential user through a sequence of models of increasing scope and complexity. This is essentially what we have done with the model above and it is what Urban has done with his new product model, SPRINTER [8]. Often, a user having learned a simple model will start to ask for just the additional considerations found in the advanced models.

As for organization, a matrix form seems to be indicated. Under this setup the manager has line responsibility but also has a commitment from operations research and/or market research in terms of somebody assigned to his area. The manager needs a person to whom he can address questions about model behavior and a person or persons who can help design measurements and do data analysis.

One of the most evident consequences of the experience to date has been that a model is a stone in the shoe for better data. Under present planning procedures many measurement problems are glossed over or suppressed. The model forces explicit consideration of every factor it contains and so pinpoints data needs.

## Appendix

### ADBUDG Model

$s_t$ = brand sales rate in period $t$ (sales units/period)
$h_t$ = brand share in period $t$
$c_t$ = product class sales rate in period $t$ (sales units/period)

(A1)
$$s_t = h_t c_t$$

$\bar{h}_t$ = unadjusted brand share in $t$
$n_t$ = nonadvertising effects index in $t$

(A2)
$$h_t = n_t \bar{h}_t$$

$\alpha$ = persistence constant for unadjusted brand share
$\beta$ = affectable range of unadjusted brand share
$\gamma$ = advertising response function exponent for brand
$\delta$ = advertising response function denominator constant for brand
$\lambda$ = long run minimum brand share
$w_t$ = weighted, normalized brand advertising in $t$

(A3)
$$\bar{h}_t = \lambda + \alpha(\bar{h}_t - \lambda) + \beta w_t^{\gamma}/(\delta + w_t^{\gamma})$$

$e_{1t}$ = brand media efficiency in $t$
$e_1^*$ = brand media efficiency reference value
$e_{2t}$ = brand copy effectiveness in $t$
$e_2^*$ = brand copy effectiveness reference value
$x_t$ = brand advertising rate in $t$ (dol/period)
$x^*$ = brand maintenance advertising rate (dol/period)

(A4)
$$w_t = e_{1t} e_{2t} x_t / e_1^* e_2^* x^*$$

$d_t$ = product class sales rate index in $t$
$\bar{c}_t$ = unadjusted product class sales rate in $t$ (sales units/period)

(A5)
$$c_t = \bar{c}_t d_t$$

$\alpha'$ = persistence constant for unadjusted product class sales
$\beta'$ = affectable range of product class sales rate (sales units/period)
$\gamma'$ = advertising response function exponent for product class

$\delta'$ = advertising response function denominator constant for product class

$\lambda'$ = long run minimum product class sales (sales units/period)

$v_t$ = normalized product class advertising rate in $t$

(A6) $$\bar{c}_t = \lambda' + \alpha'(\bar{c}_{t-1} - \lambda') + \beta' v_t^{\gamma'} / (\delta' + v_t^{\gamma'})$$

$v^*$ = maintenance advertising rate for product class sales (dol/period)

(A7) $$v_t = (v^* - x^* + x_t)/v^*$$

$m_t$ = brand contribution per unit in $t$ (dol/sales unit)

$p_t$ = brand contribution rate after advertising in $t$ (dol/period)

(A8) $$p_t = m_t s_t - x_t$$

$\sigma_t$ = cumulative contribution after advertising for periods 1 to $t$ (dol)

$T$ = number of periods considered

(A9) $$\sigma_t = \sum_{s=1}^{t} p_s$$

$\sigma_T(x_t)$ = value of $\sigma_T$ as a function of $x_t$

$\eta_t$ = the rate of change $\sigma_T$ with $x_t$, called SLOPE, and calculated by:

(A10) $$n_T = [\sigma_T(x_t + .05x^*) - \sigma_T(x_t)]/.05x^*$$

The parameters $\alpha$, $\beta$, $\gamma$, $\delta$, $\lambda$ and $\alpha'$, $\beta'$, $\gamma'$, $\delta'$, $\lambda'$ are uniquely determined by the reference case data in the input. In the reference case $n_t = 1$, $e_{1t} = e_1^*$, $e_{2t} = e_2^*$ and referring to Figure 1, the items in Table 3, and A2–A4, we obtain the following determining relations: $\lambda$ = (item 12); (item 9) = $\lambda + \alpha[(\text{item } 7) - \lambda]$; (item 10) = $\lambda + \alpha[(\text{item } 7) - \lambda] + \beta$; (item 7) = $\lambda + \alpha[(\text{item } 7) - \lambda] + \beta/(\delta + 1)$; (item 11) = $\lambda + \alpha[(\text{item } 7) - \lambda] + \beta(1.5)^\gamma / [\delta + (1.5)^\gamma]$. A similar set of relations determines the primed parameters. If the option not to consider the effect of brand advertising on product class sales is chosen, $\bar{c}_t$ is set to the initial product class sales rate of the reference period (item 22).

### REFERENCES

1. Armstrong, J. S. "Long-Range Forecasting for a Consumer Durable in an International Market." Ph.D. Thesis, M.I.T., 1968.
2. Dearden, J. "Can Management Information Be Automated?" *Harvard Business Review*, Vol. 42 (March-April 1964): pp. 128–135.
3. Little, J. D. C. "A Model of Adaptive Control of Promotional Spending." *Operations Research*, Vol. 14 (Nov. 1966): pp. 1075–1098.
4. —— and Lodish, L. M. "A Media Planning Calculus." *Operations Research*, Vol. 17 (January-February 1969): pp. 1–35.
5. Mathes, R. C. " 'D' People and 'S' People" (letter). *Science*, Vol. 164 (9 May 1969): p. 630.

6. Montgomery, D. B., and Urban, G. L. *Applications of Management Science in Marketing.* Englewood Cliffs, N. J.: Prentice-Hall, 1970.
7. Pounds, W. F. "The Process of Problem Finding." *Industrial Management Review,* Vol. 11 (Fall 1969): pp. 1–19.
8. Urban, G. L. "SPRINTER: A Model for the Analysis of New Frequently Purchased Consumer Products." Sloan School of Management Working Paper 364–69, MIT, Cambridge, Mass., 1969.

# B. The Modeling Function

## 3. DO'S & DON'TS OF COMPUTER MODELS FOR PLANNING

*John. S. Hammond III*

In recent years, the use of computer models in corporate planning has expanded rapidly. This expansion has stemmed from the growth of systematic and quantitative planning—the "five-year plan" in many corporations—and from planners' recognition that models make ex-

Editors' Note: Reprinted with permission from *Harvard Business Review*, March-April 1974, pp. 110–123. Copyright © 1974 by the President and Fellows of Harvard College; all rights reserved.

ploring the implications of strategic and environmental assumptions easy and fast.

Models can deal with complex interactions involving large quantities of data, and can show how various decisions in one part of the organization affect the rest, facilitating integration and coordination. They can also show what the risk and timing implications of alternative actions are. Better insights into the corporation can arise from using models to understand its sensitivities to numerous internal and external variables.

In spite of these important advantages, all has not been sweetness and light with this relatively new tool. Models have proved expensive. Many have taken longer than expected to create; the data requirements have been extensive and often unrealistic. Many have represented business realities improperly; and, in general, they have been inflexible. Consequently, management has refused to accept a large number of models or has used them less frequently or in a different manner from one originally planned.

With such great promise, why have so many planning models been only partial successes or outright failures? Evidence seems to indicate that the problems are more managerial than technical: few planning models fail because the technical state of the art is inadequate or because they are improperly implemented from a technical point of view.[1] It is true that some early failures were due in part to a lack of qualified modelers and to lengthy programming efforts occasioned by conventional programming languages. Both conditions, however, have since been remedied; a number of programming languages for such modeling purposes now exists, and the number of people qualified to develop such models has greatly increased—notably among MBAs.

If they are to bring the potential of the computer planning model to fruition, both line managers and planners clearly need some guidelines for deciding how and whether to use computer models as part of the planning process.

Unfortunately, most of the literature on computer planning models is not particularly helpful—it concentrates on the technical issues, rather than the managerial. My purpose here is to fill this void. After indicating what I mean by computer models for planning, I want to examine the process by which one develops and uses computer models in planning, the kinds of conditions that increase the likelihood of their success, and the things the planning manager and the modeler can do to increase this likelihood. A case history presented at the end of this article demonstrates how sensitive and complex the entire operation can be.

[1]Naomi Seligman, "Free for All," *Management Science*, Vol. 14, No. 4 (December 1967): p. B-145; and John W. Drake, *The Administration of Transportation Modeling Projects* (Lexington, Mass., D.C. Heath, 1973).

## What Are Computer Planning Models?

Computer planning models are computer-based representations of all or part of a company's current or prospective operations or of its economic environment, or both. These models are used to manipulate data as a part of the planning process. Such representations are usually of two kinds:

> The first may be a simulation of all or part of a company's operations or of its economic environment. These representations permit the user to vary (a) the conditions under management's control and (b) the assumptions about the environment, in order to test out the implications of various proposed future plans. Two types of simulation are the probabilistic (or so-called Monte Carlo), which takes specific account of the probabilities of events beyond management's control, and the deterministic, which does not. With either type, the user adjusts the variables under his control to search out the most promising plans among the proposed.

> The second may be a model designed to search automatically for "best" plans by adjusting the controllable variables by itself. These are the so-called *optimization models*.[2]

Optimization models and probabilistic simulations are relatively rare in use. Deterministic simulations are the common variety; they vary from simple models of about 100 equations requiring several man-months for development[3] to elaborate and comprehensive models requiring over ten man-years of development effort.[4] Models are used to assist a range of on-going management processes—for example, generation or consolidation of projected balance sheets and income statements, market plans (for pricing, advertising, product mix, and distribution channels), working capital plans, capital structure analyses, and cash planning. They are also used to evaluate projects of many kinds—for example, new product introductions and acquisition, merger, and divestiture analyses. Other uses for models, such as sales forecasting and capacity planning, fall somewhere between these two broad categories. The uses have varied enormously in scope, and in expense and management effort as well.

This list of applications demonstrates that planning models typically look many years into the future, a fact that distinguishes them from

[2]Leo A. Rapoport and William P. Drews, "Mathematical Approach to Long-Range Planning," *HBR* (May-June 1962): p. 75.

[3]John S. Hammond, "DYCO Chemical Corporation (A) and (B)," Harvard Business School Case Nos. 9-172-257 and 9-172-258 (Boston, Intercollegiate Case Clearing House, Harvard Business School, 1970).

[4]George W. Gershefski, "Building a Corporate Financial Model," *HBR* (July–August 1969): p. 61.

nonplanning models in a way that has important implications. Because the future is seldom like the past over the time periods covered (one to ten or more years), it is unsafe to base such models entirely, or even mainly, on historical relationships and data. To do so would be like steering the ship by watching its wake. A high degree of subjective judgment and skill is required to construct planning models, and it is impossible to validate them "objectively"—through historical evidence—as is sometimes done with models of other types.

### The Ten Stages of Models

This subjective judgment and skill must be brought to bear on all the parts of the process by which models are conceived, created, and used in planning. I myself break the process into ten steps, listed here in the approximate order in which they occur.

One danger, however, of presenting the process as a sequence of steps is that such presentation masks its iterative nature. The reader should keep in mind that much looping back occurs when inadequacies or inconsistencies stemming from earlier steps are uncovered in a later step.

(It is worth pointing out, incidentally, that most of the prescriptions I give in this article, while focused on the use of management science to support planning decisions, can be applied as well to the use of management science in other decision-making areas.)

1. Decisions must be made as to where a model may be useful. To see where models might be beneficial requires a review of the company's planning activities. I find it useful to classify planning models in these categories:

   Forecasting models provide predictive data on variables used in planning such as sales, costs, competitive activity, and industry activity.

   Project models facilitate the evaluation of a specific, significant, new activity or direction for a subunit of the company, such as capital expenditures, new product introductions, acquisitions, and divestitures.

   Corporate models support general coordination, corporate budgeting, and corporate planning as exemplified, say, in a five-year plan. These models reflect the company as a whole, often in fair detail, and incorporate such underlying processes of the business as marketing, production, and finance.[5] Corporate models have been used to generate pro forma analyses from decision-making and environmental assumptions supplied by the users; to consolidate the pro forma analyses presented by various divi-

[5]Ibid.

sions or departments; to consolidate budgets; and to test the implications of actions by one part of the organization on the rest of the organization.

Financial planning models help financial officers direct working capital, capital structure, and so forth.

2. A decision must be made whether to use a model. After a company generates a list of possible applications, it must decide whether to go ahead with one or more applications. The decision in each case depends on three considerations: Technically, is it possible? Economically, is it worthwhile? And, will the organization accept and use it?[6]

3. Specifications must be fixed. This step consists of defining the purposes of the model exactly, its primary inputs and outputs, the main aspects of its structure, and how it would be used. These specifications, in turn, determine the resources required to bring it into being.

4. A proposal must be prepared. If the required resources are significant and the procedures of the particular organization demand it, a formal proposal must be made to get (or grant) the approval to proceed.

Equally, a decision must be made as to who shall be the modeler if the company concludes that a model will be beneficial. This person might be someone within the planning group, someone inside the company but outside the planning group, or someone outside the company.

5. Actual modeling and data gathering must go forward together. Modeling usually jumps back and forth between detailed conceptualization and computer programming. Tests of early versions of the model lead to modifications of the programming to suit refined conceptualization. Collecting the required data for the model almost always parallels model construction in this respect.

6. The model must be debugged. This step consists of checking thoroughly to see that the model does what it is supposed to do on two levels: (1) Does the computer program correctly implement the intended concept? (2) Judging from the output itself, does the concept require modification?

7. The users must be educated, and the model must gain acceptance. Most of the model's users will have had little experience or education in formal techniques, and their knowledge and background must be augmented. Even more importantly, they must be filled in on the specifics of the model in question. (Much of the *general*

---

[6]McKinsey & Company, Inc., "Unlocking the Computer's Potential" (New York: McKinsey & Company, Inc., 1968).

education required should come early in this sequence of stages so the users can contribute intelligently to the model's design.)

This educational process requires an understanding of the human and organizational obstacles to acceptance, such as resistance to change, and of the actions appropriate to overcome them.

8. The process of user validation must be established. Before a model can be considered ready for use, the users must check it out to see that it is valid for the purposes for which it was intended. Hopefully, the users will have been involved in the previous steps, so that validation will be a process that continues throughout the sequence, rather than a one-shot exercise.

9. The model must be put into actual use. Successful use requires an understanding of the model's capabilities and limitations so that its output can be creatively and intelligently used in the planning process.

10. The model must be updated and modified. If the model is used on a recurring basis—for the annual planning cycle, say—several kinds of updates and modifications will be required: correcting errors unearthed as a result of use, modifying the model as a result of the experience of actually using it, refining it to reflect new sophistication on the part of the users, expanding or adapting it for new applications, and gathering up-to-date data.

With this multistage process in mind, let me now turn attention to ways in which managers can increase the likelihood that their companies will deal with it successfully.

First, let me put the case in general terms. Managers and planners must identify organizational and managerial settings where computer models are more likely to succeed; equally, they must define the actions and behavior on the part of the planner that will help to ensure success.

The situation is akin to that faced by a farmer. He must first decide whether to plant a certain crop; and naturally he will want to take into account climate and soil conditions—the givens of his situation. Once he has decided to plant the crop, he must focus on things within his control, such as seed strain, fertilizer, insecticides, and so on, to maximize his harvest.

## Organizational Climate

Thus the first question a planner must face is whether the climatic conditions in which he lives are favorable for computer planning models. These conditions are givens, by and large—the planner can do little to alter them, at least in the short run. Let me list the organizational conditions that, if fulfilled, most greatly increase the probability of success in developing and using computer planning models.

OPERATIONS ARE WELL UNDERSTOOD AND DATA ARE AMPLE. To make a useful model, the area or aspect of the business to which it will be applied must be well enough understood so that relationships that reflect planning realities can be written down. Then one must have the data necessary to "parameterize" those relationships.

Often these requirements can be met for marketing and production processes in older, more established industries—for example, steel, oil, and food processing, all well-understood industries with plenty of historical data. These industries also have large production runs requiring well-known proportions of raw materials; such continuous-flow processes are relatively easy to model.

On the other hand, an electronics company is less likely to be a "natural." It is likely to be a young company in a relatively new and rapidly changing industry.

THE RELEVANT DATA ARE EASILY ACCESSIBLE. This point sounds like part of the previous one, but it is not. The mere *existence* of data is not sufficient; they must be readily *accessible* to the modelers. Often they are available only in a form that requires a great deal of massage to be useful. And, of course, certain data points required by the modeling process may be missing.

Sometimes the difficulty in getting the data is due to organizational considerations. For example, the modeler in one food processing company could work rapidly on aspects of the company within his jurisdiction, but only slowly on the manufacturing facilities outside his jurisdiction because the necessary information was hard to obtain. Also, political considerations respecting jurisdiction over "intimate" information have often kept models from being useful.[7]

BUDGETS, PLANS, AND CONTROL SYSTEMS ARE WELL DEFINED AND QUANTIFIED. The use of models implies a highly quantitative, structured way of thinking about planning. If the company's systems are all loosely defined, then two transitions are necessary: from loose to quantitative and well-defined approaches and from not using models to using them. The second transition is seldom an easy one, and is far more difficult if the first has not yet been made. For instance, the food processor already mentioned had a well-defined pencil-and-paper budgeting system; thus model implementation was relatively easy.

---

[7]E. Eugene Carter, "What Are the Risks in Risk Analysis?" *HBR* (July-August 1972): p. 72; and Rex V. Brown, "Do Managers Find Decision Analysis Useful?" *HBR* (May-June 1970): p. 78.

MODELS HAVE MANAGEMENT SUPPORT OR, BETTER YET, A CHAMPION. If there is support or even enthusiasm for a model, more people will be committed to "make it happen." For example, at a steel company, the vice president of planning championed models; he encouraged their use, oversaw their implementation, and supported their existence. In the food processing company, the controller and top management fully supported the use of models, and another manager filled the role of the champion.

Indeed, one consultant has remarked that he would only bid on modeling projects that have the support of the very highest level of management.

MANAGEMENT SCIENTISTS ACCEPT RESPONSIBILITY FOR SUCCESSFUL IMPLEMENTA-TION. Several people have found a correlation between the success of a modeling project and the desire of the client and modelers to make it succeed.[8] Of course, a difficulty here is that the measure of success, or lack of it, in an area like this is usually the say-so of a person involved. If a person really wants something to succeed, it is quite human for him to see it as a success afterward, even though those less committed might feel otherwise. Unfortunately, objective measures of success are difficult to define.

INNOVATIONS AND FORMAL TECHNIQUES HAVE PROSPERED IN THE PAST. Allan Harvey found that the highest correlation between any organizational factor and successful implementation was management's confidence in management science solutions to company problems, and he found a high correlation between success and prior experience in using sophisticated problem-solving techniques. It goes without saying that managements of this sort are perhaps the most ready to try the techniques. He also found that, for the 31 companies he studied, all 11 of the successful applications were in companies where management had created a climate that encouraged innovation, whereas, for the 8 unsuccessful projects, a generally negative attitude toward innovation prevailed.[9] (The remaining 12 were considered partial successes.)

MANAGER AND MODELER SHARE STATUS AND BACKGROUND. Modeling and managing require very different types of knowledge and skills, and usually attract very different types of people.[10] Sometimes the difference is so great that communication and an effective working relationship are

---

[8]John W. Drake, op.cit.; and Allan Harvey, "Factors Making for Implementation Success and Failure," *Management Science*, Vol. 16, No. 6 (February 1970): p. B-312.
[9]Allan Harvey, op. cit.
[10]C. Jackson Grayson, "Management Science and Business Practice," *HBR* (July-August 1973): p. 41; John Hammond, "The Role of the Manager and Management Scientist in Successful Implementation," *Sloan Management Review*, Winter 1974.

difficult. Therefore, it helps when there is as much correspondence in background as possible—indeed, this factor correlates second highest with successful implementation in Drake's study.[11]

One very successful planning modeler in a large chemical company is a veteran line manager turned staff man. As a result of his experience, he has very strong rapport with his line clients. In another company—a large diversified manufacturer—a planning modeler reports great success in working with line managers who are chemical engineers with Ph.D.s, and who consequently have had training and experience in quantitatively modeling chemical processes.

I do not mean to imply that if all these conditions are present, success is assured, or that if all are absent, failure is inevitable—the brief case study that concludes this article will make that clear. But by comparing the list against his own situation, a manager can make a more informed judgment about whether to proceed.

### Factors within the Manager's Control

While the planning manager or the modeler can do relatively little to change the basic conditions under which he must work, there is fortunately a great deal he can do to help ensure success.

INVOLVE THE POTENTIAL USERS IN THE DEVELOPMENT PROCESS. The decision makers—the users—must be drawn into the development process right from the start. From a survey that studied the success of 36 large corporations in using computers or the lack of it, McKinsey & Company concluded that user involvement is widely neglected and that neglect is costly.[12]

The users should play an important role in the determination of the objectives. When designing the inner workings of the model, substantial attention should be paid to their perception of the situation being modeled. People tend to trust and use something they have had a hand in developing; they may not trust or use something they must accept on faith. Finally, involving the users during development enhances their understanding and decreases the educational effort required after the model is completed.

Obviously, involvement of the ultimate users must be managed judiciously so as not to consume too much of their time. If critical milestones at which they need to be involved are identified, this is easily accomplished. And if the users are too busy, it is better to involve their trusted deputies than to work in the dark.

A German magazine publisher who hired an econometrics modeling

[11]John W. Drake, op. cit.
[12]McKinsey & Company, Inc., op. cit.

consultant to produce a model to forecast sales for each issue is an illustration of the need for involvement. Working alone, the consultant produced a black-box model that management neither understood nor used. A second consultant worked with the company's marketing people to develop a forecasting model that takes account of the considerations that the executives felt were important (such as the newsworthiness of the cover story). The model is now used regularly in the planning of press runs.

DEFINE THE MODEL'S GOALS EXPLICITLY, WITH A VIEW TO THE DECISIONS IT WILL ASSIST. The initial problem is to resolve these issues: What decision is the model designed to influence? Who will use the model? For whom is the output information intended? Consequently, what information must it provide to the users? What input variables shall be used to permit the user to test alternatives and environmental assumptions? How often will it be used? How timely must the input information be?

The answers are crucial, for they define the model operationally; in turn, they become the marching orders for the technicians to implement. Obviously, there will have to be some give-and-take between what is desired and what is technically possible. But the first thing is to define the operating characteristics from the point of view of the user. I am familiar with one ambitious modeling project in particular that was well specified technically but had gone two or more man-years down the road before these crucial issues were faced. As a result, the model contained elaborate and irrelevant detail in several areas.

One common mistake is failing to design a model so that long-range plans can be linked to *current* decisions. The purpose of all planning is to help make current decisions, and hence two questions are relevant: (1) What decisions need to be made now to realize long-range plans? (2) What impact will current decisions have on the long-range plans? The whole structure of the planning model must be geared to testing current decisions as they affect and are affected by plans for the future.

EXPRESS INPUT AND OUTPUT IN FAMILIAR FORMATS. This is just another way of saying that the model should be easy to communicate with. Through years of dealing with problems in other ways, managers develop habits of thought, vocabulary, report format, and so on with which they have become extremely comfortable. Yet I have seen instances in which the computer output was in a sharply different format from what the user had come to expect. Here the models were at best qualified successes as far as usefulness to managers was concerned. There have even been cases in which the outputs were not identified in English but rather flagged by mathematical symbols. Needless to say, these models were failures.

To ensure easy communication, I like to prepare mockups of the output for the user's review early in the modeling effort.

On the input side, it is much better to let those coefficients and constants that lack clear operational meaning be calculated by the computer from inputs that are easier for the user to work with. One model, for example, works internally with projected marketing expense as a percentage of total market but accepts as input the managerially more familiar marketing expense as a percentage of sales.

STICK TO ESTABLISHED COMPANY PROCEDURES AT FIRST. These are fighting words to many planners, since they are often out to reform existing procedures as well as to introduce models. Fine, but improvements in operating procedures can come after models have been established. The planner at the food processing company verified this point: "If the model doesn't fit the normal routine, it doesn't get used." He also warned against interfering with the company's hard-copy-and-memo routine.

BE OPPORTUNISTIC. Right from the start, be shrewd in choosing projects and methods. It is well known in marketing for example, that a new product introduction is more likely to succeed if it fulfills an obvious, felt need. The same principle applies to models. An operations research department in an electronics company failed miserably in assisting planning and was later dissolved because it tried to peddle new procedures rather than solve managers' perceived problems. The solutions-in-search-of-problems approach has enjoyed broad failure.[13]

On the other hand, risk analysis was successfully introduced in a major oil company partly because of the timing. The introduction occurred when management was facing a major operating crisis precipitated by the closing of the Suez Canal in 1967. The top managers had a need and called on the management scientists to help satisfy it—and the technique worked.[14] This was the beginning of successful use of models at this company.

I know another situation in which a modeler and a planning manager at an airline had become near enemies because of the modeler's "pushy" behavior. However, after the modeler went out of his way to write a simple computer program to solve a problem for the manager in a crisis, the manager became one of the modeler's most eager supporters.[15]

START SIMPLE AND KEEP IT SIMPLE. Initially, modeling projects should be kept as straightforward and uncomplicated in design as possible. Allowances must of course be made for growth in sophistication and for changing

[13]John W. Drake, op, cit.
[14]E. Eugene Carter, op. cit.
[15]John S. Hammond, "Bud Mathaisel," Harvard Business School Case No. 9-371-252 (Boston, Intercollegiate Case Clearing House, Harvard Business School, 1972).

needs, but simplicity is the rule; and modelers must never be allowed to go overboard.

John Little, who has had much experience observing managers using planning models, has said it well:

> The manager carries responsibility for outcomes. . . . We should not be surprised if he prefers simple analysis that he can grasp, even though it may have a qualitative structure, broad assumptions, and only a little relevant data, to a complex model whose assumptions may be partially hidden or couched in jargon and whose parameters may be the result of obscure statistical manipulations. . . .

> The best approach is to lead the potential user through a sequence of models of increasing scope and complexity. . . . Often a user, having learned a simple model, will start to ask for just the additional considerations found in the advanced models.[16]

The modeler, too, needs to grow in his understanding of the particular situation he is modeling. In one airline, a technically adept modeler, who knew relatively little about airlines forecasting, produced a complicated and elaborate sales forecasting system. It went unused. Later a much simpler model was created at a fraction of the cost of the first, and it was heavily used. Companies should beware of channeling effort to the development of a mammoth model before understanding has been firmly established by both managers and modelers and scope and feasibility have been made clear.

It is far better to get a simple version of a model up and running as soon as possible, use it for a while, and then expand it on the base of enhanced understanding. A certain self-restraint is advisable in such expansions, since the tendency is to err in the direction of too much machinery and detail.

Specifically, it is wise to resist all suggestion of an "all-purpose model." A massive, general-purpose model is unwieldly, difficult to control, and requires huge amounts of data. Often, many facets of such a model are entirely extraneous to particular applications; equally, much detail in individual applications may be lost in the push to create a general purpose model. Finally, these models are much more difficult to comprehend, and therefore much more difficult for users to accept. A company that goes overboard in this direction is almost sure to regret it.

Often the top-down approach is a good way to start simple. The top-down process starts with representations of the market, company operations, and so forth, joined together in a very rough aggregate, the kind of broad-brush picture seen from the top of the company. Later, if more detail is required, some variables can be disaggregated and the de-

[16]John D. C. Little, "Models and Managers: The Concept of a Decision Calculus," *Management Science*, Vol. 16, No. 8 (April 1970): p. B-466.

scription enriched. By using this approach, the planner has a working model at all points—a great advantage.

The reverse—the bottom-up approach—requires tedious acquisition of data and modeling by product line, division, market area, and so on—or some other subdivision of the company's operation—and ultimately combining these to reflect the corporate picture. But the working model emerges quite slowly; it frequently ends up being difficult to debug and too detailed for the purposes intended.

START WITH A DETERMINISTIC, PRO FORMA MODEL. Most managers have worked with pro forma projections, or "spread sheets." Deterministic simulations are just automated pro forma generators and are therefore relatively easy for managers to understand. Furthermore, they are enormously useful for decision making and are therefore highly likely to pay off. The next step, from deterministic analysis to risk analysis, is fraught with difficulties.[17] This second step may well be worth the effort, but it should await successful completion of the first one. Once managers recognize the limitations of deterministic analysis, they may well champion the next step.

MAKE PLENTY OF ALLOWANCE FOR JUDGMENTAL INPUTS. The users like to feel that they are in control, and indeed they need to be; long horizons make planning highly judgmental. Successful modeling tends to let the user see intermediate results, to modify results prior to the next step, and to intervene in the process of model use.

In four companies studied, none of the various separate planning models were coupled together, although there was ample opportunity and reason for doing so. This was more because of the desire for human intervention at intermediate stages than because of technical difficulties. Further, because of the judgmental nature of inputs to a planning model, it is desirable to print out assumptions with the output so that the user will know the conditions under which each run from the model has been made.

BEWARE OF CREATING MISIMPRESSIONS. The first trap here is to promise delivery on a more optimistic schedule than can be met. Computer programs notoriously take longer than planned; and an unrealistic schedule can do damage to both the work and the sponsor's reputation. Worse yet, the revelation that a project is behind schedule often comes too late for remedial action to be taken. To reduce this risk, I suggest scheduling in units of a man-month of effort, with constant review of the whole schedule.

Second, the user too frequently gets the incorrect impression that the

[17]E. Eugene Carter, op. cit.

model is intended as his sole guide to decision making, rather than as an additional and important source of insight into his problem.[18]

PUT A MANAGER RATHER THAN A MODELER IN CHARGE. Ideally, the person in charge is both a manager and one who is skilled in modeling and in using the computer. However, even he should function as a manager first, to ensure that the planning goals of the model are met and that the whole effort reflects a sensitivity to the motivations and priorities existing in the organization.[19]

Unfortunately, this ideal situation is rare. In a Diebold Research Program Survey, 61% of the 2,700 executives responding said that suggestions for new computer applications were coming from technicians, not from managers.[20] The Diebold study concluded that senior management's abdication of its responsibilities to technicians was one of the prime reasons that companies have not realized the true potential from their data processing investment.

DEFINE ROLES CLEARLY. It is vital to recognize that planners make recommendations, line managers make decisions, and management scientists make models, and to define their roles accordingly. One researcher has said that this recognition is the single most important element distinguishing successful from unsuccessful projects.[21] Obviously, some overlap between roles is required, but trouble arises when decision makers abdicate decision-making responsibility to modelers or when modelers attempt to usurp the decision maker's responsibility.

In more successful projects, analysts typically sketch several alternatives and their implications, and the decision makers set the goals and criteria and make the ultimate choices. In an extreme example of the opposite behavior, modelers spent considerable time and money on an elaborate study of a single master plan for a city's transit system. The city fathers rejected it because it showed no alternatives.[22]

SCORE AN EARLY VICTORY. Model creation is time consuming and often expensive before demonstrable results are achieved. Understandably, management gets impatient with long projects or is reluctant to fund them in the first place. Therefore, it is wise to arrange matters so that some *managerially* useful results—although not necessarily the final product— can be demonstrated as early as possible.

For example, one piece of a developing model may be useful in its own right. Alternatively, victory can be achieved through picking a small, simple, but high-impact project as the first effort. This tactic is similar to healthy opportunism.

[18]John Hammond, op. cit.
[19]Allan Harvey, op. cit.
[20]Naomi Seligman, op. cit.
[21]John W. Drake, op. cit.
[22]Ibid.

Two contrasting anecdotes illustrate its value. First, in a large milk processing company, the modeler chose a simple, straightforward project for planning transportation as his initial effort. The benefits of the model were easy to measure and showed a clear improvement. Shortly he was overwhelmed by requests for additional models.

Second, and in contrast, the modelers for a tire manufacturer looked at a production planning problem and proposed a new production planning system. But, they pointed out, it would not be fully productive unless new timing devices were installed on the production machines and, "by the way, some of the machines should be replaced, too." The price tag was $3 million, plus a renegotiated labor contract. The response was rejection.

Even though these modelers could have devised a planning system that would yield some of the benefits without the capital investment or the new labor contract, they refused to do this on the grounds that it would be "prostituting themselves."

BUILD THE MODEL WITHIN THE USER'S ORGANIZATION. The modeler must understand the company and its industry, and what the managers who will use his model want. If a modeling effort is to make good progress in the right direction, then the modeler ideally will be an inside man.

The closer the modeler and the user organizationally, the more easily control, mutual understanding, and communication are maintained. As others have pointed out, this strategy enables the user to keep his most prized information close to his vest, where he wants it.[23]

Obviously, there are situations in which the absence of internal expertise dictates going outside for help. If this occurs, then control, communication, and mutual understanding must be monitored even more closely.

LEARN HOW TO USE THE MODEL EFFECTIVELY. Most managers' ways of thinking have been based on intuition, or at best on the time-consuming process of pencil-and-paper exploration of alternatives. Hence the number of alternatives they explore and the extent to which they analyze them have been relatively limited. With the computer have come expanded capabilities and speed; many more alternatives can be explored quickly. Consequently, the user must develop a new style of thinking about problems to make optimal use of the model. He should realize that decisions are seldom made based on a single run of a model. Often the result of a series of runs is a clarification and updating of his original intuitions and understanding of the problem.[24]

Further, if the user is to have an effective dialogue with a computer model, he must have fast access and fast response. This strongly argues

[23]Rex Brown, op. cit.
[24]John S. Hammond, "The Role of the Manager and Management Scientist in Successful Implementation"; and John D. C. Little, op. cit.

for putting the model on a time-sharing system or a high-priority batch system, where results are available virtually instantaneously. Of course, with a time-sharing system, the user need not sit at a console himself—he can work through technical aides and still achieve a rapid dialogue.

While the users need not become keyboard virtuosi, it is nonetheless of the utmost importance that they receive some education in the use of computer planning models to ensure that they will be able to interact with models effectively and understand the kind of information they must supply for the model to run.

In addition, an educational approach can generate considerable enthusiasm, as the experience of a major accounting firm illustrates. The partner in charge of planning had developed a time-sharing model which could be used for planning by the managing partners at each of the branch offices. It was received coldly until he made a personal tour to introduce and explain it. Great enthusiasm followed; some of the managers became so fascinated that they stayed late at night exploring alternatives and analyzing consequences.

Finally, while the users ordinarily supply a model's most important data, some vital pieces of information must come from nonusers. These people must also be educated about the assumptions they are to use in supplying their inputs, so that their inputs will be consistent with others'.

DEVELOP EXPERTISE TO MANAGE AND UPDATE THE MODEL. The battle is not over once a model is put into use, unless it is a one-shot model. Ordinarily, as soon as it goes out of date, its credibility and usefulness deteriorate. A model built for continuing use must be kept current by someone who knows the model, the company, and the industry—a combination more likely to be found inside the company than outside it. The process of keeping a model up to date might be termed "managing" the model, or, as an executive from the steel company mentioned earlier put it, "treating it with tender loving care."

A good example of effective model management comes from a major U.S. chemicals corporation.[25] Originally built by outside consultants, the model is the responsibility of one of the corporate planners who has become skilled in keeping it up to date and improving it. Through the use of adjustment factors, he can allow for certain considerations of importance not specifically programmed into the model—for example, a dock strike or the receipt of a large government contract.

TREAT THE DEVELOPMENT AND USE OF MODELS AS A PROCESS, NOT AS THE CREATION OF A PRODUCT (THE MODEL). Distinguishing between product and process is critical. Otherwise, one cannot create the frame of mind, in the modelers and the users, essential to following the advice I am outlining and to ac-

[25]John Hammond, "DYCO Chemical Corporation."

quiring benefits of modeling. Unfortunately, the product approach is the more usual; its goal is to create a working model, and those involved find it difficult to see beyond that stage in their effort. (They generally cannot see beyond the debugging stage.) For the process approach, the creation of the model is an important step along the way toward using the model to affect planning favorably.

First of all, by working with the modelers, the planners usually gain a great deal of insight into the company and its relationship to the business environment. Under the product approach, these insights are by-products; under the process approach, they are recognized as valuable benefits to be sought out, and the fact that they must be sought out increases the chances of acquiring them.

Second, the longer view of the process approach fosters a give-and-take in model design and improvement that usually continues beyond first use; it helps everyone to look ahead to how a model will be used in the future and to how the organization is likely to respond to it, and to take this information into account in its design. In particular, the process approach anticipates the need for education and organizational change in model introduction.

Finally, the process approach ensures that someone who knows the model's capabilities will be standing by to see that the model is used to full advantage. For example, one of the largest U.S. manufacturers had just completed a long-range planning model when its top management became seriously concerned over a lagging earnings trend. At first blush a model of this kind would seem to be inapplicable to such a short-term issue, but the person responsible for it saw an application. It was usefully pressed into service to explore various plans to shore up short-term earnings—plans that would have minimal long-run effects.

RECOGNIZE THAT THE PROCESS IS INDIVIDUALISTIC AND PEOPLE-DEPENDENT. Initially, one might assume the opposite; for many, models and computers are the very symbol of impersonal processes. But they depend on both the modeler and the user as individuals. Many organizations witness the demise of a model with the departure of the chief modeler or the programmers responsible for it. Good documentation can do a great deal to reduce the chances of this happening, but the documentation process is time consuming and ultimately ineffective, since everything just cannot be written down. Even with documentation, it is easy to underestimate the time another technician needs to become familiar with a computer model.

The user, for his part, has grown up with the model and has heavily influenced its character; often the original user is the only one with sufficient understanding and confidence in the model to use it. For example, there is a sophisticated and comprehensive planning model which was built for a new division of a communications-based conglomerate. The man who served as division manager at the time the model was built used it regularly. When he was promoted, one of his subordinates became division manager; since he had been in on the model from the start, he too used it. Finally, a third division manager from outside the division took over. The model is now gathering cobwebs.

BEWARE OF MISUSES OF MODELS. Once users overcome old thought patterns and really begin to take advantage of the capability of models, then a series of *misuses* often appears:

Sometimes work with a model becomes a substitute for good, hard thinking about assumptions and alternative courses of action. It becomes an unimaginative ritual, just as the annual planning cycle often becomes the "rite of fall."

The fact that the results are printed out on the computer lends an air of accuracy to the anticipated impact of plans. This may *just* be an air of accuracy.

If many alternatives are tested with the model, the one that finally is selected sometimes takes on vaunted status because it has been so rigorously tested. Thereafter it may be followed too rigidly, under changed conditions. In fact, rigid use represents a failure to use a model to full advantage; after all, one main reason for building a model in the first place is to test the implications of a modified plan under changed conditions.

In many organizations, planning is an advocacy process. In such settings, models are sometimes used to justify, rather than to explore, the implications of actions.

## A Case in Point

Some of these points of advice are more applicable to one organization than another, or to one kind of modeling than another; each situation is, after all, unique. To tie some of the points together, let me describe the experience that the corporate planning department of a large process manufacturing corporation has had with its first model.

Formally, this department reports to the treasurer, but it frequently interacts with, and holds the respect of, top management. The department is responsible for a broad range of planning and staff functions. It consists of ten professionals with educational backgrounds primarily in economics, chemical engineering, and business; many have had previous line or staff experience elsewhere in the company, but only three have management-science or computer backgrounds.

The department had long considered using models. Finally, one January, a member decided that a combined forecasting and simulation model was technically feasible and managerially worthwhile. It would provide pro forma forecasts of company sales, earnings, and other financial statistics from the economic forecasts provided by an economic forecasting service, as well as from other inputs.

Hopefully, this model's output would augment the company's usual forecasts. These forecasts were assembled, by hand, from information supplied by the several divisions—information that was seasoned with, and perhaps inflated to accord with, the division's goals. Since the model's output would be based partly on aggregate economic data from a neutral source, it could possibly provide a top-down check on the divisions' numbers. Maybe the model would even produce forecasts of sufficient accuracy to supplant the hand forecasts. Perhaps, too, it would provide a means of rapidly updating forecasts that depend on changing conditions.

The reader might note that these definitions for usage of the model were not entirely crisp. Specifically, no mention was made of the decisions the model was to influence.

While potential modelers existed within the department, their time was already committed. Consequently, nothing happened until July. In July, the department accepted a proposal to build the model from an economics forecasting company, of which the department was already a client and with which the model had already been discussed. The modeling was started immediately afterward, and by September data had been gathered and the model debugged. The forecasting firm then turned the model over to a member of the department who tested and refined it—for example, by substituting direct calculation of certain investment tax credits in the place of an earlier statistical approximation.

By the following March, the department was running the model in parallel with the customary hand forecasts. The planning manager found that, while the model offered a useful check, the planners still relied more heavily on the hand forecasts. For about a year afterward, the department member responsible for the model updated it regularly and continued to make improvements, but recently he has been confronted with the need to make substantial changes: the company has made two major acquisitions. Since he has other duties, the modeler has not taken the time to modify the model to accommodate these acquisitions, and he does not feel he has a mandate to pursue the issue.

IMPORTANCE OF MANAGERIAL FACTORS. While by no means a failure, the model has been less heavily used for planning than the planners had hoped, and it has not yet earned the same trust as the hand forecasts. Why? The themes of this article give some insight into the answer.

Most of the organizational factors were favorable to modeling, but not all. Processes and markets were well understood and easy to model. Most of the required data were available from the department's files, but some massage was necessary; for example, historical figures needed restatement to allow for acquisitions. The planning, budgeting, and control systems were quantitative and well defined, but less highly developed than in some other companies in the same industry.

The treasurer and the planning manager supported the modeling effort strongly, but stopped short of championing it. Previously, another model, built for another purpose by another department, had not been well received by top managers; they found it complex, hard to understand, and unresponsive. This precedent put salutary pressure on the modelers to keep their model simple; nonetheless, the absence of a champion reflected a somewhat negative attitude at the top.

Thus, although not all the organizational factors favored success, more were favorable than unfavorable. The problem lay, rather, with management's failure to deal with some of the factors under its control. Principally, the goals of the model had not been defined crisply in operational—that is, planning—terms. As the planning manager remarked, "It was like motherhood to say that a model would be useful. We never specifically addressed the question *For what?* until after it had been created. This was probably our biggest mistake."

On the other hand, the potential users—the planners themselves—were firmly in control and thoroughly involved in the development process. Their perceptions of problems were constantly drafted into the model's formulation, and, through adjustment factors, they could intervene with judgmental inputs when the model was used. Schedules were set and met, in two-week blocks. Role definition was easy, since only the planners would use the model. Formal education on model use was slight; but, instead, the planners' knowledge grew through actual experience with the model, initially side-by-side with the modeler. Input and output were expressed in familiar formats. Company procedures were strongly respected— the model was eased into the department's operations gingerly. Documentation was excellent.

The outside modeler, both a technically competent and a management-minded MBA, enjoyed great rapport with and respect from his department clients, with whom he had worked during the year prior to the building of the model. Two department members were assigned to work with him, and all supplied him with data. These facts, plus his knowing the company well, compensated for the fact that he was an outsider.

The modeling effort had both a product and a process orientation. Heavier emphasis was placed on creating a working model, but at all times the department was concerned that it would be favorably reviewed by top management.

On the negative side, again, no golden opportunity was exploited by selecting this particular project in the first place. Instead of reviewing the department's activities carefully to find an activity on which a quick victory could be scored, or where it was easy to start simple, or that would provide an occasion for a healthy opportunism, the department simply selected a seemingly "natural" project.

Not only that, but one golden opportunity had to be passed by after the model had been installed. Management was concerned about the long-term effects of the oil embargo of late 1973, but because the model had not been modified to accommodate the company's recent acquisitions, it could be of no help. This was unfortunate.

Still, this model was orders of magnitude simpler than the vast corporate planning models we often hear about. The development time was several months, rather than several years, and that indicates that the effort was not grossly over scale. In spite of this, the model was probably more sophisticated than anyone realized at the outset. For example, the amount of effort necessary to keep the model up to date had been grossly underestimated. That, in fact, is why the changes in the model to take account of the acquisitions were not made.

Over the three years since development began, the department's expertise in constructing and using models has grown as a result of this modeling effort. The planners have subsequently developed a series of simpler models addressed to specific planning issues—for example, the financing implications of earnings growth plans. The direct benefits of the model have been somewhat disappointing to the planning manager, but these indirect benefits are a solid payoff.

I cannot help but wonder, however, if the department would have made better progress if these simpler models had come first. Then a more extensive model might have been built with very specific planning objectives in mind, and with a firm base of experience and expertise.

### Concluding Note

It is unquestionable that the skill and art of management are needed to supplement technical efforts if models are to be created and used successfully. And success, when it comes, will not come quickly. Hence my final word of advice is—be patient. Most of the successful users I know say that success has taken a number of years, with inevitable failures along the way. I believe that some of the advice offered here will shorten the time and reduce the failure, but one must be prepared to be very patient.

# 4. WHAT KIND OF CORPORATE MODELING FUNCTIONS BEST?

*Robert H. Hayes and Richard L. Nolan*

---

## What Is a "Success"?

To date there is no consensus on what constitutes a successful corporate model. In fact, the history of corporate modeling—that is, of providing formal images of whole companies—reveals many efforts that were unsuccessful by *any* measure. For this reason, businessmen generally regard corporate modeling with considerable skepticism; hence the defensive attitude of corporate modelers. However, our friend described a "success" as a fairly detailed corporate model that has been used for at least a couple of years to help senior managers make strategic decisions. His success criterion focused directly on the model itself, as complex, integrated, and relatively static. He visualized it as distinct from the corporate decision-making process it was designed to serve.

This criterion, while pragmatic enough, ignores the fact that a model is and can only be part of a broader process for management decision making and development. It must fit that process; and as the process evolves, so must the model. A simple process requires a simple model; a changing process requires a flexible model. Consequently, trying to identify the inherent characteristics of a corporate model that is "successful" according to our friend's definition is wrongheaded.

Some very inelegant models, which *we* consider successful because they have evolved and been integrated into a management decision-making process, might be rejected as failures by our aforementioned friend either because of their simplicity or because they evolved over a period of time. In some of these cases the original model was scrapped entirely and a new one developed to fit the particular management process in question. To us, it is the process that is important, *not* the model.

Granted this criterion, a more optimistic picture of the present and future of corporate modeling emerges. While the past has indeed been grim, it has taught us some extremely valuable lessons about what models, modelers, and corporate modeling can, and cannot, be and do.

Exhibit I shows the three distinct periods through which corporate modeling has progressed. The most salient feature characterizing each period is the particular management approach to modeling that was

*Part III: Modeling*

| Design approach | Period | Prevailing computer technology | Feasible applications | Modelers | Major focus of attention | Major fallacy | Lessons learned |
|---|---|---|---|---|---|---|---|
| BOTTOM-UP | 1956–1963 | Second generation: batch processing high-level programming languages | Corporate models designed and implemented by technically oriented personnel | Operations researchers | The model | Models of operating processes can be utilized as planning tools | 1. Planning models are different from operating models<br><br>2. Operations researchers ("outsiders") do not understand the management decision-making process well enough to build general models |

*Exhibit I—Continued*

| TOP-DOWN | 1964–1969 | Third generation: disk storage; time sharing; model programming languages | Large models (both in size and in data required) easier to build with special languages | Management scientists and systems analysts | The model | Large, "realistic" models are required for planning, and can be responsive to decision making | 1. Large models are relatively inflexible<br><br>2. Large models overwhelm the manager's ability to understand the assumptions of the model and to integrate its output into the decision-making process |
| --- | --- | --- | --- | --- | --- | --- | --- |

| INSIDE-OUT | 1970–present | Third-plus generation: mass low-cost storage data bases teleprocessing minicomputers | More efficient use of corporate data Sharing data and programs among geographical areas | Ad hoc project team: managers, systems analysts, management scientists | The process | Undetected, but doubtless there | 1. The manager must be intimately involved in the model-building process 2. Simple models are usually the way to start 3. The model should evolve in complexity or size as required by the decision-maker, and at *his* pace |
|---|---|---|---|---|---|---|---|

used: bottom-up, top-down, or inside-out. To appreciate the lessons of the past two decades, one has to analyze the environment in which each corporate modeling period flourished and the changes in this environment that led to the onset of a new period. The current period, characterized by the inside-out approach, appears likely to be the longest period yet, and a successful one at that.

### From the Bottom Up: 1956–1963

The bottom-up approach to corporate modeling can be characterized by the phrase "corporate modeling as an afterthought." It began with the first commercial use of computers in the mid-1950s. Businessmen were then presented with a powerful new tool that not only promised to increase the speed and reduce the cost of much clerical work, but would also allow them to attempt things that had never been possible previously.

Automating clerical work was a manageable task: the manager could always compare the output of the computer with the output of the previously existent operation, and he needed to defer to the computer specialist only on matters of machine efficiency and speed. Because early computers were difficult to use, the priority issue was simple enough: how to master the machine to do traditional chores better.[1]

However, once early success at improving routine tasks—like payroll and accounts receivable—began to whet management's appetite for new horizons in the use of computer technology, the trouble began. Management information systems and corporate planning models were hovering in the mist of the future, it seemed, but who was to lead the manager into the unknown? Who was there to even tell him which unknowns were conquerable?

The only people available were the same computer specialists who had played such supportive roles in automating the familiar tasks. Who were they? Generally, people with mathematical or scientific backgrounds, often with some training in the (then new) field of "operations research," seldom with much business training or experience. They tended to regard the computer with a mixture of awe, affection, and scientific curiosity. In leading the manager by the hand into the unknown, they tended to choose those applications and problems that would cause the computer to shine most brightly and that would stretch its capabilities, and theirs, to the maximum.

One direction they chose was to develop computer "models" of various aspects of the business and to analyze the behavior of those models under

---

[1]For a lucid discussion of the main concerns of organizations in the use of computers, see Robert I. Benjamin, "A Generational Perspective of Information Development," *Communications of the ACM* (July 1972): p. 640.

*Part III: Modeling*

various assumptions, through simulation. Usually the parts of the company that were chosen for modeling were operating units: a plant, a distribution center, or even a department within a larger unit.

There were several reasons for this early emphasis on *operating* models:

Operations researchers had developed a number of effective frameworks for analyzing operational processes.

Operating units are very often structured sufficiently well to permit the quantification of their important activities.

Operating units are relatively easy to observe, and the kind of quantitative data required in the construction of a computer model is generally either already available or easy to obtain.

The events that occur in operating units are fairly predictable, and many of the decision procedures that were being used at that time for responding to these events involved rather simple rules of thumb, which could be readily translated into computer programs.

These events usually occur with such frequency that the operations manager is under continual pressure to respond; hence he is often delighted at the prospect of a computer providing him assistance in the analysis and resolution of these repetitive and pressure-laden problems.

In manufacturing, where most of these early attempts at modeling were made, the manager usually had an engineering background that made him appreciative of the capabilities of the computer and also allowed him to communicate easily with the computer programmer.

Hence it appeared to be possible for someone without extensive business training, but with some scientific detachment and good powers of observation, to develop an adequate operating model.

DISASTER BY ADDITION. Once an operating model had been demonstrated to senior management, someone, in the flush of enthusiasm, was bound to ask how and when such a model could be adapted to provide information for corporate planning purposes. The reasoning seemed impeccable:

1. If a company can develop a model for one function, such as plant operations, then a company can develop a model for all functions of the plant (plant operations, purchasing, accounting, personnel, and so forth).
2. If a company can develop a model for all the functions of one plant, it can develop a model for all the plants.
3. If a company puts all these models together and adds a "corporate functions" model to them, then presto—a corporate model will emerge. (Such a model, of course, will require "a slightly larger computer" than the existing one.)

Impeccable though this reasoning appeared, it simply did not work. Attempts to build corporate models in this fashion, from the bottom of the company upward, led to incredible Frankenstein monsters which fortunately died before they could do much harm. For example:

A large, integrated wood-products company successfully used a computer model to improve the performance of one of its sawmills in the early 1960s. Then it developed similar models for other plants, and attempted to coordinate and optimize the activities of a group of plants. Next, using this coordinated, "optimized" model as a base, the company tried to develop, evaluate, and compare alternative long-range plans. The pyramid of operating models began to crumble as more and more were added, and it collapsed completely when the new burden of long-range planning was added. Today this company has largely abandoned computer planning models.

A major defense contractor developed a computer model (essentially a job-shop simulator) at one plant to help coordinate and expedite the job flow and improve delivery estimates. The model was quite effective as long as it was used for these purposes, but its extension to long-range planning so discredited it in the eyes of management that it was eventually abandoned as an operating tool.

In retrospect, the reasons for these disasters are obvious. Operating models—which embrace a variety of inputs, operations, and outputs, and where events occur and decisions are made almost continuously—must contain a wealth of detail. In those days the amount of programming detail and data required for even a simple job-shop simulator was substantial; for a distribution network it was incredible; for a whole complex of plants and distribution centers it was simply infeasible. By the time all the data required to run such a model had been collected, they were out of date, and new data were required.

Face with such a dismal Sisyphean task, the corporate modeler did exactly what any sane person would do in a similar situation—he made a game out of it. The game was to continually polish the model, adding "realism" and "precision" to it. Thereby, he was able to pass off his efforts as "research." The fruits of this research were reported to his colleagues through the various professional journals that sprang up during this period.

As the game continued and the model became more complex and sophisticated, more information was required to operate the model, it took longer to produce results, and it was used less frequently. And not only was the output which it generated dissimilar to the actual operating results of the company, but there was often no way to ascertain where and why this divergence existed. The model, in time, became an end in itself.

After a year or so of funding this kind of nonsense, companies quietly dispatched both the model and the modelers; only a stack of boxes filled with punched cards was left to molder quietly in some dark corner. These lessons, however, emerged from the bottom-up period:

1. Operating models are not planning models. The kind of information required is different, procedures are different, and the output required is different.
2. Planning models cannot be built by specialists who are not familiar with the company and its planning process. Knowledge of why and how planning is actually accomplished is necessary.

### From the Top Down: 1964-1969

By the mid-1960s, then, the bottom-up approach had fallen into a much deserved disrepute. Meanwhile, a new generation of computers had arrived. They were faster, had larger capacities for storing and retrieving data, and functioned with higher level, user-oriented computer languages. These technological improvements provided a major impetus to corporate modeling activity; one survey indicates that 28 out of 36 companies studied initiated corporate modeling efforts after 1964.[2]

In addition, the increased use of computers in organizations induced specialization among computer personnel and associated groups. Some of these people called themselves management scientists, others, systems analysts, but they all tended to be more aware of practical management problems than their predecessors.

They were also more familiar with the advantages and limitations of the use of computers in organizations. Systems analysts had become conscious that operations models are not usually appropriate for addressing planning problems, and had begun to develop a better understanding of the organizational contexts in which information-gathering and planning take place. They knew by now that the manner in which the enterprise organizes to collect information often determines the kind of planning activity that is possible.

However, the biggest change took place in the echelons of upper management. Somehow—through friends and associates, through books and articles, through speeches and seminars, and through their own inability to deal effectively with a world that was changing faster than ever before—these upper managers "got the faith." A planning model became not just an interesting possibility, one that could be classified as a kind of basic research from which no immediate usefulness was anticipated, but an absolute necessity.

[2]Richard L. Nolan, "Strategic Simulation as a Process: Using the Computer in Major Business Decisions," unpublished research study, Harvard Business School, 1974.

DISASTER BY DECREE. In the pursuit of a competitive advantage (and the "modern image" that publicity about the company's corporate model would engender), upper managements sent forth orders to "create a corporate planning model." This is what we mean by the top-down approach. Earlier corporate modeling experiences were discounted because of lack of commitment, poor technique, or some other equally superficial explanation, and top management directed that a new start on a global model be made.

The first response to this decree was usually the establishment of a corporate modeling group, generally as a subunit within the corporate planning department, but often reporting directly to a senior officer. The people staffing these departments were a mixed breed; some were old-time operations researchers, some were professional planners who were wise in the ways of the corporate jungle, and some were of the new breed of management scientist, often fresh out of business school. Created by fiat, grafted awkwardly onto the organization chart, and peopled largely by outsiders, such groups were often resented by existing personnel right from the outset.

Suspicions were further aroused by such a group's initial activities. Rather than ask what kind of model was wanted (because nobody really knew), the members attempted to capture in a computer program whatever planning process the corporation was currently using. This required that various people in the organization submit to a rather lengthy interview in which they were asked to describe the decisions they were responsible for, their methods of obtaining the information used to make those decisions, their individual decision-making processes, and the systems by which they transmitted their decisions to those farther down the line.

Nothing, of course, could be more threatening to a middle manager at the staff level, who, on paper, may not *appear* to do work of very much significance, and who has recurring nightmares about being displaced by a computer. The same is true of a line manager, who is usually already burdened by staff people poking their noses into things they know very little about. Their reactions, almost invariably, were to misinform, either by omission, inaccuracy, or exaggeration. Even those that took the effort seriously found it difficult to respond to such glib questions as: How do you make decisions? (As some have pointed out, this question may be impossible for the manager to answer.[3])

Having collected this information with all the intensity and devotion of priests trying to extract the future from the entrails of animals, the corporate modeling group retreated to its aluminum tower and began to build its model. And what a model it was! This time it was the budgetary process and the flows of funds and resources throughout the company that got the major attention, but the result was the same:

[3]Russel L. Ackoff, "Management Misinformation Systems," *Management Science* (December 1967): p. B-147.

The model required incredible amounts of data, the useful life of which was often less than the collection period required.

The model took a long time to run, and it produced piles of output that nobody bothered to look at.

Such models produced another stream of articles, speeches, and comments in trade journals. One such model, for a large petroleum company, was initiated with a team of qualified planners, management scientists, and MBAs. Design efforts began with high level meetings to decide what level of detail would be appropriate for the model, whether optimization or simulation techniques should be used, whether the model should be probabilistic or deterministic, and what data should be collected. Unfortunately, what the model was actually going to be used for was never stated very clearly. As the project continued, support dwindled, and four years later a merger permitted the model to die a merciful death.

Another such model, for an aerospace company, was championed by the vice president for corporate planning. A team designed a four-module model, comprising a manpower module, a facilities module, an overhead module, and a financial module. The need for and purpose of these modules was clear: to permit analysis of the impact of various contracts and programs on the company's resources. The model was developed, but it proved incredibly difficult to use because of its size and inflexibility. The staff was just unable to keep the model up to date, or utilize it as a planning tool.

HISTORY REPEATED. History seemed to have repeated itself; the result of the second corporate modeling approach was the same as for the first approach. The corporate model was a myth. It was built by nonmanagers who had no clear concept of how its output was to be used to resolve specific problems, or by whom. By and large, nobody within the corporation had a vested interest in its success, except the modelers themselves. It took so long to build (on the order of two or three years), that by the time it was ready to be demonstrated, its original justification had largely evaporated, as had many of the people who willed its creation. These were the lessons of the period:

1. Top-management commitment to a corporate model is not enough; the managers must actually *understand* the model.
2. Large, all-inclusive, corporate models pose formidable design and data problems. Moreover, they are almost impossible to understand, except for the people who created them.

The time was then the late 1960s, and the recessionary profit squeeze was on. In many corporations, a new head of corporate planning appeared and was given the mandate to "streamline the operation." Most of the people originally involved in building the model had drifted away, attracted by opportunities to build new and better models for other companies or consulting firms. The corporate model, already infirm, was quietly dispatched, and the new planning director now appeared at corporate planning conferences to give speeches with titles like "The life and death of a corporate model"—addressing the populace over the tyrant's dead body, as it were. Exit the corporate planning model, an unworkable idea condemned by its own naïveté to an early demise.

Or so it seemed.

## From the Inside Out: 1970-?

During the past five years computers have become much more accessible and easy to use. Teleprocessing, time sharing, and user-oriented languages (such as BASIC and APL) now enable managers and analysts to use the computer directly; it is no longer necessary to work through intermediaries such as computer specialists, data processing department managers, operations research staffs, planning departments, or whatever.

Nor do managers have to rely on others to decide what their problems are and to define the nature of their solutions. They now have direct access to the power of the computer and to canned programs for many of the simple things they need (for example, breakeven analyses, cash flow projections, and market segment analyzers). Without a conscious effort—without even realizing what is happening—many corporations have begun to use the computer to actually develop plans. This is what we call the inside-out approach, and it is in full, if unheralded, swing right now:

A typical example of the inside-out approach is an interactive budgeting model recently developed for a large commercial bank. The president of the bank had routinely used the budgets of the bank's divisions for control purposes and as a basis for determining bonuses. Consequently, the management of each division had devoted considerable time to these budgets and plans, as well as to analyzing the impact that various business alternatives would have on their budgets.

Then a young MBA went to work for the bank as assistant vice president; within a year he had automated the budget spread sheet preparation for his division, using a computer time-sharing service. Soon the budgetary and planning process had been automated for all the divisions. The model has continued to evolve through the addition of features such as "trend history" files for revenues and expenses, and statistical tools for analysis and forecasting.

A second example is provided by the development of the AAIMS interactive planning system at American Airlines. In much the same way as the interactive budgeting system was started at the bank, AAIMS was initiated by some planners who needed computer assistance with their tasks.

By automating their procedure for assembling forecasts from all parts of the company through a modern programming language (APL), and by designing their key files so that they could be shared among programs, these planners reduced the time required for first-cut planning by 61%. They were then able to shift their major efforts from clerical preparation tasks to "what if?" analyses—of alternative schedules, routings, expense patterns, and the like. (As an added benefit, more and more MS techniques are being assimilated into the company's planning.) Now AAIMS is widely used throughout the company.

These models are not "corporate models," in what has become the conventional connotation of the term—namely, a model that *encompasses* the strategic planning function of the corporation. Such a model is clearly infeasible; yet this was the illusory objective (although not usually expressly stated) of corporate modeling in the first two periods.

The models resulting from the inside-out approach are designed to exploit the use of the computer *within* the planning function. Often they simply duplicate activities that had previously been carried on manually. But they respond to genuine, specific needs and are being used intelligently; their output is having an impact on corporate planning decisions. In effect, the inside-out approach has reconciled the requirements of the computer modeling process with those of the corporate planning process.

WHY IS THIS APPROACH BEST? First, decisions are made by *people*, often while working together in an unstructured fashion. The process by which alternatives are formulated, refined, analyzed, pruned, resolved, and, finally, sold to others is a lengthy and complex one. Seldom does an important corporate decision ever emerge automatically and stand on its own merits; it must be nurtured and defended, often in a hostile environment. And it needs at least one powerful champion—someone who believes in it strongly enough to devote major effort to its acceptance.

No computer can provide this kind and quality of advocacy. Nor will any manager be likely to take on the role of champion unless he believes in both the decision and the analytical process that supports it. Therefore, at best, a computer can take only a secondary role in the decision-making process. Moreover, the computer model must be closely tailored to the person who will use it and assume responsibility for its advocacy. It must make sense to him, and, above all, it must not threaten him.

This sounds obvious, but it lays waste a large part of the conventional wisdom that has surrounded corporate models until recently. For example, it calls into question the validity of "realism" in a model (at least to the extent that "realistic" is equated with "detailed"). What is important is not that the model contain a complete, or even a correct, representation of reality, but that it matches the manager's (or company's) own understanding of the reality that exists. We must replace the concept of "realism" with the concepts of "adequate" and "useful."

Moreover, this viewpoint calls into question the whole concept of a *general* model—that is, one that can be used by a variety of people for a variety of purposes over a long period of time. Problems, and the environment, change with time. Further, different people look at these problems in different ways and require different kinds of information and different forms of output. A corporate model that attempts to appeal to too many people and address too many problems will often represent an unworkable compromise, too simple to achieve wide credibility, yet too complex to be easily used, updated, and explained. In addition, such models take too long to develop. Models whose expected useful life is only two or three years should certainly require no more than half a year, total, to be created.

Finally, managers are beginning to realize that the real value of a model comes not just from *using* it, but from *creating* it. Just as a person advances his understanding of a situation under the tutelage of experience, so does his understanding evolve during the modeling process. Over 50% of the value comes from "getting there"; a model provides an opportunity to gain synthetic experience. As the model is developed and used, it will begin to challenge implicit assumptions of the user and to suggest opportunities for improvement. Hence a good corporate model is not only a decision-making aid, but also a powerful educating and developing tool for management.

LESSONS OF THE PERIOD. Three important facts have emerged from this stage of corporate modeling:

1. The manager must be involved in the process of developing the model. Not only does this ensure that he understands the model and is aware of its shortcomings, so that he is not tempted to make stronger claims than are justified, but it becomes a factor in his own development as a manager.
2. Simple models are best at the outset. One should start with something simple and begin working with it as soon as possible. Often the first model will be based largely on intuition. But as experience is gained, a richer understanding emerges, the level of detail increases as required, and the model becomes more comprehensible and explicable; hence it is more useful for the advocate. Moreover, simplicity tends to ensure that the model's development time will not exceed its expected lifetime.
3. Models (plural), not a single model, are involved in the corporate modeling process. The models should be responsive to the require-

ments of the problems at hand and should effectively exploit the computer and the modeling resources available.

## Inherent Problems

Ironically, however, one thing is clear. The facilities and infrastructure that most companies have created to assist the development of more formal corporate models will probably work *against* the inside-out approach. In our work with companies we have been struck repeatedly by the uneasiness that our work, and even our presence, has created among the resident management scientists. Rather than regarding us as promoters and champions of their efforts, they often regard us as betrayers and usurpers.

In all fairness, in some cases they have proved to be rightly suspicious— it did not require a blazing intellect to determine that some of these people were contributing nothing of value to their companies. Nevertheless, in most cases we were there to encourage and enlarge their activity. Why then do they regard the inside-out approach as a threat? To answer this question, one must look at the typical backgrounds of the people who staff these departments and at the ways these departments are funded.

First, planning departments are ordinarily staffed by professional planners; OR departments, by professional operations researchers; and corporate modeling departments, by professional modelers. These people have special training in the techniques and theories associated with their particular disciplines. They tend to be analyzers, observers, conceptualizers—and *outsiders*. Their role is usually defined as "in-house consultant." They are rarely intimately familiar with their organizations, nor do they have close working relationships with many of their organizations' line managers. In fact, they tend to work most comfortably and effectively with each other, not with managers.

As a result, they usually prefer to work in teams, relatively isolated from the organizational problems being dealt with. Their only contact with the managers involved generally consists of a rather limited and sterile dialogue. First, there is an initial attempt to understand the problem. Next, some clarifying questions are raised during the course of their analysis. Finally, a formal report is submitted.

As far as funding is concerned, these departments are usually set up as cost centers. The problems associated with assigning costs to projects increase enormously as the number of projects increases, of course, as do the overhead costs associated with manning and scheduling people's time. Moreover, it is much easier to garner publicity, assign rewards, and negotiate for higher budgets for the following year if the projects are large and highly visible. So, in the natural course of events, a few large projects tend to be preferred to many smaller projects.

Hence, most of these departments, because of the inclinations of the people in them and the type of budgetary and control process they are subject to, tend to work on major projects in teams of several people, over long periods of time. Then administration is easy, specialization is possible, training is provided by the team/project orientation, and "career paths" are identifiable. Further, the chances of some sort of perceived success are higher because such projects take so long and are so demanding of resources that the company tends to becomes psychologically committed to them. In consequence, the initial reaction to their completion is generally favorable.

Under these conditions, it is not surprising that most management scientists feel threatened. Their teamwork-oriented methods, their relative isolation from the rest of the organization, and their quasicynical attitude toward funding and the other organizational pressures that bear on long-term, highly complicated projects are antipathetic to the inside-out approach, which is geared toward simplicity and management involvement.

## How to Begin

A manager who wants to try this technique needs someone who can offer advice on how to translate a decision process into a computer model; on how such a model might be structured so as to make maximum use of the company's data base; and on how it would relate to others that are being developed. But this adviser needs to be an insider, one who is familiar with the organization and its personnel and who shares the interests of the manager as well as the technician.

To make the inside-out approach work, therefore, the corporate modeling department should be comprised of a few high-caliber people who work informally with a number of managers on an on-going basis. They must have a variety of skills, both managerial and technical, since one of their functions is to recognize the interrelationships between their clients' activities and what is going on in the rest of the organization. Project proposals and funding, except in a very informal sense, are simply not appropriate responsibilities for this kind of group.

Such people might come from a consulting firm—but only if that firm has a long-standing, retainerlike relationship with the company in question, and only if it is understood that the specific consultants will be assigned to this activity over a period of several years. More likely, however, these people will come from within the company itself.

And where would the company get such people? The following scenario seems likely, in our opinion:

A young man—or woman—joins the company and works in two or more line positions over the course of five years or so. At this point he is identified as a "comer," and the process of grooming for higher responsibility begins. He is given a new job in a functional area with which he is not familiar. Once he has a broad grounding in the overall activities of his company, he takes part in a management development program, of which instruction in both planning and the use of computer models is an integral part.

His charge, on returning from the program, is to develop some simple computer models to aid the decision-making or planning activities he performed in his previous positions. He is also transferred to a special "planning consultant" group, where he is then freed from the day-to-day distractions of line management. This assignment lasts a predetermined time, perhaps a year. While he is with this group, he is also asked to serve as a consultant of the type we described. His ability to inspire confidence and work effectively with those who request his assistance will be one of the bases for his performance evaluation when the time comes for him to be reassigned.

The specific progression is not the most important feature of this scenario. The really valuable points are (a) that assignment to such a group is regarded as a natural and attractive step in a person's career path, (b) that highly capable people are appointed to that group, and (c) that these people are regarded by the organization as having special assignments, rather than as being permanent specialists. The funding of such a project should be modest, because excessive funding tends to create a dysfunctional pressure: more modeling might be done, but there will be less real commitment to it.

Achieving full utilization of the computer resource in the planning process under this approach will be a rather long process, probably taking a minimum of five years. We regret to say that no shortcuts appear to be available.

Perhaps once a "critical mass" of modeling has been accomplished and models have achieved a certain amount of credibility in an organization, the process will speed up considerably.

### The Issue of Urgency

Corporate modeling is emerging from adolescence and approaching maturity as a top management tool. As with many other innovations, it was introduced too quickly, sold too enthusiastically to people who had neither the inclination nor the experience to use it effectively, and then debunked and discredited too emphatically. But in the process of compiling a rather dismal ledger of errors, we have learned much. More important, a cadre of experienced, computer-wise managers has been created. Today models are being used pragmatically and effectively in corporate planning and decision-making processes.

However, there still appear to be so many potential pitfalls associated with corporate modeling that many senior managers may question the advisability of getting involved with it at this time. "Wouldn't a wait-and-see strategy be advisable?" We argue *no* for two reasons:

First, the cost of the inside-out approach is minimal, and the returns can be great. This approach enables the manager to probe tough strategic planning problems—involving markets, products, technologies, and competitive tactics—more deeply and comprehensively than ever before. Moreover, models serve as effective integrative mechanisms; they focus the attention of a number of different people—line managers, planners, and analysts—on a common problem and a common set of data and facilitate communication among them. The value of the model as a communication and educational device is probably as great as its value as a decision aid.

Second, the growth of technology and technological sophistication in management is quickening. There will be more progress in the use of computer models in the next five years than there has been in the past fifteen, for a couple of reasons:

The cost of computer logic and storage devices has been reduced by more than half every three to five years, and within the next few years it promises to shrink even more rapidly. Consider the hand calculator. Three years ago it cost $250 and few executives used it routinely; two years from now it will cost $25 and almost all executives will use it. Measuring either by cost or by expertise required, the step from hand calculators to desktop computers and communication terminals is not much greater than the step from the scratch pad to the hand calculator.

The technology of building computer data bases, through which the basic data about a company's operations can be assessed and used by a computer model, is now available; in five years many organizations will have developed this kind of base. Management will use these bases in precisely the kind of context represented by the inside-out model.

Nothing will ever replace experience and good judgment. But in a competitive arena that is becoming increasingly skill-laden there will be many management teams with experience and good judgment. As has always been the case, success will be a matter of determination and willingness to innovate. Modeling is an idea whose time has come. The technology is here; the cost is down; the people are available. How much longer can one afford to wait?

# Part IV: Implementation

# A. *The Implementation Partnership*

## 1. THE RESEARCHER AND THE MANAGER: A DIALECTIC OF IMPLEMENTATION

*C. W. Churchman and A. H. Schainblatt*

### Introduction

It is a commonplace that science is having more and more impact on human decision-making in all areas of our culture. What is neither commonplace nor easily determined is whether the impact is healthy for the human race and how the impact should occur. Some scientists believe

Editors' Note: Reprinted with permission from *Management Science*, February 1965, pp. B69–B87, published by The Institute of Management Sciences.

that because they think clearly and rationally in their own disciplines they are particularly adept at thinking clearly and rationally about almost any important decision problem. Many managers are shocked by the claim that scientists can penetrate the extreme subtleties of managerial decision-making in sufficient depth to accomplish anything but the superficial.

Much of management science has been conducted under the very naive philosophy that a certain kind of reason must prevail, and that once this reason has been made clear, the manager will either accept it or be charged with gross negligence or, still worse, gross stupidity. The counter philosophy consists of asserting that the goals and decisions of managers are so complicated, so elusive, so creative, that they must forever be closed secrets to a mind trained in the objectivity of so-called scientific method. For example, Colonel Francis Kane, USAF, believes that today's military planning:

> . . . is inadequate because of its almost complete dependence on scientific methodology, which cannot reckon with those acts of will that have always determined the conduct of man. So long as the security planner uses science and its methodology, however modern, as the foundation for his plans, he will be limited in knowing how to act by the bounds that science cannot pass in dealing with human affairs ([1], p.146).

There is also the attitude of the scientist to be considered. Above all he wants to maintain the hallmarks of the tradition of science: honesty, reason, warranted evidence. He believes that he can always be called to task to retrace his analysis, repeat his experiments, reveal his evidence. He may feel threatened by the call to assist the manager, to appear on panels that raise obscure questions, or to make recommendations in the face of little evidence.

Thus there is a national problem of the interrelationship between the scientist and manager. The word "education" seems necessary here. The managers need to be educated about the scientist, to understand what he is trying to do and why he tries to do things the way he does. The scientists need to be educated about the managers, to understand their personal and organizational goals, and their particular techniques of accomplishing them.

So large a task of education almost overwhelms us. But in the last two decades, the activities and reflections of operations researchers and other related social scientists provide a very rich background in which to study the problem. The great advantage of this segment of the history of science has been that the scientist has not posed merely as an expert using only his own disciplinary background, but rather as a conscientious researcher trying to discover the problem and the relevant information for its solution. The manager, too, has learned to respect this type of research and to regard it as something quite different from a recommendation whose only force is to be found in the scientific prestige of the one who recommends it.

In this paper we intend to examine what operations researchers and social scientists have had to say about the educational process through which management and science may know each other better. It is obvious that they have had a great deal to say, and that in the saying of it they have tended to emphasize one point of view rather than another. These viewpoints are important in themselves, for they help us better to understand the nature of the educational problem and what kinds of research may best be used to help solve it.

This paper, therefore, is designed to classify opinions about how the relationship between the manager and scientist should be studied and improved. It is a paper for those who think that this problem is important and that it is not now adequately solved. We shall use the term "implementation" to refer to the manner in which the manager may come to use the results of scientific effort. The "problem of implementation" is the problem of determining what activities of the scientist and the manager are most appropriate to bring about an effective relationship.

We cannot deny a bit of arrogance as well as courage in attempting to classify the opinions of contemporaries. It might be better to wait until the present crop was gone, because the historian finds no such difficulty in cataloging the opinions of the past. But the urgency of creating a debate we can live to enjoy, leads us to the present attempt. Rather than say that a specific man espouses a specific opinion, we shall rather say that the opinions are "in the air," and on occasion one of them gets expressed. Whoever expresses it may not believe in all its implications, and need not be labeled at all as far as the debate is concerned.

With this in mind, we classify four distinct opinions about the relationship between manager and scientist. The first considers the two functions, management and research, as essentially separable. The task of the scientist is to prepare as complete a plan as possible, taking into account as many aspects of the problem as possible, and conforming above all to the standards of scientific research. The completed plan is then presented to the manager, whose responsibility it is to accept or reject what is proposed. We shall call this response to the problem of the manager-scientist relationship the *separate-function* concept. In some extreme cases, the concept is interpreted as though the scientist ought not to do any more than present a model with a formal solution. But a far more sophisticated version is that the scientist must consider the detailed operational phases of the design he recommends.

In other words, the scientist must also lay down the specific steps by which his plan will be carried out. In discussing this phase of the scientist's work, system designers often refer to it as "implementation," but we should be aware that this meaning of the concept is peculiar to this line of thinking, just as the other three opinions will also have their own meanings of implementation.

The second position argues for creating more understanding on the part of the manager, i.e., for creating better lines of *communication*, a label we use to identify this position. The word "understanding" is critical here. We shall mean something quite definite and strong by the term. A pure sensor can track the behavior of another object simply by setting up a one-to-one response pattern between each change in the object and a subset of its own behavior. This simple tracking is clearly not understanding; merely to sense how something behaves is not to understand its behavior. In order to have understanding, the sensing organism must be able to translate the *goals* of the thing observed into responses that serve the sensing organism's ends. Thus a manager, $M$, understands how an engineer works if $M$ senses what the engineer is trying to do and why he acts as he does, in order that $M$ accomplish his own purposes. Another example is the tennis player who does not merely respond to the other player's behavior, but senses his opponent's intentions in order to defeat him. Such an astute player may be said to understand his opponent. We might refer to understanding as "purposive tracking," to emphasize that the tracker senses the intention of the other person and uses this information to further his own goals.

Hence, those who are concerned about communication, i.e., getting the manager to understand the scientist, want to do a great deal more than have the manager *accept* the recommendations, because mere acceptance might be mere purposeless tracking. For the proper communication to take place, the manager must understand what the scientist is trying to do and why he does what he does. Here the problem of implementation is the education of the manager. After a successful implementation, the manager himself becomes "more of a scientist."

A quite different point of view is that the scientist must come to understand the manager, by sensing what makes the manager what he is, and what the manager is really trying to do. Many of the experienced operations researchers have come to feel that most of OR is thoroughly naive, simply because it ignores the important issues facing the manager. It assumes, for example, that inventory control or price optimization are really serious managerial problems, when they may in fact be trivial housekeeping matters for the manager. With such a naive concept of the manager in mind, the operations researcher will waste his time. No wonder, then, that so little OR is "sold" in many companies. The proponents of this third position argue that the problem is *not* to get the manager to understand the scientist—since the former is too busy—but to get the scientist to understand enough about the manager so that he can persuade him to accept the results. Hence we label this group the *persuaders*; their attitude is not too different from that of market researchers who see their task to be one of learning enough about consumers to sell them. Here "implementation" means the process of selling the manager on the validity of the scientist's approach.

Finally, there is the position we shall want to argue for, in which *mutual understanding* must take place. A phrase as benevolent as "mutual understanding" is likely to suggest a weak conclusion for a position that intends to assert something quite radical, unless one recalls what "understanding" is taken to mean. The manager understands the scientist only by becoming something of a scientist himself, because he must purposefully respond to what the scientist *qua* scientist is trying to do. The scientist understands the manager only by becoming something of a manager himself, because he must purposefully respond to what the manager *qua* manager is trying to do. Evidently, we do not mean anything as simple and passive as "mutual appreciation" when we talk about "mutual understanding." Indeed, we mean something that is quite complicated and obscure, so complex that we believe extensive research is required to discover its real implications.

Hence, the ultimate aim of this paper is to prepare the groundwork for further research on implementation, i.e., to propose an area of behavioral research that will be of value to social scientists and managers.

We begin with four sections in which we review some literature on each of the four positions mentioned in order better to define what each opinion means. We then proceed to make the classification more precise.

### The Separate-Function Position

As we mentioned, the different opinions about the possible relationships between scientist and manager can be derived from the different meanings of implementation. What does it mean to implement a scientific finding? In the case of the separate-function position, it means essentially an adaptation of a mathematical model to a specific set of conditions. One such adaptation is the simplification of the model in terms of a set of rules that can easily be followed. Thus Orr [2] uses the theory of random walk to develop a model of inventory; he then derives simple rules as follows: identify three inventory levels, $a > c > b$, and three production rates $h > n > l$, with the operating instructions:

$$P_t = \begin{cases} h & \text{if } I_t \text{ passes } b \text{ from above} \\ n & \text{if } I_t \text{ passes } c \\ l & \text{if } I_t \text{ passes } a \text{ from below} \end{cases}$$

where $P_t$ and $I_t$ represent the dated rate of production and the "on hand" level of inventory. Orr's conception of the "implementation" of such a policy consists of making simplifying assumptions which enable him to treat the inventory random walk generated by the $(a, b, c)$ policy as a diffusion process. The diffusion representation provides a tractable model of inventory behavior which permits him to determine the six decision parameters of the $(a, b, c)$ policy.

In a more complete form of the separate-function concept, "implementation" is the process of translating the theoretical solution into an "operational" solution. The operational solution is generally a specification of the physical changes that must take place in the organization in order for it to be able to accommodate the optimal theoretical solution. This problem of designing the operational phase is well described by Hanssman, [3]:

> Therefore, one of the first and most important steps in implementation is to organize a formal forecasting activity. Similarly, procedures for the use of the decision rules must be spelled out. In this area, new problems may arise for such simple reasons as the fact that inventory records are often out of phase with the actual inventory. This difficulty can be met by incorporating the reporting lag in the mathematical model (i.e., by setting higher reorder points). Alternatively, one may try to reduce the reporting lag by organizational changes. Sometimes, the use of electronic computers may be warranted to obtain up-to-date inventory information. . . . As mentioned earlier, the cost of a formal forecasting activity as well as any other change in procedures must not be overlooked. If after consideration of all factors the savings are small, one will usually prefer to avoid the disturbance which is inevitably caused by the introduction of a new system ([3], p. 99).

The operational solution also deals with the problems of transition:

> The period of transition from an existing to a new control system poses a considerable problem in most applications. For example, when greater lot sizes are recommended, more storage facilities may be required; the higher inventories must be financed; in production, care must be taken that the occurrence of shortages is not drastically increased in the transition period; to realize savings staff reductions are necessary. Companies often shrink back from layoffs so that the staff reduction may have to be accomplished through attrition. All in all, it will seldom be possible to make a quick transition. Especially in production, lot sizes must be changed gradually in the direction of economic-lot-sizes. In one case, the installation of economic-lot-sizes for the production of parts had to be planned over a period of two years.
>
> Even when an inventory reduction is ultimately expected under a new system, the transition period may lead to peak inventories since all items with too low inventory levels under the new system are immediately ordered, but no compensating effect is present for those items with too high levels under the new system. Sometimes it is necessary to change the system only for a few items at a time ([3], pp. 99, 100).

Starr and Miller devote the second part of a book on inventory control to the "implementation" phase in which the emphasis is on specifying the steps required to go from a theoretical model to specific operating procedures. They break the implementation phase into three parts: (a) the evaluation study: design of the inventory study; (b) the inventory study: design of decision procedures; and (c) the data-processing study: design of operating procedures [4]. Detailed approaches are presented for accomplishing each part—approaches which are assumed valid no matter who the manager is.

In both of these examples, the emphasis is on a design that permits the realization of a plan independent of the persons involved. More precisely, neither scientist nor manager is required to carry out the "implementation" steps, once the "implementing" plan is made clear. This point is made clear by Pennycuick [5]:

> So far in this chapter implementation has been used in the sense of agreeing to accept the results of Operational Research and to put the recommendations of research into practice. It, also, rather implies that once the recommendations have been made the problem is put into a neat pigeonhole and forgotten by all except the man who is taking the advice prescribed. Such circumstances do, of course, occur. If the Operational Research project has been on a much larger scale and results in recommendations for major changes in organization, it is very unlikely that these will be worked out to the last detail by an Operational Research team. It is much more likely that a separate implementing team will have to be set up to plan the method in which changes are to be made, rather than make the actual changes ([5], pp. 296, 297).

Pennycuick then proceeds to give examples illustrating the nature of the problems that may confront the implementing team. These problems are of the same kind as those discussed by Hanssman, Starr and Miller.

It must be admitted that there is something very attractive about the concept of separate functions. The scientist has the responsibility of generating a workable model and the implementing team has the responsibility of making sure that the application is successful. The only confusing aspect of the picture is the manager. Of course, it is his responsibility to decide whether to accept the scientist's recommendation and the implementing team's design. But how can he assure himself that he is carrying out his responsibility correctly? He may do so by examining the past record of the scientist or implementer; or by intuition he may come to feel that the recommendations are acceptable. In either event, he cannot be said to understand the scientist, in the sense of responding to the scientist's behavior. His mere acceptance (or rejection) is not understanding; the separate functions of manager and scientist preclude the need for any such interaction. In the end, the scientist's analysis is never understood by the manager, and the scientist is largely a mystery, albeit a very useful one. Also, managerial decisions lie beyond the analysis of the scientist; for him decision making is largely a mystery, albeit sometimes a profitable one.

# The Communication Position

According to this second opinion, "implementation" means educating the manager, i.e., getting the manager to understand the aims and methods of the researcher. The techniques for producing understanding in the manager are generally called "communication" techniques. These techniques are often considered to be universal in the sense that they are assumed to be applicable in all implementation situations, regardless of who is managing.

Hankin [6] gives the following argument for better communication as a part of implementation:

> Michael Faraday said that there were three steps in useful research: the first to begin it, the second to end it and the third to publish it. In operational research I suggest that to publish it is not nearly enough. In the broadest possible sense of the word we have to "*communicate*" it. The aim must be to get the results and conclusions studied, respected, understood and fully considered in the formulation of policy. I suggest that the success of operational research must in the end be judged by the influence that it has upon the making of sound policy. If this is true it is very important indeed because it means that the duty of all operational research workers is not only to use scientific methods to analyze a situation or to deduce a most suitable line of policy. In subtle ways they must also use every part of their work to influence the making of policy without treading on the toes of those responsible for it. Some scientists may regard this as unethical; but what is the use of their work unless they take all permissible steps to make it effective ([6], p. 293).

Of course, the problem is how to communicate. Wynne [7] suggests a "simplification" technique:

> It has been stated that the purpose of OR is to support executive decision. You (management scientists) are adequate judges of whether a particular research project has been successful. Generally, your research is successful but not every patient implements good diagnosis, no more than he always survives good surgery. In addition to performing successful research, the OR practitioner is faced with another problem in whose solution he is not always so successful. To be insistent, it is one of communication.
>
> The practitioner's ability to convey an understanding of the results of his research and a feeling of confidence in it measures his ability in establishing good communication between himself and his consumer. Failing in this, he does not really have an accomplishment, for the report is not the desired end result. It is but a tool whose use by management may cause action to be taken. This action is the end result desired from the research authorized by management . . .
>
> The successful executive is skilled in the evaluation of relevant factors and in judging how their alternative interactions could affect the business enterprise. The successful research man is trained in the objective determi-

nation of elements of an abstract problem and the prediction of the results of alternative combinations of these elements. The success of each is determined by the imagination and the rigor in his approach to problems. The problem in communicating research results to the executive mind thus consists of stripping the research argument of its mathematical complexities and irrelevancies while retaining the rigorous logic for the executive's understanding. Only with this understanding and acceptance of the research findings can the executive successfully combine them with his judgment of untreated and often intangible factors which bear on the business decision ([7], pp. 17–18).

The Earl of Halsbury [8] goes even further. He views the art of exposition as the means for transferring information and understanding from the operations researcher to the manager, and he seems to argue that even fairly sophisticated mathematical concepts can be transferred:

> In expounding work to laymen we must, I think, use the method of the catalogue so that the reader has before him a long list of problems which, though they may appear physically diverse, are nevertheless structurally similar and therefore describable by a single mathematical formula. We want the layman to recognize a queue under its diverse manifestation so that by thinking of service times and waiting periods he can call us in to help him with problems that have occurred to him as problems, not as Acts of God, or the Queen's Enemies.
>
> Distributions—Poissonian, binomial and normal—require to be explained by examples from occurrences and by graphs for the purpose of illustrating properties. There is no reason why the layman should not learn to recognize a distribution that is Poissonian. It is as unnecessary for him to know about its mathematical description as it is for a spinbowler to know the mathematics of gravitation and aerodynamics. Above all, this illustration must be in concrete terms and *copious*. An abstract presentation coupled to a solitary instance will achieve nothing.
>
> Results need to be presented graphically and the graphs must be described in clear prose stating what they represent. Not even the simplest terms such as maximum and minimum should be hurried over. They may represent unexpected difficulties to some layman and deserve a paragraph at their first occurrence and a sentence on subsequent occurrences. And, of course, graphs must be clearly labelled in practical units so that they come alive for the reader ([8], pp. 14, 15).

The three authors just cited seem to imply that communication is a fairly direct process, once the scientist appreciates its need. That is, there is "one best way" to communicate, independent, for the most part, of the personality of the manager, though perhaps somewhat dependent on his educational background. In any event, the three authors seem to imply that a true understanding of the manager is not essential, and in this regard they offer an opinion different from the third position, in which such understanding is essential. The point is that the philosophy being discussed here conceives of the manager as a type, and thinks that there are general principles of education applicable to most members of the managerial class. Of course, individual differences will appear, as they always do in the educational process, but nonetheless the major task of implementation is to discover the general principles of communication. Others, like Jordan [9], realize that these general principles may not be obvious, and their development may require the special expertise of a "social engineer," whose main function would be to bridge the gap between the researcher and the manager, but who still develops methods that hold good for all managers:

> It was mentioned earlier that the gap between laboratory results and their application in real life is not restricted to the social sciences but is also true for the physical sciences. Yet there is no great problem in applying the results of academic research in the physical sciences to the needs of industry and the government. This is the result of the development of a large and highly competent, experienced, mediating profession—the engineers. Chemical engineers, mechanical engineers, electronic engineers, etc., are as a profession, at home both with the basic research done in the universities and the actual needs and realities of the line organizations.
>
> The social sciences lack a similar profession. True, social scientists are playing a greater and greater role in industry and government and a social engineering profession is slowly emerging. But it is growing up like Topsy, and is developing in an unplanned manner. This is a rather inefficient way of doing things. A reasoned plan, even though it may be mistaken in many ways, is generally more efficient in getting things done than letting "nature" take its course unaided. Steps should be taken to set up a viable social engineering profession as soon as possible. Industry, government, and the interested professional disciplines should organize a social engineering curriculum in the American colleges and universities, modelled after the physical engineering curriculum. It should lead to a terminal Bachelor or Master degree—not a Doctorate—and turn out people who are at home both in the world of the academic investigator and the practical administrator. The prime responsibility of these engineers will be to eliminate the pitfalls and difficulties to be found in the present attempts of applying academic research ([9], pp. 50, 51).

Quite another technique is to let the manager live in the environment of the researcher. Then, the argument goes, no matter what kind of a manager he may be, he will "eventually" come to understand the researcher. Thus Stillson [10] suggests that

> One way to provide the requisite training is to include this person on the team at the inception of the study. As a team member he will receive "on-the-problem" training and be allowed to participate in the formulation and solution of the problem with which he will be associated. Thus, he will understand the underlying reasons for each component of the model as well as become familiar with its manipulation. Perhaps the inclusion of such a

team member should be standard practice in every operations-research study! ([10], p. 147).

Perhaps the most far-reaching proposal within the Communication position is offered by Hertz [11]. He would have a program of universal education in the management sciences:

> If the processes of management in business and government are to be improved, we must make sure they are understood. We have castigated ourselves and been castigated by management for not being able to "communicate," and I believe this difficulty is a more profound one than we recognized a few years ago. Wherever scientific methods—say operations research—have been effectively used in management, I have observed that this use has involved the re-education of virtually an entire management group. In these groups there have been changes in language, and in methods of thought, that were reflected in the entire organization. If the management sciences are to make their maximum contribution to our society, a similar educational process must be extended to virtually the entire population. The methods used by management scientists to assess the consequences of alternatives must be put into reasonably common terms, so that the proposals of policy and the disposals of action may be debated by an enlightened public.
>
> Thus, far from relegating management sciences to a handful of experts who advise top managers, I am saying that, if scientific management is to be effective, there must be at least the glimmerings of understanding of what it is all about on a wide scale. This is precisely the base that the physical sciences are achieving. When it became clear that the world was going to depend upon science and technology, not alone for new knowledge, but for security and survival as well, the currently well-known campaign for education in the sciences began. "Understand in order to help make and be responsible for the tough scientific decisions" became the underlying theme. While there are obviously top scientists, the next-to-the-top and so on down the hierarchy, it was agreed by many that these layers must be broadened to an almost universal base of "some" knowledge. This is what we must have in the management sciences as well.
>
> To repeat what I said earlier: this education of all for understanding in the management sciences may be at least as important, if not more so, than future advances in the biological and physical sciences. For, with today's scientific knowledge, the world could be fed, sheltered, and ministered to peaceably, if only we could *manage* it ([11], p. 97).

To appreciate the spirit of this philosophy, it is important to realize that the implementation is essentially one of understanding science. That is, communication techniques are to be developed by means of which the manager can properly appreciate what the scientist is like, what he is trying to do, what he is not trying to do. It is only natural to ask whether the reverse communication process is also a part of the implementation. This is our third position.

## The Persuasion Position

The persuader views the implementation problem to center around an understanding of the role of the manager. Emphasis on understanding the manager seems to be far more prevalent among social scientists than operations researchers with engineering backgrounds.

Now there are two ways of looking at the problem of understanding the manager. On the one hand, a scientist might want to grasp enough of the personality of the manager to be able to overcome his resistance, i.e., to be able to "sell" him. On the other hand, the scientist might realize that all so-called solutions to organizational problems need to be "tailor made," i.e., need to be modified to fit the particular styles of the managers. Perhaps a stronger way to state the second position is to say that a large part of the process of running an organization is extremely elusive, and cannot be learned simply by studying the technological side of the organization. There is no one English word that captures both of these meanings. Because for the moment we wish to continue to think of the recommendation as being initiated by the scientist, we shall discuss in this section the first purpose of understanding the manager, namely, breaking down his resistance. In the next section we turn to the alternative purpose of including managerial style in the model. Since this section talks about the selling job, we call its advocate the "persuader."

The persuader seeks methods for overcoming managerial resistance to change, altering managerial attitudes, and gaining managerial acceptance to recommendations. Tarkowski [12] stresses these psychological aspects of the implementation problem:

> To take a decision in the absence of adequate information is always difficult. The difficulty is further increased when various experts offer contradictory advice. More especially, when the advice is not obvious or easily intelligible on common-sense grounds and, even worse, goes against the spontaneous inclination of a manager based on his intuition and experience, it may produce a strong emotional reaction and be a cause of considerable stress.
>
> Examples of this are provided by the well-known difficulties of accepting recommendations of an operational-research team referring to the level of stocks or the range of products. Objections, predominantly of an emotional nature, are supported by invoking tradition and by arguments based on apparent common sense. These objections are counteracted by mathematical or statistical reasoning and it is hardly realized that in a state of emotional stress the ability to follow new and unfamiliar ways of thinking is very seriously diminished.
>
> An analogy has been drawn already during the present conference between operational research and medicine, insofar as there are some similarities between medicine and industrial diagnosis. It may be useful, therefore, to point out that the understanding of the personality and the moods of the patient are almost as important to the successful practice of medicine

as is the understanding of the physical processes taking place in the patient's body. To a biochemist, whose task is to analyze a sample of a body liquid, the personality of the patient may be of no import and he may be able to confine himself to the strict limits of his scientific discipline. But a practitioner or a specialist, who has to deal with a human being as a whole, must take these various factors into account and his bedside manner is as much a part of the treatment as are the physical measures.

The same remarks apply to operational research work. An industrial organization is composed not only of buildings and machines, but also of human beings. The materials and the processes they undergo are obviously of great importance and so are the methods of financial and production control. No less important, however, are the personalities, the moods and attitudes, of people who form a part of the whole system. As with the biochemist, a backroom statistician or scientist may be able to neglect the human aspect of the situation, but members of an operational research team who are in direct contact with the management or labour must possess an adequate understanding of these factors and must display accordingly, an appropriate "bedside" manner. Also, the form and content of operational research reports and recommendations must be partly dictated by these considerations ([12], pp. 121, 122).

In a more general discussion, and in an attempt to delve deeper into the essential problem of decision making, Festinger [3] argues that decision making is a source of considerable stress or "dissonance" as he calls it. A manager faced with a choice between several alternative courses of action will go through a process of evaluating each alternative, considering the desirable and undesirable features of each, and then choosing that course of action that seems more desirable to him relative to his ends. After the manager has made a choice and committed himself to a course of action, all the information and knowledge he has concerning the desirable features of the chosen action are consonant with his chosen action. But in the process of making his choice he also acquired information concerning the attractive aspects of the courses of action he rejected. These cognitive elements are dissonant with the chosen action. Hence, Festinger concludes, "dissonance is an almost inevitable consequence of having made a decision." Furthermore, he believes that the existence of dissonance between cognitive elements and an individual's action choices produces pressures to reduce or eliminate this dissonance. These reductive pressures can act to change the behavior or to alter some of the cognitive elements. Thus the important question for the researcher who produces dissonance in the manager when he presents the desirable features of his recommendation, is whether the manager will reduce the dissonance by accepting the recommendation or by rationalizing away the attractiveness of the recommendation.

Various other attempts have been made to account for attitude change in terms of the arousal and reduction of inconsistency among the cognitive, affective, and behavioral components of attitude. For example, there are the studies conducted within the Yale Communication and Attitude Change Progam [14] which until his death was guided by Hovland. This group is primarily interested in persuasibility. In addition to the problem of attitude organization already mentioned, the group has studied the effect of the order of presentation [15]. For example, two aspects of "order" can be studied: (a) the order of a series of successive recommendations; and (b) the order of different elements within a single recommendation. The first case is concerned with the relative impact on attitude change of "primacy" and "recency"; the second case is concerned with the optimal organization of the recommendation.

A third aspect of persuasibility research has occupied the Hovland group. The two end points in the communication process involved in persuasion are the communication stimuli and the communication effects. These events are identifiable or observable. To account for the inter-relationships between them, two types of theoretical constructs are used: *predispositional factors* and *mediating processes*. Predispositional factors have been formulated to account for the different effects observed in *different people* when the communication stimuli are *held constant.* Mediating processes are used to account for the different effects of *different* stimuli on the *same people*. The Yale group would hope to use such constructs in making estimates concerning the probability of an attitude change in response to a given communication [16].

Creelman and Wallen [17], also basing their argument on a strictly psychological approach, emphasize "overcoming resistance":

> A third phase of OR in which the psychologist can make a unique contribution is that of implementing the decision. We can understand this point better if we survey OR activity from a broad point of view. Essentially, OR attempts to find rational solutions for the relief of some organizational disturbance. But the discovery of a rational solution to a problem does not insure its acceptance. An alcoholic will often admit, for example, that it is sensible for him to stop drinking, but this conviction seldom results in his reformation. The same thing applies to an organization that is confronted with a proposal for rational change. All too often, OR findings are not applied because the proposal arouses fears of loss of prestige. It may produce resentment because it seems to rob supervisors of their independence of action. It may be resisted because of the sheer effort of having to learn a new way of doing things. Social psychologists know something about over-coming irrational resistance to organizational change. If they are to use this knowledge effectively, however, they must be associated with the research team from the very beginning of its efforts ([17], p. 119).

Many social psychologists stress the group to which an individual belongs as the crucial determinant of his feelings, beliefs, and behavior [18]. A principle frequently applied by the "group dynamicist" to achieve change in managers is the group participation principle [19]:

Strong pressure for changes in the group can be established by creating a shared perception by members of the need for change, thus making the source of pressure for change lie within the group ([19], p. 390).

Marrow and French [20] used this principle in overcoming a stereotype (prejudice) concerning the ability of older women in a garment factory:

> Our experiment at the Harwood Manufacturing Corporation demonstrated that whereas arguments and persuasion had failed to uproot a strong institutional stereotype crystallized into company policy, other methods succeeded. Chief among them were participation of management in research and participation of supervisors in group discussion and decision. Thus, through a process of guided experiences which are equally his own, a person may be reoriented so that he gradually takes on within himself the attitudes which he would not accept from others ([20], p. 37).

As one reads over the pages of OR and other social science literature on the subject of communication and persuasion, one is tempted to say that these are two sides of the same coin. But it is more correct to say that the persuasion position takes persuasion to be fundamental: education presupposes selling. The communication theme is, of course, the modern version of the philosophy of enlightenment: if managers come to understand what is being said to them, their resistance will disappear, and they will be persuaded. On the other hand, the persuasion theme is the modern counterpart of all classical theories of irrationality or nonrationality: before a man can become "enlightened" he must become conscious or even self-conscious. One can "brief" a reluctant manager endlessly without accomplishing anything, unless one comes to realize his hidden resistances and strives to bring them up to consciousness in some way. Hence the persuader believes that his effort must precede the effort to communicate.

Nevertheless, the reflective reader must feel that underlying the discussion and quotations of this paper there has been a certain type of naivete. The point was made in a very succinct manner by Hertz in his presidential address to The Institute of Management Sciences [21]. He points out that many scientists think they are wooing management, think that management is the passive and somewhat coy lady, and think that management must be "sold." Such an attitude on the part of the scientist is surely naive. As Hertz points out, management is aware of what the scientist is trying to do and has made its own decision about how science should be used, namely, to tackle the important but relatively uninteresting technological problems of government and industry: data processing, traffic control, inventory, advertising, etc. In some real sense, management has understood the scientist far better than the scientist has understood management. At the beginning of this section, we hinted that the problem of the scientist's understanding the manager is far deeper than merely understanding enough to sell the manager on an idea. Of course, one clue to this greater understanding is the scientist's realization that even while he acts as a scientist he is also acting as a manager. To understand the scientist is to understand what kind of manager he really is.

## The Mutual Understanding Position

To borrow a well-turned phrase from Singer, "this *Dialectic of [implementation]* would have been of interest to none but the historian did it not suggest to one who has followed its argument, that so much as it has reviewed is badly in need of a future if a satisfactory theory of [implementation] is ever to be developed" ([22], p. 83).

We have designed a classification of opinion in order to persuade the reader of a viewpoint about the future. The separate-function position, attractive as it is to the technologist, simply ignores the heart of the problem of management science, namely, the relationship to be established between the manager and scientist. At best this position argues that the relational problem is easy, namely, a "translation" of technical findings into "simple" terms. Ackoff [23] has so well stated the point about simplicity, namely, that to be simple is one of the most difficult tasks the human mind faces:

> The researcher should not consider this translation problem as a chore, but as a challenge. He should appreciate the fact that in making such a translation he subjects his work to the most severe critical evaluation of which he is capable. It is very easy to conceal glib assumptions from oneself and others by the use of symbols and technical jargon. As one approaches expression of Basic English, however, self-deception and deception of others become increasingly difficult. Simplicity of expression, like brevity, is the result of extended distillation and evaluation of ideas; it takes a long time and much effort to attain ([23], p. 426).

In other words, simplicity is the result of intensive research on minds and their capabilities of receiving information.

The communication and persuasion positions seem to us together to pose the critical problem, but they must be extended far beyond the trivial "let the manager learn science" or "let the scientist learn how to sell."

Of the many terms one could use to describe this fourth position, the best seem to be politics and the unconscious. To the consciously observing mind of the scientist, a great deal of managerial activity is political, and the reasons given for decisions are rarely the real reasons, i.e., are almost always unconscious. On the other hand, once a decision has been made, the manager seeks to find perfectly conscious and justifiable reasons why this decision is best. These are contained in the statements he makes to the rank and file, the press, the directors, or whomever.

*Part IV: Implementation*

The scientist may abhor what he takes to be either dishonesty or at least self-deception in the managerial process. But he ought to realize, as we have said, that his own way of arranging his affairs is little different. Science knows very little about its basic decision making: the creation of new ideas, the trends in research effort, the debates that go on to establish a line of attack on a new problem, the resistances set up to radical ideas. But once a project is under way, science can call into play all its set of rationalities: objective evidence, mathematical models, experimental design and analysis. Indeed, science is proud of the mysteries of its unconscious life.

Much of the discourse about science and management is concerned with the comparison of the rational, conscious and apolitical side of each. OR attempts to modify the reasoning and justification process of management by putting it in the setting of more elaborate and finer models than the manager can create. Once the basic, political and unconscious decision has been made, management can only be grateful to the scientist who adds such magnificent strength to the justification process. Thus, if it has been decided politically to build a freeway through a certain part of a city, the managers are grateful to anyone who sets out to minimize delays on entrances and exits; they provide an excellent "justification" of the design.

Neither managers nor scientists want to understand their unconscious processes. Managers refer to them as "intuitive," scientists as "creative." Managers claim that no one is ever going to put their decision making on computers; scientists claim that the creative process of genius is eternally a mystery (some go so far as to describe it as "random"!).

The fourth position then is neither obvious nor palatable, for its very mild phrase "mutual understanding" calls for an intellectual attack on the mysteries of management and science. On the side of management, it calls for an understanding of the politics of decision making, and on the side of science it calls for an understanding of the creative process. This call is threatening to both.

And yet the scientist must feel uncomfortable indeed if he merely thinks of himself as someone who finds justifications for managers' decisions. And the manager may feel uncomfortable if he thinks that the large part of his support of research goes into activities that cannot be analyzed and therefore cannot be controlled. The fourth position may not be palatable, but perhaps it must be tasted, nonetheless.

This fourth position is programmatic. As such, it does not tell the manager how he can better understand, i.e., better manage, science, any more than it tells the scientist how he can better understand, i.e., better rationalize, management. The program, however, seems to be just the program that "management science" is committed to follow, namely, a program aimed at a "unified science of management," which must seem very dangerous to the managers, *and* a "unified management of science," which must seem dangerous to the scientist. But "dangerous" is not the same as "inappropriate," we hope.

## Appendix: A Formal Classification

The preceding discussion has been stated in language that might possibly misrepresent our intent, especially with regard to the meaning of "understanding." We now proceed to give this concept, as well as the meaning of the four positions, greater precision. We shall use Singer's [22, 24] logico-historical method as a means of providing a sharp focus.

This method enables one to display all possible alternative positions relative to a set of basic propositions. The number and choice of these propositions are dictated by the aim of the researcher and the history of the problem. Thus, the logico-historical method provides a classification of opinions which is guaranteed (a) by logic to possess exclusiveness and exhaustiveness and (b) by history (in our case by relevant literature of the last two decades) to be significant in content.

We begin by introducing certain concepts. The basic formal language of this discussion is to be found in Churchman and Ackoff's *Psychologistics* [26], but is also described in the following more accessible references: Ackoff [23, 27], Churchman [25], Churchman and Ackoff [28, 29], and Singer [22], pp. 257–343). The key concepts are "producer-product relation," "morphological behavior," "potential behavior," "teleological behavior," "means," "ends," "environments," and "personality." To recapitulate the most relevant part of this language, we say that by "teleological behavior," we mean behavior that can be perceived by an observer in terms of the following scheme:

(a) *Manager M*—referring to the decision-making unit under consideration, whether it be one person or a group of persons. Managers may be individuated on the basis of scales which we shall call "personality" measures.

(b) *Means (BP_i)*—behavior patterns which are "potentially producible" by M. That is, Means represent the alternative courses of action which are potentially available to the manager.

(c) *Ends (E)*—representing potential products of $BP_i$. Ends are often referred to as objectives or aspects of a state of nature, which may occur after the choice of a Means.

(d) *Environment (N)*—consisting of all other potential co-producers (relative to $BP_i$) of $E_j$. N may be described by a matrix of efficiency measures $(p_{ij})$ where, for example, $p_{ij}$ might represent the probability that $BP_i$ will produce $E_j$.

(e) *Values (V_j)*—measures associated with $E_j$.

It needs to be emphasized that the ends in particular, but also the means,

*Part IV: Implementation*

are not necessarily in the conscious mind of the manager. That is, the class of ends are not the same as the class of goals he claims to want. Nor are they the goals he may reveal when asked his preferences in either the loose manner of consumer surveys or the more refined manner of von Neumann "gambles" [30]. The intended ends are the potential products of actions he freely chooses, whether or not he expresses conscious preferences for them. Without pursuing in greater depth the obscure problem of "intended consequences," we merely note that this is a problem of measurement requiring a very careful specification of operational rules; for further detail, see [25].

Following Singer's method, we proceed to our classification of contrasting opinions by first specifying certain notions which we shall take to be common to all positions. These common notions will clarify the meaning of the basic propositions relative to which we can express the positions.

*Common Notion 1:* Decision making is teleological behavior.

*Common Notion 2:* There exists for any $(BP_i)$, $(N)$, and $(V_j)$ the optimal means, $BP_i^*$, i.e., the means that $M$ ought to produce.

*Common Notion 3:* The determination of $BP_i^*$ presupposes "scientific inquiry." Put another way, Common Notion 3 acknowledges the existence of a reflecting mind, i.e., the researcher, who is able to determine $BP_i^*$. We have thus distinguished between two minds: the manager who must decide, and the researcher who has determined the best decision. The activity of implementation must in some sense "bring together" both minds.

In this paper we have talked about the understanding one of these minds may have for the other. What this concept means is of course obscure. In the spirit of the formalism of this Appendix, we suggest that understanding is a kind of "teleological tracking," in which the understander responds to the purposes of the one who is understood; see also [26]. Whether this way of viewing understanding really captures the depth of the concept as it is used in philosophy, literature and psychoanalysis is neither obvious nor altogether relevant to our present purposes.

*Common Notion 4:* The degree of understanding of a decision-making unit concerning a teleological stimulus is the rate of change of the probability of the unit's teleological reaction choices ($BP$'s) in response to the stimulus as the efficiencies of the $BP$'s are changed.

Thus we say that an individual understands a stimulus if he responds to the stimulus in an efficient manner relative to his ends. We have also placed a restriction on the nature of the stimulus: it must be a purposive behavior pattern, i.e., the stimulus must be another mind or decision-maker. Understanding, then, connotes the workings of two minds, one a stimulus, the other a response, each distinguishable by its own teleological framework consisting of means, ends, environment, and values.

Consider, for example, the assertion, "the manager understands the researcher." This statement means that the manager reacts to the teleology of the researcher, i.e., what the researcher is trying to do, in a manner that improves the manager's chances of attaining a purpose empirically assigned to him. Consequently, the manager would react in the same way to a morphologically different researcher having the same teleology, although he would react differently if the researcher were replaced by a lawyer having a different goal or purpose.

If we assume now, that the nature of the relationship between the manager and the researcher is central to any theory of implementation, then every opinion concerning implementation must imply either the affirmation or the negation of a proposition specifying a particular relationship. A set of such propositions which are mutually independent and consistent can be used to construct a classification frame for the various opinions that have been expressed.

Thus, everyone who expresses an opinion on the problem of how to implement must accept or reject each of the following two propositions:

Implementation presupposes that,
    A. The manager understands the researcher.
    B. The researcher understands the manager.

The following matrix displays the four possible ways of affirming and denying the propositions and the names that we have assigned to the different positions. We have used the prime symbol to indicate negation:

|    | B                    | B′                   |
|----|----------------------|----------------------|
| A  | Mutual Understanding | Communication        |
| A′ | Persuasion           | Separate Function    |

REFERENCES

1. Kane, Col. Francis X. "Security Is Too Important to Be Left to Computers." *Fortune*, April 1964.
2. Orr, D. "A Random Walk Production-Inventory Policy: Rationale and Implementation." *Management Science*, Vol. 9, No. 1 (October 1962): pp. 108–122.
3. Hanssmann, F. *Operations Research in Production and Inventory Control.* New York: John Wiley and Sons, 1962.
4. Starr, M. K., and D. W. Miller. *Inventory Control: Theory and Practice.* Englewood Cliffs, N.J.: Prentice-Hall, 1962, pp. 170–329.

5. Pennycuick, K. "Presentation and Implementation of the Results of Operational Research." In *Operational Research in Management*, edited by R. T. Eddison, K. Pennycuick, and B. B. Rivett. New York: John Wiley and Sons, 1962, pp. 288–298.

6. Hankin, B. D. "The Communication of the Results of Operational Research to the Makers of Policy." *Operational Research Quarterly*, Vol. 9, No. 4 (December 1958): pp. 293–301.

7. Wynne, B. E. "A Pattern for Reporting Operations Research to the Business Executive." *Management Technology*, Vol. 1, No. 3 (December 1961): pp. 16–23.

8. Halsbury, Earl of. "The Art of Exposition." *Operational Research Quarterly*, Vol. 11, Nos. 1–2 (March–June 1960): pp. 1–15.

9. Jordan, N. "The Application of Human Relations Research to Administration." *Management Technology*, Vol. 1, No. 3 (December 1961): pp. 42–51.

10. Stillson, P. "Implementation of Problems in O.R." *Operations Research*, Vol. 11, No. 1 (January-February 1963): pp. 140–147.

11. Hertz, D. B. "Universal Education for the Management Sciences." *Management Technology*, Vol. 3, No. 2 (December 1963): pp. 93–99.

12. Tarkowski, Z. M. "Symposium: Problems in Decision Taking (3)." *Operational Research Quarterly*, Vol. 9, No. 2 (June 1958): pp. 121–123.

13. Festinger, L. "The Relation Between Behavior and Cognition." *Contemporary Approaches to Cognition*, a Symposium held at the University of Colorado. Cambridge: Harvard University Press, 1957.

14. Rosenberg, M., and C. Hovland (eds.). *Attitude Organization and Change*, Vol. 3. New Haven: Yale University Press, 1960.

15. Hovland, C. (ed.). *The Order of Presentation*, Vol. 1. New Haven: Yale University Press, 1957.

16. Hovland, C., and I. L. Janis (eds.). *Personality and Persuasibility*, Vol. 2. New Haven: Yale University Press, 1959.

17. Creelman, G. D., and R. W. Wallen. "The Place of Psychology in Operations Research." *Operations Research*, Vol. 6, No. 1 (January-February 1958): pp. 116–121.

18. Cartwright, D., and A. Zander (eds.). *Group Dynamics, Research and Theory*. Elmsford, New York: Row, Peterson and Co., 1960.

19. Cartwright, D. "Achieving Change in People: Some Applications of Group Dynamics Theory." *Human Relations*, Vol. 4, No. 4, 1951.

20. Marrow, A., and J. French. "Changing a Stereotype in Industry." *Journal of Social Issues*, Vol. 2, No. 1, 1945.

21. Hertz, D. B. "The Unity of Science and Management." *Management Science*, Series B, 1965.

22. Singer, E. A. *Experience and Reflection* (ed. C. W. Churchman). Philadelphia: University of Pennsylvania Press, 1959, pp. 72–85.

23. Ackoff, R. L.; S. K. Gupta, and J. S. Minas. *Scientific Method: Optimizing Applied Research Decisions*. New York: John Wiley and Sons, 1962.

24. Singer, E. A. "Mechanism, Vitalism, Naturalism: A Logico-Historical Study." *Philosophy of Science*, Vol. 13, No. 2 (April 1946): pp. 81–99.

25. Churchman, C. W. *Prediction and Optimal Decision*. Englewood Cliffs, N.J.: Prentice-Hall, 1961.

26. Churchman, C. W., and R. L. Ackoff. *Psychologistics.* Philadelphia: University of Pennsylvania, 1947, Chapter V (mimeographed).
27. Ackoff, R. L. *The Design of Social Research.* Chicago: University of Chicago Press, 1953, pp. 49–82.
28. Churchman, C. W., and R. L. Ackoff. "An Experimental Measure of Personality." *Philosophy of Science*, Vol. 14, No. 4 (October 1947): pp. 304–332.
29. —— and ——. "Purposive Behavior and Cybernetics." *Social Forces*, Vol. 29, No. 1 (October 1950): pp. 32–39.
30. Luce, D. R., and H. Raiffa. *Games and Decisions.* New York: John Wiley and Sons, 1957.

# 2. THE ROLES OF THE MANAGER AND MANAGEMENT SCIENTIST IN SUCCESSFUL IMPLEMENTATION

*John S. Hammond*

## The Problem

This article explores ways in which a manager, faced with a one-shot decision problem, can derive more benefit from the application of management science to his problem. Starting with the observation that few applications result in benefit anywhere near potential and many result in virtually no benefits, it will be shown that the reason is seldom inadequate technical tools or technically inadequate models. Rather, the reason is usually inadequate interface between the manager responsible for the decision and the management science model and analysis.

It is a well-documented fact that managers too often receive little or no benefit from management science analyses.[1] In the early days of operations research they received, more often than not, no benefit. A survey of the authors of articles in *Operations Research* over the first six years of its publication (1953–1959) revealed no good evidence that the recommendations of the reported studies had been accepted by management.[2] More recently, the record seems to have improved. In 1972, Drake surveyed twenty-five transportation modeling projects and for many of these was able to get an answer from both the project director of the management science effort and his manager client to the question, "How would you characterize the results

[1]See Huysmans [22], Hammond [19].
[2]See Churchman [11].

Editors' Note: Reprinted with permission from *Sloan Management Review*, Winter 1974, pp. 1–24.

*Part IV: Implementation*

of the completed project?"[3] The results were reported on a scale ranging from worthless (0 points) to complete success (10 points). In only one instance did a manager rate a project 10. More usual numbers were in the range of 6-7, and a significant minority gave scores in the range of about 2. More importantly, of the dozen projects which were rated by both parties, in only one did the client give a score higher than the project director and in seven instances the reverse was true. The remaining four were rated equal by both parties. Assumptions by management scientists about the benefits they create are apparently inflated.

To explore why the benefits are below potential, the kinds of decision making situations on which this article focuses will be discussed first. Next, the process by which a manager makes a decision and some aspects of cognitive behavior will be examined. This will allow an exploration of the ways in which quantitative analysis can help. Finally, the obstacles to reaching these benefits are addressed and then ways in which the realization of the benefits can be enhanced are suggested.

This article presents a progress report on the early phases of ongoing research; the conceptual scheme included still is evolving. It brings to bear on the problem the work of behavioral and cognitive researchers, most of which has been done in applications other than the implementation of management science. At this stage the hypotheses posed here are stronger in diagnosis than in prescription, but they have sufficient face validity and relevance to make them useful to both managers and management scientists.

## The Applicable Decision Making Situation

The applicable decision making situation is where a top or middle manager or a small group of managers has the responsibility for making an important nonrecurring decision such as an acquisition, divestiture, new product introduction, significant shift in manufacturing strategy (such as an automobile manufacturer deciding whether to begin manufacturing its own glass), new facilities, or new financial strategy. The important thing to notice is that these are problems of concern to upper level management; excluded are most of the "classical" applications of management science or of management science systems designed to facilitate operations, such as inventory control systems. As a consequence, applications of interest are those which permit a *specific individual* (with unique characteristics) or a specific group of individuals to reach an important decision as opposed to a system designed to help an *organization* make recurring decisions, independent of the particular individuals responsible for those decisions. Further, these are problems that are inherently less structured than the classical applications. Finally, Lindblom has identified this type of decision as an in-

[3]See Drake [16].

tegral mixture of value and fact to the manager.[4] The type of help that the manager will want in such situations is a kind of "personalized rationality."[5] Problems like this are frequently addressed by decision analysis.[6]

While this article focuses on the roles of the management scientist and manager in dealing with a relatively unstructured, important, one-shot decision, many of its observations apply to other settings, too. First, much of it nonetheless applies to the use of management science to support other types of decisions, for example more structured, recurring problems. More importantly, most of what is said below applies to the conduct of good, high-level staff work, independent of whether management science is used.

## The Process by Which the Manager Reaches Decisions

Classical management science analyses assume that the manager is a rational, economic man taking action to optimize his organization's best interest. Implicitly, it is assumed that he has the same objectives as the organization and that the management scientist's abstraction of the decision making situation will be so close to his that he will adopt the course of action indicated by such an analysis. Rationality is defined in some external, universal sense, rather than in the manager's terms.

In fact, this is seldom what happens. As Churchman and many others have pointed out, part of the problem is that the manager's goals are often different from his organization's goals.[7] Often this is the result of the organization's reward and incentive system (its so-called control system) inducing behavior different than what the organization intends. For example, it is well known that individual managers are often more risk averse regarding risky decisions than is in their organization's best interest or is their organization's intent.[8] Another reason for lack of congruence of the manager's goals with the organization's goals is specialization and functional division of labor, which results in units of the organization having different and sometimes incongruent subgoals.[9] For instance, the marketing department may emphasize increasing sales while manufacturing may be concerned with reducing production costs.

Furthermore, it is recognized by many that instead of addressing a whole management problem, management science analyses usually deal with analyzable parts of it.[10] Hence, the actual decision making is done by the manager, blending the results of management science analyses with considera-

[4]See Lindblom [25].
[5]See Wagner [41].
[6]See Schlaifer [35] and Raiffa [30].
[7]See Churchman [11].
[8]See Swalm [40].
[9]See Lawrence and Lorsch [24] and Cyert and March [13].
[10]See Wagner [41].

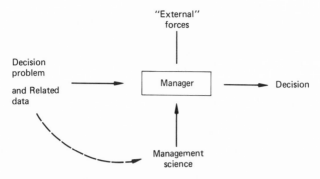

Figure 1: *Forces influencing a manager's decision making*

tions not covered, partially covered, or covered with some distortion in the management science analysis.

Consequently, it is important to know how the manager thinks about a decision problem to understand better how his thinking can be enhanced by management science. For this one relies on a model of the human thought process adapted from the work of those who have studied human reasoning over the past few decades and those who have more recently applied this line of thinking to decision support systems.[11] The resultant conceptual scheme is shown in its simplest, most schematic form in Figure 1. The person responsible for the decision is in the center of the diagram. Impinging upon him and thus affecting the resultant decision are external forces such as his organization, his role within it, his social and political relationships with other individuals, generally accepted and new management principles, the behavior of competition, and so on. These not only affect his perception of the problem (for example, because of his position he is expected to respond in certain ways to problems), but also can directly affect the way he responds to management science assistance (for example, he may be less willing to share information with a management scientist from a corporate O.R. department than with someone who reports directly to him).[12] Second, there are the nature and characteristics of the decision problem itself and data relating to it. Decisions will vary according to their complexity, the degree of structure inherent in them, the amount of data available, the nature of the data (quantitative vs. verbal), the importance of the decision to the decision maker and organization, and time pressure.[13] Each varying dimension will affect the way he responds to and copes with the decision. Finally, there are management science analysis and the management scientist. (The dashed line from the problem to the management scientist indi-

[11]See Simon and Newell [38], [39]; Bruner, Goodnow, and Austin [8]; McKenney [28]; and Keen [23].
[12]See Brown [7].
[13]See Anthony [2] and Simon and Newell [39].

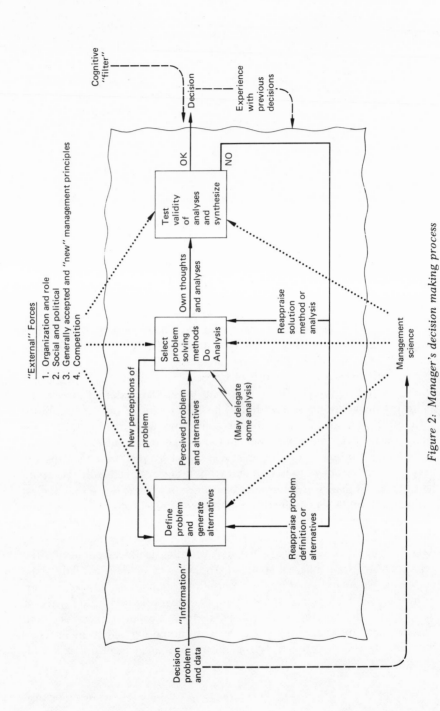

Figure 2: *Manager's decision making process and factors affecting it*

*Part IV: Implementation*

cates that data about the problem can reach the manager via the management scientist as well as directly.)

What are the processes that affect how the manager reaches a decision? To explore this, Figure 1 has been elaborated in Figure 2, with particular emphasis on what happens inside the box labeled "Manager." The manager's thought process shown in the center, is a fairly standard representation, consisting of:

1. Defining the problem and generating alternative courses of action.
2. Selecting ways for analyzing the problem and doing the analysis or analyses.
3. Synthesizing the results of various analyses and testing their validity.

As indicated by the feedback loops, the process is iterative. At any step the decision can be made to loop back to an earlier step if inadequacies are discovered in the results of the earlier step on the basis of working with its results in a later step. Further, at any point the decision can be made to gather additional information. It is important to note that while some managers go through the steps shown in a conscious manner, many are unconscious of these steps as they solve problems. In the latter case a process, little understood by them, occurs which finally results in a decision.

On the basis of this diagram one can discuss the traditional role of management science. Frequently, a general manager will delegate aspects of the middle step, particularly data gathering and analytical efforts to members of his staff. He often will reserve for himself the right to define the problem (or at least to authenticate the definition), the right to decide on alternatives to be tested, and the final decision making authority. Reinforcing this traditional relationship of line to staff is a general perception of management science as "problem solving"; thus, management science efforts generally have the greatest impact on the middle step of the process. However, the diagram shows that management science and the external forces can potentially impact all steps.

A significant aspect of the diagram is the cognitive filter or attention-focusing mechanism surrounding the thought process. It is well documented that limitations in human information processing capacity often require a selection of a portion of incoming stimuli for processing.[14] A classical example of this is the individual who is involved in one cocktail party conversation and who overhears his name mentioned in another conversation to which he seemingly has been oblivious.[15] His filter, in fact, had been "listening" to the other conversations but filtering most of them out.

The result is that what is "data" in the external world is filtered by the individual, a process called cognitive filtering. This is a transformation process that produces information for use in the reasoning processes. There is

[14]See Broadbent [6], Miller [27], and Cherry [10].
[15]See Cherry [10].

considerable difference among individuals in the way this filtering process occurs, and it is affected by many things such as personal background, education, previous experience, organizational role, motivation, the nature of the problem currently being faced, the source of the external stimulus, whether the information supports a favored alternative, and so on.

There are two aspects of cognitive filtering worth emphasizing. First, different people can be exposed to the same external stimuli and end up with different resultant information in their thought processes. For example, a production and a marketing manager might each read the same consultant's report regarding a particular new product, and one would "see" information regarding production and the other marketing. Each has an internal "cognitive map" that is heavily colored by his experience and his specialized role in the organization. What "clicks" with one person is largely ignored as being irrelevant by the other. Second, the same set of data coming from two separate sources can have different effects on a decision maker. For example, precisely the same words regarding a new product introduction can be used by either a marketing manager or a director of computer services in an organization. The manager who hears them probably will internalize and assign more credibility to them when they come from his marketing director instead of from the EDP man, because he thinks the marketing man knows more about marketing. What the manager pays attention to and how he perceives things is a very personalized thing that can have considerable impact on his problem solving. Given the fact that his time is perhaps his scarcest resource, what he pays attention to is one of the most important decisions he makes.

A number of other relevant aspects of human cognitive processes affect what is shown on the diagram but are not included in it: the fact that the human memory is an associative one, the process of concept formation, the role of cuing, the notion of mental set, and the finite information processing capability of the human mind. These ideas are neatly related. The first is that the human memory is an associative one; ideas and information are stored by related concepts as opposed to physical location in memory.[16] This means that to bring past experiences, information, and problem-solving approaches to bear on a particular current problem requires establishing a conceptual relationship between the current problem and the past information. Often the conceptual relationship is a seemingly tangential one, such as a relationship in time or space. For example, things that occurred at the same time might be stored together, such as some ideas resulting from a particular management meeting.

The process of establishing the required relationship has been dubbed by psychologists, "cuing." For instance, the recognition that the opening of a new medical clinic is in fact a marketing problem allows all of one's previous experience and knowledge related to marketing to be applied to the

[16]See Broadbent [6] and Bartlett [3].

problem. The realization or "cue" of this relationship might have been stimulated by a conversation with a colleague, the reading of an article, and so on.

As a result of thinking about the problem and gathering data and cues, one forms concepts useful in solving the problem. These concepts are analogous to models in the mathematical sense but are considerably less formal. They consist of vocabulary, categories, interrelationships, etc., that allow one to manipulate ideas.[17] For instance, a manager, faced with cost cutting on a feed lot for cattle, may make great headway in thinking of his operation as a production facility rather than an agricultural operation. Then the ideas of inventory, flow of materials, and so on can be applied to his problem.

However, there is the barrier to effective thinking that arises from mental set (known to some psychologists as functional fixedness).[18] Mental set consists of perception of the problem and a set of concepts for dealing with it, which plays the useful role of economizing mental effort. Mental set has a significant impact on cognitive filtering, thereby influencing what the decision maker pays attention to and his perceptions. Unfortunately, the mental set often becomes too rigid ("tunnel vision") and blocks redefinitions of the problem, recognition of new alternatives, the application of related and useful experience, and the use of relevant information. A classical and simple example of this is the well-known old lady-young lady problem.[19] Individuals are each shown either a picture of an old or a young lady and then all are shown an ambiguous picture which can look like either an old or a young lady. Those who were originally exposed to the old lady see an old lady, and those who originally saw a young lady see a young lady. It is difficult for those in either case to convince the others that the other type of lady can be seen in the ambiguous picture.

An instance in the management science sphere occurred in one of my consulting relationships. I offered to do a quantitative analysis of various potential licensing arrangements for a patent which was about to be issued. It seemed to me that the lawyers, who would be negotiating, would benefit from having a better understanding of the economic trade-offs between various percentage royalty, fixed fee, and other arrangements. The offer was rejected, the lawyers replying that the licensing arrangement was a matter of negotiation not of analysis. The mental set, based on past experience of how to handle a licensing arrangement, had kept them from seeing how analysis could make their negotiations more effective.

Finally, Miller has demonstrated man's finite capacity to process information; most individuals can deal simultaneously with about seven "chunks" or qualitatively different pieces of information at a time.[20] This is

[17]See Bruner, Goodnow, Austin [8].
[18]See Glucksberg [17], deBono [14], Gordon [18], and Schon [36].
[19]See Boning [5].
[20]See Miller [27].

an important constraint to problem solving and poses a challenge of coding as much information as possible into each chunk. Thus it is important to group and name things and form concepts which will permit one to remember, to retrieve and manipulate as much information as possible, and to find external devices to augment one's limited information processing.

## The Potential Benefits of Management Science

In terms of the foregoing, what are the potential benefits of management science? They can be articulated under six major headings which partially overlap.

1. PROVIDES A STRUCTURE TO A SITUATION WHICH IS INITIALLY RELATIVELY UNSTRUCTURED TO THE MANAGER. This is usually the first step in a management science analysis and if properly interpreted to the manager can have significant impact in the problem-definition phase of his own analysis. Initially he will have a structure for the problem but it will be somewhat amorphous. The management science structuring can make him aware of the important decision and environmental variables, cause the formalization of objectives, and define interrelationships and assumptions. The result of this process can be a new, sharper and useful view of his problem. For instance, a management science team assisted the management of a subsidiary of a major equipment manufacturer in reviewing its product policy. Management implicitly had viewed its product line as a set of separate items which would be replaced one-by-one as they neared the end of their product life cycles. After working with the management scientists, the problem was restructured as a series of products with a common core of technology, and serious questions were raised about the future viability of the underlying technology.

2. EXTENDS THE DECISION MAKER'S INFORMATION PROCESSING ABILITY. This benefit arises primarily because management science provides the structure necessary to bring the computer to bear on the decision maker's problem. This generally takes the form of providing optimum-seeking algorithms that permit the manipulation of large amounts of data in complex situations (as with mathematical programming) or testing the logical implications of alternative courses of action or environmental assumptions (as with simulation). It is especially noteworthy that the relatively low cost and short time required for additional computer runs allows the decision maker to explore aspects of the problem which formerly were considered to be peripheral, because they were too costly or time consuming to explore. Once examined they may turn out to be central.

3. FACILITATES CONCEPT FORMATION. First, the various management science

paradigms can provide concepts, vocabulary, and distinctions which greatly facilitate informal reasoning about problems. For instance, the distinction between risk (probability) and attitude toward risk (utility) which decision analysis makes is an insight that allows the manipulation of ideas in ways not possible without this distinction. Most decision makers confound their analysis by mixing these two ideas together.[21] The concept of shadow prices in mathematical programming has similar power. In addition to the general concepts, the particular representation of the decision problem that the manager and management scientists evolve can have great impact on the manager's concept of the problem. For instance, the concept that recruitment and training of airline stewardesses is a replacement problem or an inventory problem allows fresh ideas to be applied to a problem formerly viewed as a hiring or training problem.[22]

4. PROVIDES CUES TO THE DECISION MAKER. While this benefit can occur at any stage in his relationship with the management scientists, it can become particularly important after the analysis is under way. The cues can result from testing the implications of alternatives, the collection of new data, the manipulation and display of data in useful ways, sensitivity analyses, etc., and the results can be new concepts useful in dealing with the problem, new alternatives for consideration, or new definitions of the problem.

For instance, from the early results of a decision analysis of whether to open an innovative medical clinic and if so where, it emerged that the main financial risk was due to the large salary expense of doctors. Once this was clear, new salary schemes were explored which would shift some of the risk to the doctors. The problem as redefined, and new alternatives entered the picture. It is important to note that the management science analysis itself does not create the alternatives or redefine the problem; it is the decision maker who does it, cued by previous results. Further, the cues from the analysis can provide a better understanding of the organizational entity, its markets, or other aspects of its business environment, which are useful not only for the solution of the current decision problem, but also for coping with subsequent problems.

5. STIMULATES THE COLLECTION, ORGANIZATION AND UTILIZATION OF DATA WHICH MIGHT NOT OTHERWISE BE COLLECTED. Although the manager may be aware of the existence of some relevant data, he will not assemble and utilize it since he does not know precisely how it bears on his problem. It will not make it through his cognitive filter. The management science model may make the relevance of the data more explicit, and it then will become real information to the decision maker. In addition, the management scientist may collect data of which the decision maker was unaware.

[21]See Hammond [20].
[22]See Sasieni, Yaspan, and Friedman [34].

6. FREES FROM MENTAL SET. The initially different way of approaching a problem with the assistance of a management scientist combined with the constant new insights coming from the emerging analysis has a great potential for freeing the decision maker's mind. For instance, the management of one small firm was long convinced that a particular product line was the key to reaching its sales goals and took action accordingly. This persisted until a computer model demonstrated persuasively that even under the most optimistic conditions the product line could not sustain the required growth. Subsequently, new avenues including acquisition were explored.

These benefits imply a mutual problem solving effort between the decision maker and the management scientist, where the manager's thinking about the problem is augmented and stimulated by the services provided by the management scientist, a form of personalized rationality. They play down the more traditional role or benefit, namely the delegation to the management scientist of analytical responsibility with the implicit understanding that the analysis will identify the best decision (through some optimum-seeking algorithm applied to a model) or point the way to the best decision (through testing a series of alternatives with a simulation model so that the alternative which scores highest according to some criterion can be chosen).[23] They imply a more frequent interplay between the management scientist and manager with different objectives than normally assumed. These benefits, if they are achieved, can be considerable, but they seldom are realized. In the next section some obstacles to their attainment are explored.

## Obstacles to Reaching Benefits

In general, few of the implementation failures of management science are due to inadequate or incorrect analyses from a technical viewpoint, and this is also true for the benefits described here.[24] The obstacles appear to be human.

In a given situation let us assume applicability of management science to the problem and technical competence on the part of the management scientist. Under such circumstances there are three main, interrelated reasons why the benefits fail to be realized:

1. Improper expectations about the purposes of the analysis and of each party for the other.
2. Strongly held preconceptions by each about the nature of the problem or about a preferred alternative.
3. Sharp differentiation between the characteristics of the management scientist and the decision maker which impede an effective interface.

[23]See Churchman, Ackoff, and Arnoff [12].
[24]See Ackoff [1], Drake [16], Hammond [19], and Huysmans [22].

IMPROPER EXPECTATIONS ABOUT THE PURPOSE OF THE ANALYSIS AND ABOUT THE APPROPRIATE ROLES OF EACH IN THE EFFORT. The previous section described the more usual expectation about a management science analysis as being the delegation of the analysis of a relatively well-defined problem to the management scientist, the analysis leading to a "solution" of his managerial problem which, if sufficiently on the mark, will be adopted. The expectation implies a specialization of roles and a compartmentalization of activities. The manager is the "problem giver"; the management scientist is the "problem solver"; finally, the manager is the "problem decider." Each effectively does his own thing with a minimum of overlap. This image of the relationship also is implicit in the way researchers on implementation usually define successful implementation, namely whether management adopts the recommended course of action.[25] Further, others write of the main benefits implied above as "byproducts."[26] The cart is placed before the horse. Because of this, both the analyst and the decision maker will have a set of expectations (indeed, a mental set) which reduces the chance of achieving the main benefits. Each is geared up mentally for the wrong priorities.

The expectations affect their relationship and their roles in the problem-solving effort. Without structuring the relationship in a manner that actively seeks these benefits, they often are missed or only partially achieved. Meetings while the analysis is under way are held more to answer the management scientist's questions and to seek data than to discuss the problem. Preliminary results usually are not brought to the manager's attention, since they are only interim steps en route to the management scientist's "solution." Changed signals on the part of the manager regarding his perceptions of the problem are annoyances to the management scientist rather than progress in problem solving. The management scientist is perceived as a technical expert, and consequently suggestions of a business nature do not make it through the manager's cognitive filter. After all, what does a management scientist know about marketing or finance? Further, the management scientist often perceives himself as a technical expert and avoids exploring the nontechnical issues.

STRONG PRECONCEPTIONS. As mentioned in a previous section, functional fixedness, an overly strong mental set, can impede effective thinking about a problem. Such behavior can occur on either side of a manager/management scientist relationship. The manager may have a strongly held concept of his problem definition which is difficult to shake despite fresh insights from the management scientist. His mind already may be all but made up regarding the best course of action, making it difficult for him to accept analysis which strongly indicates that other alternatives may be preferable.

[25]See Ackoff [1] and Huysmans [22].
[26]See Buzzell [9].

In fact, he may have taken a public position from which it is difficult to retreat without loss of face.

For his part, the management scientist may be overly wed to a particular view of the problem, especially if it relates to a particular management science methodology. For example, it is not unusual for a management scientist to conclude quickly that a particular management problem is a "linear programming problem" or a "simulation problem" and then to view the problem from the resultant more narrow viewpoint. Indeed, he may feel a near compulsion to reach such a conclusion, because he is a technical expert and his strength lies in his expertise. If he has not formulated the problem in some management science framework, he feels he has not used his expertise and therefore has not done his job. The penchant to go in a particular direction may be heavily influenced by the person's particular management science expertise (for instance, he might be predominantly a mathematical programmer) or by the conventional wisdom of the literature (for instance, blending problems are linear programming problems). Having selected a methodology, he may have a particular formulation which strongly colors his perception of reality. The model becomes reality.

DIFFERENTIATED CHARACTERISTICS. The manager and management scientist are, with very rare exceptions, very different types of people along dimensions important for successful implementation. These differences can be the source of a fresh viewpoint which is the genesis of many potential benefits to the manager. On the other hand, they also can be obstacles to achieving those benefits.

The situation is akin to that observed by Lawrence and Lorsch where departments within organizations are differentiated along four dimensions.[27] Such differentiation is essential to the functioning of each department yet an obstacle to the departments working effectively together. Lawrence and Lorsch write about appropriate integrating mechanisms which allow for the benefits of differentiation yet permit the organizational units to work effectively with one another. The material in this section is inspired heavily by their notions of differentiation and integration, except that it is applied more to individuals than to departments.

There are eight dimensions along which such differentiations can be made, which have great influence on how the individuals work and think. As shown in Table 1, they are goal orientation, time horizon, comparative expertise, interpersonal style, cognitive style, problem definition, validation of analysis, and degree of structuredness required. In the following discussion, the characteristics of prototypical managers and management scientists along each of these dimensions are described. While these descriptions are intended to represent the model case, individual managers and management scientists may not have all their respective characteristics ascribed to

[27]See Lawrence and Lorsch [24].

them. What matters in the final analysis is the differentiation between the particular individuals involved.

The first dimension is goal orientation, goals and objectives that in turn motivate behavior. There are four aspects of goal orientation differences. First, the individual manager usually is oriented toward the subgoals of his particular department which are derived from the organization's overall goals. For instance, the marketing department seeks to increase sales whereas the production department seeks to reduce costs. In short, the individual manager tries to look good along dimensions on which he believes he is measured and which consequently affect his career and compensation.

The management scientist, on the other hand, while often interested in organizationally related goals, frequently is motivated by the desire for professional recognition in the eyes of other management scientists within his organization and externally (through writing articles).[28] While this goal orientation leads to high professional quality, it also is counterproductive in that the management scientist feels the need to be technically "elegant" or innovative when such elegance or innovation adds little to the managerial problem-solving power of his analysis.

The second aspect of differences in goal orientation is in the organizational viewpoint which is reflected in the explicit or implicit objectives or objective function used in the analysis of a decision. The manager is more likely to reflect the goals of the particular subunit with which he is affiliated, whereas the management scientist often reflects the goals of the organization as a whole. This difference is due in part to training (for example, it is "rational" for subunits of large organizations to maximize expected value for decisions that are small for the organization as a whole) and in part to organizational affiliation of the management scientist (he is often a member of a corporate staff). While the position taken by the management scientist is often in the best interests of the firm (or at least different), it conflicts with the way the managers respond to corporate control systems. For instance, a management scientist might prescribe that a regional manager in charge of exploration for an oil company should drill a particular well since its expected value of return is quite positive. However, the manager, whose compensation may in part be determined by the number of successful wells drilled, may prefer to attempt a safer well, whose expected value is less positive, because it has a higher success probability. Such subunit-versus-overall confrontations also arise when there are significant political considerations entering into a decision.

A third goal-oriented difference is the pragmatic, action orientation of the manager as contrasted to the normative, truth-seeking orientation of the management scientist. In his desire to make things happen, the manager seeks operational solutions given economic, human and organizational considerations and sees highly refined analysis, focusing primarily on eco-

[28]See Blau and Scott [4] and Heany [21].

Table 1: Potential sources of interface problems: differentiation of management scientist and manager

|  | Manager | Management Scientist |
| --- | --- | --- |
| Goal Orientation | 1. Things recognized by control system: Sales, Profit, etc. (career)<br>2. Subunit goals<br>3. Pragmatic<br>4. Active, decision (ends) | 1. Professional recognition (career)<br>2. Organizational goals<br>3. Normative<br>4. Instrumental, analytic (means) |
| Time Horizon<br>1. Time for analysis<br>2. Time covered by analysis | 1. Shorter<br>2. Shorter | 1. Longer<br>2. Longer |
| Comparative Expertise | 1. High context<br>2. Low formal decision-making technology | 1. Low context<br>2. High formal decision-making technology |
| Interpersonal Style | Task or relationship | Task |
| Cognitive Style | Heuristic or analytic | Analytic (almost always more analytic than manager |
| Problem Definition | Loose, less explicit, often broader scope | More explicit, but narrower scope |
| Validation of Analysis | "Fit" and man who does analysis—shared values, track record, the way the analyst presents his results | Internal logic of model and sensitivity analysis |
| Degree of Structured-ness Required | Low/Medium | High |

nomic considerations as having relatively little incremental benefit over a looser analysis of broader scope. The management scientist, on the other hand, is wed to the code of the scientific method. He seeks the truth and the "right" answer with less consideration to the time and expense it takes to obtain it, how workable the solution is, or how acceptable it is to the human begins who have to implement it.[29] On the one hand, the careful reasoning of the scientific method is a powerful advantage, but many a manager becomes impatient with the time and energy requirements necessary to achieve its advantages, especially when the advantages of the extra effort are not all that clear to him.

[29]See Heany [21].

A final source of goal-oriented differentiation is that the management scientist is instrumental or means oriented and the manager is active or ends oriented. The management scientist is very interested in his methodology and the nature and content of his analysis. They are his ends. The manager cares about the resultant decision. By analogy, the management scientist is interested in the mode of travel whereas the manager is interested in arriving. This is a useful division of labor and attention, but it is also the source of conflict when the management scientist becomes so involved in his analysis that he loses sight of the decision problem that was its source or when the manager presses on with a decision without benefit of the management scientist's completed analysis.

The second major source of differentiation is between the individuals' time horizons. The manager's time horizon is usually shorter, being heavily influenced by the speed with which he gets feedback about the appropriateness of his actions or by the speed with which he is rewarded by the corporate control system. Ambitious, he wants the soundness of his decisions to be recognized quickly so he can advance in the corporate ladder. He often seeks quick payback alternatives, sometimes at the expense of others with a higher present value but longer payback.[30] Even when he is at the top of the corporate ladder, his time horizon is sometimes shortened by the fact that retirement is near, and he wants a superlative record while he is an incumbent. Further, he needs answers quickly to be responsive to competitive pressures and also must be responsive to deadlines in the corporate administrative protocols such as budgeting and planning.

The management scientist, on the other hand, takes a longer viewpoint. First, his analyses tend to optimize over the longer run. Second, while he tries to be accommodating to managerial deadlines, he frequently considers his job finished when he feels his analysis is "right" rather than when a decision is due. Further, this is exacerbated by the fact that completion times of his efforts are difficult to forecast due to the vagaries of computer program debugging and to the fact that the direction of his analysis cannot be plotted with certainty at the beginning. Unforeseen contingencies bias his time estimates on the optimistic side. These are a considerable source of frustration to the manager.

Another dimension of differentiation is their comparative expertise. The manager is more expert regarding the institutional aspects of the decision problem. For instance, a marketing manager knows more about marketing generally and marketing his line in particular than most management scientists. Concerning expertise in formal decision making methodology, the situation is reversed. The manager usually has little formal training in management science or advanced mathematics. At best, he is a former engineer whose mathematical skills have atrophied.

This difference in comparative expertise is at once a source of an ideal

[30]See Weingartner [42].

division of labor and a considerable problem in communication. The manager is frustrated that the management scientist speaks a strange and formal language and appears to have abstracted away important parts of his problem or to have made it unduly complex in a formal sense. He frequently concludes that the management scientist is impractical. The management scientist, on the other hand, is frustrated at the manager's inability to understand his analysis or its "obvious" implications. Because the manager lacks academic credentials and has difficulty understanding the analysis, and because he frequently does not see the "truth" or "wisdom" in the results of the analysis, the management scientist occasionally ends up thinking of the manager as "stupid." Of course, as soon as the manager senses this or the management scientist senses the manager's scorn, the relationship between the two is further strained.

Regarding language, there is a double danger of miscommunication. First, there is the danger of plain, simple misunderstanding, which is apparent to at least one of the parties at the moment. Second, there is the danger of seeming understanding when in fact there was miscommunication. Language and jargon have a way of permitting people to talk about things where the words they use have meanings they do not really understand. The author has done some interesting analysis with Drake's raw data, which indicates an asymmetry in feeling about ease of communication between project director and client, the project director more frequently feeling communication was easier than the manager did.

Another dimension of difference, often a less sharp one than the foregoing, is interpersonal style.[31] Management scientists are more likely to be preoccupied with getting the job done when they deal with others (so-called task-oriented interpersonal style) whereas managers may be task oriented or they may pay more attention to maintaining relationships with their peers (so-called relationship oriented). One might expect, for example, a plant manager to be task-oriented whereas sales and marketing managers, who are accustomed to being concerned with customer relations, might care more about fostering positive social relationships among their coworkers. When such a difference exists between the manager and management scientist, it can lead to frustrating interpersonal relationships, which unlike some of the previously mentioned differences do not have associated positive benefits.

Cognitive style is a dimension of differentiation which is receiving increasing attention in management science literature, and it is certainly one of the most important.[32] Many schemes for classifying cognitive styles exist. Most distinguish between people who are analytic or systematic in their reasoning (have a conscious problem-solving method in mind as they deal with a problem) and heuristic or intuitive (have a less formal problem-

[31]See Lawrence and Lorsch [24].
[32]See Huysmans [22], McKenney [28], Morris [29], and Doktor and Hamilton [15].

solving approach which is less conscious). Whatever classifying scheme is used, it is generally acknowledged that the management scientist is at the analytic end of the scale and that the manager is more likely to be at the heuristic end or, if somewhere in between, less analytic than the management scientist.

For instance, Huysmans characterizes the analytic cognitive style as reasoning through a more or less explicit model built up from a core set of underlying relationships to search for an "optimal" solution.[33] The heuristic approach relies on analogies with familiar, solved problems, common sense, intuition and unquantified "feelings." It is difficult to discover the mechanisms that lead to a decision under heuristic reasoning. (In terms of Figure 2, it would be difficult to chart the progress of a particular decision through the processes shown.) The analytic approach considers "externalities" not explicitly in the model only insofar as they might require a significantly different course of action than the one suggested by the model solution. The heuristic approach has no externalities, since all is considered to be an organic whole. From laboratory experiments with subjects dealing with business issues, Huysmans concluded that the chance of adoption of management science recommendations was higher with analytic managers. Further, from among those who had adopted the recommendations, heuristic managers needed continual follow-on support to insure continued use of the management science results, whereas analytic managers often could operate independently with the results of the management science analysis once introduced.

The consequences of the frequently observed difference between the cognitive styles of the manager and the management scientist are both positive and negative. Clearly, systematic problem-solving approaches associated with an analytic style are powerful tools for increasing the quality of decisions in many situations. However, the frequent assumption (especially by management scientists) that analytic is universally better, is incorrect in important situations. Heuristic problem solvers tend to be very good at solving unstructured problems.[34] For instance, Roy and Miller report an experiment where a complex, deterministic problem-solving task was solved quicker by experimental subjects educated in the social sciences than those educated in the natural sciences.[35]

When the two people have different reasoning styles, interface is difficult. Having been steeped educationally in the need for clearly articulated, logical reasoning and being analytic and intelligent himself, the management scientist gets impatient with the seemingly "sloppy" reasoning of the manager. Worse yet, he may often react scornfully to the manager's thinking, or at least the manager frequently feels that he does. The manager

[33]See Huysmans [22].
[34]See Reitman [31].
[35]See Roy and Miller [32].

sometimes feels as if he has been put in a straight jacket with the rigidly prescribed decision-making protocols of the management scientist.

Closely related to cognitive style is the way the two participants define problems. The management scientist's definition frequently is very explicit but somewhat narrower, abstracting out dimensions of the problem that do not lend themselves to quantitative treatment. On the other hand, the manager's looser, broader definition includes considerations not covered in the management scientist's definition. Further, the manager's test for the correctness of his definition is based on internal criteria, which include a heavy input of his own values, whereas the management scientist's definition is validated by external criteria, in some sense "universals." Since good problem definition is essential for good solution, the two approaches are potentially complementary, the management scientist helping the manager to sharpen his problem definition and the manager providing breadth. However, again, this can be the source of discord, the manager rejecting the management scientist's definition as being too narrow and the management scientist becoming impatient with the manager for being too vague.

Just as they differ in problem definitions at the beginning of the problem-solving process, so do they also differ at the end, when an analysis is being validated. The management scientist validates his analysis primarily on the basis of its internal logic and the appropriateness of its input. If they are correct, then the output should be correct. The manager will look less at the logic and inputs than at the results. He will check the way that they seem to "fit" with what he expects and what seems reasonable from a business viewpoint. He also will base his validation in part on his assessment of the management scientist. Rosenblum has shown that when a manager must act on the advice of others in complex situations outside his field of expertise, he will judge the quality of the analysis by the man who does the analysis.[36] This includes the track record of the analyst; the degree of confidence the analyst projects in presenting his analysis; the degree of shared values, problem-solving style, and experiences between him and the analyst; and the use of advisors to evaluate advisors.

Unfortunately, most management scientists are not mindful of this difference when they present and justify their results to their manager clients. They tend to overemphasize the logic and internal workings of their models rather than the sensibleness of the results from the management viewpoint and the dimensions mentioned by Rosenblum. The result is considerable miscommunication.

A final dimension on which the two differ is in the degree of structuredness required in situations. Because the manager is accustomed to dealing with inherently less structured situations, with more than one "right answer," it is less troublesome to him to work in a world of low structure. Reaching conclusions and taking action without chasing after every dimen-

[36]See Rosenblum [33].

sion of the problem is routine. Ambiguity is more a source of anxiety to a management scientist, used to a structured way of viewing everything and having everything specified before deciding. The inability to "prove" a right answer is a source of great frustration. The result is over structure on the part of the management scientist or the tendency to deal only with the more structured parts of a problem, a source of frustration to the manager. A complementary feeling on the part of the management scientist is serious doubt about the quality of the manager's decisions reached without externally apparent structure.

To reiterate, the above discussion of commonly observed differences between managers and management scientists is not intended to indicate that in a given situation the manager and management scientist will be differentiated along all lines according to Table 1. The discussion is intended to describe the kinds of differences that can be expected and their impact on the potential success of a joint effort. Indeed, there is a real danger of stereotyping a particular manager as being "management" instead of dealing with him according to his unique characteristics, and a similar danger in lumping all management scientists into a single class, a mistake which is frequently made.

### Summary and Implications

This article has focused on a particular type of problem where management science has had relatively less impact to date, namely the relatively unstructured, one-shot decision that is the responsibility of an individual manager. Taking a cognitive viewpoint, it has asserted that if management science is to be fully effective in dealing with such problems, it must offer a form of "personalized rationality" which requires a close relationship between the manager and management scientist.

An implication of this is a new role for management science in the analysis of these decisions, namely as a decision prosthetic rather than a decision maker. The goal of such analyses should be to augment, stimulate, and otherwise assist the reasoning of the manager instead of finding a "solution" of the management problem arising primarily from the management science analysis. The measure of successful implementation then becomes the degree to which the manager's problem solving is augmented and stimulated rather than whether the conclusions of the management science analysis are adopted.

Further, the relationship between the manager and management scientist must become a *process* leading to a decision by the manager rather than the creation of a *product*, namely the creation of a "solution" by the management scientist. This suggests more frequent interaction between a management scientist and manager, more intermediary results (interpreted in the manager's terms), analyses that are more responsive to the questions and concerns of the manager as his problem solving unfolds, behavior and analyses on the part of the management scientist which are purposely stimulating to the thought processes of the manager, and that the supporting models and formulations be flexible and evolutionary and have a quick turnaround. It also suggests that the management scientist attempt to draw out the manager's thinking in their encounters and that the manager in turn speak as freely as possible to the management scientist.

Because perceptions will affect their behavior, it is essential that the two participants clearly understand the difference between the decision-prosthetic and the decision-making role of management science and between the process and the product nature of their relationship and behave accordingly. Further, they must understand the benefits and pitfalls in their differentiated characteristics in order to make them worth living with on the one hand and easier to live with on the other. The goal should not be to eliminate the differences but rather to find ways of reducing their negative consequences while maintaining their positive ones. To put it in terms of a slogan, it is "specialization without compartmentalization."

One way of doing this is for each party to take conscious account of his own and the other's characteristics in their dealings and to respect one another's differences. Another is the possibility of using an integrator as a go-between.[37] This should be considered when the differentiation between the two parties is so extreme that a helpful, direct interface is impossible. The integrator then becomes the one who has the dialogues with the manager, interprets results and conveys and interprets the conversation to the management scientist, and the reverse. It is important that this integrator have characteristics and values shared by the manager and additional characteristics in common with the management scientist so that he can move effectively between the two camps. The author has seen this role being effectively filled at the top level of two large U.S. corporations. In each case the integrator was a respected vice-president acting as a bridge between senior management and younger analysts.

With proper understanding of this different role of management science in this setting and proper understanding of the obstacles to achieving the resultant benefits, the chances of successful results with this sort of decision should be considerably enhanced.

The prescriptions proposed here are not going to be easy to implement. The practices that they seek to change, the delegate the analysis-come back with a solution syndrome, are deeply ingrained in the way staff work generally and management science work particularly are usually done. The resultant roles of manager and analyst, compartmentalized ones, are well established and will be difficult to restructure. The interpersonal skill and mutual tolerance required to make it work are substantial. In addition, the mode of problem solving proposed is somewhat more time consuming than the traditional kind. Furthermore, since the benefits articulated here are

[37]See Lawrence and Lorsch [24].

more difficult to measure than the adoption or rejection of a recommendation, they will be more difficult to justify. Finally, the differentiation between manager and management scientist is substantial and real. Skill and art are required to obtain the benefits of the differentiation without destroying it.

As indicated at the outset, most of the diagnosis and prescriptions articulated here apply to good, top-level staff work, not just to the use of management scientists. The main difference is that management science, as a highly skilled, differentiated specialty, has the problems in the extreme.

### REFERENCES

1. Ackoff, Russell L. "Unsuccessful Case Studies and Why." *Operations Research* 8 (1960): 259.
2. Anthony, Robert N. *Planning and Control Systems, A Framework for Analysis.* Boston: Harvard Business School, Division of Research, 1965.
3. Bartlett, R. *Remembering.* London: Cambridge University Press, 1932.
4. Blau, Peter M., and Scott, W. Richard. *Formal Organizations: A Comparative Approach.* Scranton, Pa.: Chandler Publications, 1962.
5. Boning, Edwin G. "A New Ambiguous Figure." *American Journal of Psychology* 42 (1930): 444–445.
6. Broadbent, D. E. *Decision and Stress.* New York: Academic Press, 1971.
7. Brown, Rex V. "Do Managers Find Decision Theory Analysis Useful?" *Harvard Business Review*, May-June 1970, pp. 78–89.
8. Bruner, Jerome J.; Goodnow, J.; Austin, G. A *Study of Thinking.* New York: John Wiley & Sons, 1956.
9. Buzzell, Robert D. *Mathematical Models and Marketing Management.* Boston: Harvard Business School, Division of Research, 1964.
10. Cherry, Collin. *On Human Communication, A Review, A Survey, and A Criticism.* Cambridge: Massachusetts Institute of Technology, Technology Press, and New York: John Wiley & Sons, 1957.
11. Churchman, C. West. "Managerial Acceptance of Scientific Recommendations." *California Management Review*, Fall 1964, pp. 31–38.
12. Churchman, C. West; Ackoff, Russell L.; and Arnoff, E. Leonard. *Introduction to Operations Research.* New York: John Wiley & Sons, 1957.
13. Cyert, Richard M., and March, J. G. *Behavioral Theory of the Firm.* Englewood Cliffs, N.J.: Prentice-Hall, 1963.
14. deBono, Edward. *Lateral Thinking: Creativity Step by Step.* New York: Harper & Row, 1972.
15. Doktor, Robert H., and Hamilton, William F. "Cognitive Style and the Acceptance of Management Science Recommendations." *Management Science* 19 (1973): 884–894.
16. Drake, John W. *The Administration of Transportation Modeling Projects.* Lexington, Massachusetts: D. C. Heath, 1973.
17. Glucksberg, S. "Functional Fixedness—Problem Solutions and Functions of Observing Responses." *Psychonomic Science* 52 (1964): 117.
18. Gordon, William J. *Synectics.* New York: Harper & Row, 1961.
19. Hammond, John S. "Do's and Don'ts of Computer Models for Planning." *Harvard Business Review*, March-April 1974.

20. Hammond, John S. "Better Decisions with Preference Theory." *Harvard Business Review*, November-December 1967, pp. 123–141.

21. Heany, Donald F. "Is TIMS Talking to Itself?" *Management Science* 12 (1965): E-146 to B-155.

22. Huysmans, Jan. *The Implementation of Operations Research*. New York: Wiley-Interscience, 1970.

23. Keen, Peter G. W. "The Implications of Cognitive Style for the Design of Computer Systems." Harvard Business School Working Paper, HBS 72-43, November 19, 1972 (Quoted by permission).

24. Lawrence, Paul R., and Lorsch, Jay W. *Organization and Environment Managing Differentiation and Integration*. Boston: Harvard Business School, Division of Research, 1967.

25. Lindblom, Charles E. "The Science of Muddling Through." *Public Administration Review* 19 (1959): 79–88.

26. Little, John D. C. "Models and Managers, The Concept of a Decision Calculus." *Management Science* 16 (1970): B-466 to B-485.

27. Miller, George A. *The Psychology of Communications*. Baltimore: Penguin Books, 1969.

28. McKenney, James L. "Human Information Processing Systems." Harvard Business School Working Paper, HBS 72-74, 1972 (Quoted by permission).

29. Morris, William T. "Intuition and Relevance." *Management Science* 14 (1967): B-157 to B-165.

30. Raiffa, Howard. *Decision Analysis: Introductory Lectures on Choices under Uncertainty*. Reading, Mass.: Addison-Wesley, 1968, pp. 264–266.

31. Reitman, Walter. *Cognition and Thought: An Information-Processing Approach*. New York: Wiley, 1965.

32. Roy, J. E., and Miller, J. G. "The Acquisition and Application of Information in the Problem-Solving Process: The Electronically Operated Logical Test." *Behavioral Science*, Volume 2-4, October 1957, pp. 291–300.

33. Rosenblum, John. "General Managers and Technical Advisors." Unpublished Harvard Business School Doctoral Dissertation, 1972.

34. Sasieni, Maurice; Yaspan, Arthur; and Friedman, Lawrence. *Operations Research Methods and Problems*. New York: John Wiley & Sons, 1959.

35. Schlaifer, Robert O. *Analysis of Decisions under Uncertainty*. New York: McGraw-Hill, 1969.

36. Schon, Donald A. *Displacement of Concepts*. London: Tavistock, 1963.

37. Simon, Herbert A. *New Science of Management Decision*. New York: Harper & Row, 1960.

38. Simon, H. A., and Newell, A. "Information Processing in Computers and Man." *American Scientist*, 1964.

39. Simon, H. A., and Newell, A. *Human Problem Solving*. Englewood Cliffs, N.J.: Prentice-Hall, 1971.

40. Swalm, Ralph. "Utility Theory—Insights into Risk Taking." *Harvard Business Review*, November-December 1966, p. 123.

41. Wagner, Harvey M. "The ABC's of O.R." *Operations Research* 19 (1971): 1259–1281.

42. Weingartner, H. Martin. "Some New Views on the Payback Period and Capital Budgeting Decisions." *Management Science* 15 (1969): B-594 to B-607.

# B. Communication and Implementation

## 3. ORGANIZATIONAL FACTORS RELATED TO OPERATIONS RESEARCH PROJECT GROUP EFFECTIVENESS

*Robert D. Amspoker, J. Randall Brown, Robert D. Smith, and Robert H. Culhan*

### Introduction

An empirical investigation was initiated in late 1971 of fourteen operations research project groups to identify and evaluate organizational fac-

Editors' Note: Reprinted with permission from American Institute for Decision Sciences *Proceedings*, Fall 1973, pp. 102–105.

tors related to group effectiveness. The operations research groups studied were concerned with a wide range of technically oriented tasks within a billion dollar, diversified, industrial corporation.

The project groups which were studied functioned for varying lengths of time from 1967 through 1972 and were generally comprised of less than 13 members. Each group was comprised of employees from three corporate areas—the operations research department (OR), the corporate division which requested OR assistance (USER), and the management information organization (SYSTEMS).

The general procedure followed by an operations research project group can be described as follows: The operating division initiates a request for help from the operations research department for solution of an existing problem. An operations research analyst is appointed to work on the problem with a representative of the operating division. Either at this point in the life of the project group or shortly thereafter, a representative from management information organization is included in the operations research project group. The group members then jointly determine their course of action and the information which will be required to solve the existing problem. To follow this procedure, a high degree of interaction is required among the project group members. The USER representatives must provide the OR analyst with a detailed description of the problem and the inter-workings of the operating division. The OR analyst must have a knowledge of the available operations research techniques and models and how these tools can be used to help the operating division. The SYSTEMS representatives must provide technical programming help as well as financial and accounting data needed by the project group. A great amount of information, therefore, is transferred among group members as well as between group members and individuals external to the project group.

The operations research groups which were evaluated in this research effort were concerned with a variety of projects in the corporation's operating divisions. Table 1 provides a brief description of the project groups investigated.

## Data Gathering Techniques

The availability of published information on the functioning of operations research project groups is extremely limited, but that which is available tends to indicate that the problems and difficulties of the groups which were investigated in this study are typically encountered. Radnor and Rubenstein [2], [3] indicate that there are a number of factors which influence the effectiveness of operations research project groups. Among these factors are relations with clients and top corporate management, the backgrounds and personality characteristics of group members, and

| Project Group | Project Description |
|---|---|
| Pilot Study | Management information system |
| 1 | Division planning model |
| 2 | Inventory control model |
| 3 | Cold draw tube simulation model |
| 4 | Division venture analysis |
| 5 | Long range planning model |
| 6 | Detailed parts forecasting model |
| 7 | Ingot weight calculation model |
| 8 | Material selection model |
| 9 | Business planning model |
| 10 | Corporate venture analysis |
| 11 | Project selection model |
| 12 | Production scheduling model |
| 13 | Component parts forecasting model |

the role taken by the group leader. Consideration of these factors plus a comprehensive review of the small group literature [4] resulted in an investigation and evaluation of 12 organizational variables. Each organizational variable was evaluated relative to the empirically determined differences in project group effectiveness.

The research data for the study was obtained from personal interviews with group participants. The interview was initiated with a brief statement about the purpose of the study and that it was being conducted with the approval and cooperation of corporate headquarters. Interviewees were guaranteed anonymity in their responses.

The interview consisted of 65 questions which were asked of each interviewee. The initial questions were concerned with a definition of the particular problem under study and a listing of the members on the operations research project group. A series of questions then attempted to obtain information about the internal and external communication patterns of the project groups. Demographic information on each interviewee was gathered by a series of questions related to the group member's educational and industrial background. Finally, information related to the project group positive interaction qualities and the individual personalities was obtained from the last two series of questions. Initially, it was thought that the length of the interview might be detrimental to obtaining interviewee cooperation. The reaction of the interviewees, however, to the method of data gathering was extremely gratifying. The vast majority of the project group members showed a great enthusiasm in not only supplying information but also in learning of the research results.

It has been hypothesized that the project groups being investigated had significantly different degrees of success in completing their stated objectives. Since this study considers project group effectiveness as the dependent variable under investigation, considerable discussion will be given regarding the measurement and evaluation of project group effectiveness.

Each interviewed project group member was asked to evaluate the effectiveness of his project group by responding to the following interview question.

How effective do you feel your group was
in completing its objectives?

completely       1   2   3   4   5       extremely
ineffective                              effective

This particular method for evaluating project group effectiveness was selected for two reasons: (1) *group members seemed to provide very candid responses to the effectiveness interview item, and (2) the effectiveness responses which were obtained, represented the viewpoints of OR, USER, and SYSTEMS corporate area employees.*

The project group effectiveness measures for the operations research project groups were averaged to provide a single group evaluation score. The average project group effectiveness scores ranked from a low of 2.50 to a high of 5.00. Inspection of these average effectiveness measures indicated four distinct sets of project groups: Set A (project groups 1, 2, and 10); Set B (project groups 6, 8, and 13); Set C (project groups 7, 9, 11, and 12); and Set D (project groups 3, 4, and 5). Set A contains the least effective project groups; Set D contains the most effective project groups.

Jonckheere's k-sample test [1] was used with the empirically obtained data to test the null hypothesis that the average effectiveness scores for the four sets of project groups are not significantly different. This null hypothesis is tested against the alternative hypothesis that the effectiveness scores are arranged in ascending order from Set A through Set D. Jonckheere's test involves the procedure of counting the number of items which are larger in all succeeding samples. The maximum number of larger sample items is then subtracted from twice the observed larger items to give Jonckheere's test statistic S.

Jonckheere has shown that with a fairly large number of items in each group, the distribution of S approaches a normal curve with a mean of zero and a calculable standard deviation. The research data resulted in a standard normal deviate of 2.563. The probability of obtaining a z value of 2.563 by random chance is only .0104. The null hypothesis that the average effectiveness scores for the four sets of project groups are equal can be rejected at approximately a 1% significance level. The statistical test results, therefore, support the hypothesis that there was a significant difference in project group effectiveness. Specifically, the average effectiveness of the project group sets increased from A through D.

Jonckheere's k-sample test was also used within each of the four project group sets to determine whether differences existed in the average effectiveness of the project groups within each set. In all four sets, the calculated test statistic S was negative indicating acceptance of the null hypothesis that no significant difference exists in the average project group effectiveness scores within each of the four groupings.

## Organizational Factors and Project Group Effectiveness

There was a significant difference between the four sets of project groups in terms of the perceived effectiveness with which they met their stated objectives. It was concluded that there was not a significant difference between the four sets of project groups in average group size, group member demographic characteristics, group member personality characteristics, or perceived task sophistication. The significant differences in effectiveness were, therefore, not attributed to these group or individual characteristics.

Members of each of the project groups studied communicated with individuals external to the group. In evaluating the methods used for external communication, the four sets of project groups exhibited definite preferences for face-to-face rather than telephone or written communications. This preference existed regardless of the effectiveness of the project group set.

The average number of external contacts made per project group set was evaluated in relation to effectiveness. It was concluded that the average number of external contacts made by the four sets of project groups was not significantly different. The average number of external contacts made by the perceived group leaders was also compared between the sets of project groups. Again it was concluded that the perceived group leaders within each of the four sets did not differ in their number of external group contacts. The significant differences in grouping effectiveness were not attributed to the average number of external contacts per project group set or to the number of external contacts made by the perceived group leaders.

There was, however, a significant positive relationship ($\tau = 0.5345$) between the number of external contacts made by the perceived group leaders and their group effectiveness ratings. The higher the number of external group contacts made by the perceived group leader, the higher the group leader's group effectiveness rating. This relationship has been interpreted to indicate that a bargaining process takes place between the perceived group leader and individuals external to the group. The result of this bargaining is inferred to result in a compromise between what the perceived group leader wants the group to accomplish, and what individuals external to the group expect the group to accomplish. If this line of reasoning is correct, the number of external contacts made by members of the most effective project groups will be larger than the number of contacts made by the less effective groups. This situation was observed, but the number of ordering inversions was too large to conclude that the average number of external contacts made by members of the most effective groups was significantly greater than the average number of contacts made by members of the less effective groups.

Five reasons were identified for using external group communication. The frequency of use and perceived importance for each reason for external communication was evaluated in relation to effectiveness. In reviewing the frequency-importance ratings for the five uses of external communication, it is felt that a great deal of the external contact was politically expedient, but did not help the group accomplish its "technical" task. It was concluded that the group members did differentiate between the frequency of use and the perceived importance of the five reasons for external communications, but the agreement between frequency-importance ratings was poor. The groups were not using external communication for the reasons which they perceived most important for successful project completion.

The internal communication patterns of the operations research project groups were evaluated in relation to the amount of time spent on internal communication, the group members to whom communication was directed, and the content of the internal communication. It was determined that the project groups, regardless of the effectiveness set to which they belonged, spent essentially the same average number of hours on internal communication.

There was, however, a significant difference between the average hours the perceived group leaders in the four groupings spent on internal communication. The perceived leaders in the least effective set of project groups spent significantly more time on internal communication than did the perceived leaders of the three more effective project group sets. Perceived leaders in the most effective project group set spent less time on internal communication than did the leaders of the least effective project group set but significantly more time than did the perceived leaders of the two moderately effective project group sets. In evaluating these test results, there appears to be a plateau effect associated with the amount of perceived leader internal communication. The perceived group leader must be an active participant in internal group communication. To a certain point, the more active the perceived leaders are in internal group communication, the more effective will be the group. However, there seems to be an upper limit to this phenomenon. If the perceived group leader monopolizes internal communication, the average effectiveness of the group declines.

The distribution of communication within each project group was also evaluated. It was concluded that the average number of communication hours directed toward the identified members of each project group was not significantly different.

It was determined that the most effective project groups directed a significantly higher average number of internal communication hours toward representatives from the USER corporate area than did the less effective groups. Due to this internal communication distribution, the project groups in the most effective set were felt to have developed a better understanding of what the USER expects the project to accomplish. Based on this understanding, the members of the most effective groups perceive a better chance for successful project implementation than did the members of the less effective groups.

The operations research project groups had definite preferences for face-to-face rather than telephone or written methods of internal communication. This preference was evident regardless of effectiveness. The perceived group leaders in the least effective project group set also spent more time using face-to-face internal communications than did the leaders in the more effective sets. These findings support the conclusions previously reported regarding the amount of internal communication attributed to the perceived group leader. An excessive amount of face-to-face communication is apparently not conducive to project group effectiveness. It is felt, therefore, that a balance between the three methods of internal communication must be achieved to promote group effectiveness. This balancing is viewed as a method of assuring that vital internal information is shared among all group members.

The four project group sets did not differ in their perceived adequacy of internal group communication. The four project group sets did differ, however, in their average positive interaction qualities. The most effective set had the highest positive interaction qualities and the least effective set had the lowest positive interaction qualities. The positive interaction qualities are measures of the extent to which the members of a project group are friendly, cooperative, share important information, and are judged competent in performing their assigned tasks. The higher positive interaction qualities of the most effective groups are considered to be closely related to the internal communication characteristics of these groups. The perceived group leaders, by being active participants in internal group communication, are felt to be providing the guidance necessary to develop a friendly, cooperative atmosphere in which important information is shared among group members. The most effective project groups also directed more communication toward group USER representatives. This communication characteristic appeared to promote a feeling of group single-mindedness in reaching a task solution that would be useful to the operating division.

Conversely, in the least effective groups, the perceived leaders monopolized internal communication time which seemed to have a negative influence on group positive interaction qualities. The least effective groups also did not differentiate between corporate areas in the distribution of their internal group communication. It is felt, therefore, that the members of these groups did not develop a strong feeling of providing help to the operating division.

## Conclusions

The operations research project groups which were investigated in this research study differed significantly in several organizational factors which are felt to be related to group effectiveness. Initially it was determined that a significant difference exists in the effectiveness with which the operations research project groups met their stated objectives. This difference in effectiveness could not be attributed to differences in group size, group composition, or the perceived sophistication of the operations research techniques used.

The perceived group leaders in the least effective groups appeared to monopolize internal group communication. The perceived group leaders in the most effective groups took a more active internal communication role than did the perceived leaders in the moderately effective groups, but they did not monopolize internal communication. The most effective operations research project groups also directed a greater amount of their internal communication to representatives from the USER corporate area than did the less effective groups. These internal communication characteristics, both individually and collectively, are felt to have resulted in the high feeling of trust and cooperation which existed in the most effective groups.

While a significant difference existed in the perceived effectiveness of the operations research project groups, all groups were considered to have completed their "technical" task requirements with essentially the same degree of success. The differences in measured effectiveness are thought to be dependent upon how well the group members perceived the project could help the operating division and upon the probability of successful implementation. These two characteristics were positively influenced by the internal communication patterns of the most effective groups and negatively influenced by the internal communication patterns of the least effective groups.

There was also evidence that considerable portions of the external communication used by the project groups did not help the groups accomplish their "technical" task but probably increased the chance of successful project implementation.

REFERENCES

1. Jonckheere, A. R. "A Distribution Free k-Sample Test Against Ordered Alternatives." *Biometrika*, KLI, No. 2 (1953): pp. 133–45.
2. Radnor, Michael; Rubenstein, Albert H.; and Bean, Alden S. "Integration and Utilization of Management Science Activities in Organizations." *Operations Research Quarterly* XIV, No. 2 (1968): pp. 117–41.
3. Rubenstein, Albert H.; Radnor, Michael; Baker, Norman R.; Heiman, David R. and McColly, John B. "Some Organizational Factors Related to the Effectiveness of Management Science Groups in Industry." *Management Science* XIII, No. 8 (1967): pp. B508–18.
4. Selected citations from the literature survey are listed below.
   a. Allen, Thomas J., and Cohen, Stephen I. "Information Flow in Research and Development Laboratories." *Administrative Science Quarterly* XIV, No. 1 (1969): pp. 12–19.
   b. Burgess, Robert. "Communication Networks and Behavioral Consequences." *Human Relations* XXII, No. 2 (1969): pp. 137–59.
   c. Carzo, Rocco, Jr. "Some Effects of Organizational Structure on Group Effectiveness." *Administrative Science Quarterly* VII, No. 4 (1963): pp. 393–424.
   d. Hackman, J. Richard. "Effects of Task Characteristics on Group Products." *Journal of Experimental Social Psychology* IV, No. 2 (1968): pp. 162–87.
   e. Hackman, J. Richard and Vidmar, Neil. "Effects of Size and Task Type on Group Performance and Member Reactions." *Sociometry* XXXIII, No. 1 (1970): pp. 37–54.
   f. Hayes, Donald P.; Meltzer, Leo; and Lundberg, Simon. "Information Distribution, Interdependence, and Activity Levels." *Sociometry* XXXI, No. 2 (1968): pp. 162–79.
   g. Huff, Frederic, W., and Piantianida, Thomas P. "The Effect of Group Size on Group Information Transmitted." *Psychonomic Science* II, No. 10 (1968): pp. 365–66.
   h. Morris, Charles G. "Task Effects on Group Interaction." *Journal of Personality and Social Psychology* IV, No. 5 (1966): pp. 545–54.
   i. Mulder, Mauk. "Communication Structure, Decision Structure, and Group Performance." *Sociometry* XXIII, No. 1 (1960): pp. 1–14.
   j. Pelz, Donald C., and Andrews, Frank M. *Scientists in Organizations: Productive Climates for Research and Development.* New York: John Wiley, 1966.
   k. Steiner, Ivan D. "Models for Inferring Relationships Between Group Size and Potential Group Productivity." *Behavioral Science* XI, No. 4 (1966): pp. 273–83.
   l. Zimet, Carl N., and Schneider, Carol. "Effects of Group Size on Interaction in Small Groups." *Journal of Social Psychology* LXXVII, No. 2 (1969): pp. 177–87.

# 4. THE COMMUNICATION OF THE RESULTS OF OPERATIONAL RESEARCH TO THE MAKERS OF POLICY

## B. D. Hankin

Michael Faraday said that there were three steps in useful research; the first to begin it, the second to end it and the third to publish it. In operational research I suggest that to publish it is not nearly enough. In the broadest possible sense of the word we have to "*communicate*" it. The aim must be to get the results and conclusions studied, respected, understood and fully considered in the formulation of policy. I suggest that the success of operational research must in the end be judged by the influence that it has upon the making of sound policy. If this is true it is very important indeed because it means that the duty of all operational research workers is not only to use scientific methods to analyse a situation or to deduce a most suitable line of policy. In subtle ways they must also use every part of their work to influence the making of policy without treading on the toes of those responsible for it. Some scientists may regard this as unethical, but what is the use of their work unless they take all permissible steps to make it effective? In this approach lies the philosophy behind this paper. It is one of the reasons why operational research is so fascinating and is the main reason why I consider operational research to be quite as much an art as it is a science.

### Factors Affecting the Acceptance of Operational Research Results

The table which follows analyses the principal factors which I consider may contribute to the acceptance of the results of operational research at management level.

From the analysis contained in Table 1 I draw the important conclusion that the acceptance of the results of a piece of operational research does not begin at the report stage. The process starts at the beginning of the project and is greatly affected by all previous work.

### Effect of Stages Leading Up to the Report

I think it will be readily accepted that the reputation of an operational research section is based on past work and that this certainly has a bearing

Editors' Note: Reprinted with permission from *Operational Research Quarterly*, March 1958, pp. 293–301.

*Part IV: Implementation*

on the acceptance of the results of any new work. My contention is that nearly every detail in the execution of any new project also contributes to the ease with which the results can be communicated and to the chance that they will be accepted. I suggest that the following are important.

TERMS OF REFERENCE. These need very careful study and drafting, usually by operational research personnel in conjunction with management. Well-chosen terms of reference help to get a good job done in a reasonable time. They help to steer the operational research approach and to prevent management saying at a later stage, "You have not done what I wanted, your results are of little interest."

AGREEMENT ON THE TIME AVAILABLE. It is important both to management and to the operational research section to reach mutual agreement on the time scale in mind before a project starts. Most work can take years to complete if it is done extremely thoroughly or if it has only a small effort allocated to it. On the other hand, management may be better satisfied by something a little less complete, carried out much more quickly. The speed with which a project can be completed, and the meeting of an agreed date has an important effect on the interest with which management will study the results and on the chances of their being accepted.

BUILDING UP CONFIDENCE. Every stage of the work must be directed towards building up confidence in the accuracy, impartiality and value of the results which eventually come out. In my own organization certain projects are tackled by committees whose chairman and secretary are operational research men, and whose members are from the departments who are affected by the particular project. The bulk of the work must be done by research staff assisted by suitable observers who come under their supervision. The departmental members are useful in making arrangements for research within their departments, for expressing departmental viewpoints and for conveying information and confidence to their departments as the work proceeds. This system may slow down the work slightly, but it can be very valuable in getting the results speedily accepted.

There are many other ways of assisting in building up confidence. I will mention only a few:

1. Enthusiasm, efficiency and thoroughness on the part of all concerned in the research.
2. Preparedness to "get dirty," to really understand and share the lives and hardships of human beings who may be involved in aspects of the study. (To study soldiers you must live with them. To study bus conductors it is best to begin by doing their job, if only for a relatively short time.)
3. Reaching the stage where it is accepted that research staff know more about many aspects of the problem than anyone else.

*Table 1: Principal factors affecting the acceptance of operational research results*

| Principal Factors Affecting Acceptance by Management | | Supporting Details | Lessons for Operational Research Section |
|---|---|---|---|
| Reputation of the operational research section | | Sincerity<br>Impartiality<br>No desire for personal kudos<br>Square, honest co-operative dealing<br>Thoroughness<br>Reliability<br>Accuracy<br>Usefulness | Choice of operational research personnel of suitable character and quality at all levels. They all contribute to the reputation produced by past and present work |
| Confidence in the work and methods used in a particular project | | A conviction is necessary that the methods used are likely to have produced reliable results and are going to add something useful to the knowledge or understanding already available | Nothing less than the most enthusiastic, well planned and thorough examination possible with the time and staff available<br>Visits by appropriate members of customer dept. to observe research in action<br>Co-operation in the project by the department involved who will feed back impressions of how the work is undertaken |
| Some prior knowledge of results of the particular project | | New information is often more readily accepted and understood if it is fed in gradually | Participation in the work by the user department where possible. Feeding in and discussion of results and drafts prior to final report |
| Methods of presenting results | Any information | Simplicity<br>Clarity<br>Well argued and logical<br>Capable of speedy absorption<br>Attractively presented | An important part of the work of all but the most junior operational research personnel. Both arts and science are equally involved |

*Table 1: Continued*

| Principal Factors Affecting Acceptance by Management | Supporting Details | Lessons for Operational Research Section |
|---|---|---|
| Unpleas- ant in- forma- tion | Tact<br>Recipient should be helped to avoid losing face or appearing foolish<br>Gradual and early infor- mation to avoid shock and to give opportun- ity to put it right | |

PLANNING FOR INTELLIGIBILITY AND ACCEPTANCE. The operational researcher is constantly faced with decisions as to how he should plan his data collection or his analysis. How should he classify something? What measures or stan- dards should be adopt? He should constantly bear in mind that his methods must be practical, realistic and as simple and intelligible as possible to those who will study his report. In this way the planning and execution of his work can assist in getting it accepted. I would not rate his skill by the length of his formulae or the scientific jargon he displays. What counts is that he should get results which really matter and see that they are under- stood.

WOOING THOSE IN RESPONSIBLE POSITIONS. The responsibility for accepting the results or recommendations of a report is often in the hands of a small num- ber of people and their advisers. Throughout a piece of operational re- search, it is clearly wise to study the mentality, views and reactions of these individuals, with the object of securing their interest and co-operation, and thus preparing them to accept the results of the work. If any part of the data collection phase is of interest to them, it is sometimes useful to invite them to pay a visit to see it being carried out.

CIRCULATION OF DRAFT REPORT. The circulation and discussion of a draft report is a most valuable way to assist in "communicating" it and getting it accepted. The user department is warned of the results in advance and can start to act on them if it wishes. The operational research section should make the draft as near perfect as possible, but if there is misunderstanding, or if there is wrong emphasis, it can be discussed and cleared up. The con- clusions and recommendations can be debated and challenged without either side losing face.

## Use of a Report for "Communicating" Results

I have purposely given considerable emphasis to the stages prior to a report, because I think their importance from the point of view of "communication" is not well understood by some operational researchers. The presentation of a good report is also a very important part of any operational research.* It requires much imagination and skill and far too little attention is given to it by many workers.

## Deciding on the Objectives

Before writing an operational research report the author should clarify his objects, which are frequently as follows:

1. To "communicate" the results of work to policy makers and to stimulate action if recommendations have been included.
2. To inform others who may be interested.
3. To provide a tidy record of scientific data and method for easy reference.

Every report should be considered on its merits which should be adjusted to suit the particular objects in view. Many authors would improve their reports out of all recognition if they would apply the following dictum:

> The material in the main part of an operational research report should be severely restricted. Without failing in its objects, it should minimize by all available means the time and mental effort demanded from the policy maker. Everything else which may be necessary should be relegated ruthlessly to appendices.

## Factors Affecting Good Communication by Means of a Report

If the time and mental effort demanded from the reader of a report is to be reduced to a minimum, it is worth examining the factors which affect them. They depend on a complex interaction of many effects which include the following:

1. Pre-knowledge of the subject by the reader.
2. The intelligence, quickness and freshness of the reader.
3. The quantity of information to be communicated.
4. The ability of the report to foster or maintain the interest of the reader.

*It is of interest to note that some operational research workers are experimenting with methods of presenting results to management in a "presentation session," thus reducing the labours of report writing and report reading.

5. The method or combination of methods chosen for communicating each part of the information (e.g., prose, table, diagram, photograph, etc.).
6. The skill with which the chosen methods are used (layout and visual appeal, style, selection of material, clarity, etc.).

It can be assumed that at this stage the author cannot do very much about (1) or (2), and that in his mind he has already reduced (3) to the minimum. He is then left to do his best with (4), (5) and (6). In tackling these three aspects of his problem he must draw heavily on his imagination and artistic experience, and rather less on his scientific training. It is also apparent that the imaginative and artistic skills required are similar to many of those commonly used by authors, journalists, advertisers, schoolmasters and artists. Operational researchers should therefore study these professions and borrow from them everything which may be of use to them.

### Methods for Communicating Information in a Report

In communicating information in a report the author has four principal methods to choose from:

1. Words in the form of prose (or slightly simplified versions, such as notes)
2. Tabulated information
3. Diagrams and charts
4. Photographs

It is common experience that information can frequently be communicated more efficiently (i.e., understood in a shorter time and with less effort on the part of the reader) by some form of visual presentation rather than by the use of words.

It is also considered by many people that information acquired from a visual presentation is more easily remembered than when it is received through the medium of the printed word. These statements suggest the need to exploit visual aids to the full in the presentation of our reports.

### Skillful Use of the Chosen Methods

It would be quite impracticable to attempt to describe all the skills connected with the presentation of material. I will mention only a few.

STYLE OF WRITING. Good English is a foundation for any good writing, but I venture to suggest that an operational research report needs a style very different from that usually demanded in a work of high literary merit. The former will probably be "skimmed" by a very busy man in an office, while the latter is intended for pleasure in an armchair at home. I think that we have much to learn from the concise, crisp style of writing taught to military staff officers. The technique is based on the demands and experience of battle where it is important to save time and words, to be absolutely clear, and to communicate with very busy people who may be extremely tired.

LAYOUT, EMPHASIS AND VISUAL APPEAL. Aesthetic satisfaction in the visual sense is produced by a subtle interrelationship between the shapes, sizes, colours and textures of the component parts forming a whole. Emphasis can be produced by suitable arrangements of shape and colour in relation to the background and adjoining areas. Examples of this can be seen in the "appointments vacant" pages in newspapers and periodicals; the modern tendency is to buy more advertisement space than is necessary, in order to attract attention by leaving some of it empty. Good layout and good visual appeal have an important effect on the communication of information.

PAPER AND PRINT. Some operational research sections are forced to try to save a pound or two per report by using cheap paper. This may be a false economy by virtue of the bad effect it produces on the readers. The texture, quality and colour of paper and the spacing and variety of the print can assist in "readability" and in variation of emphasis. I recommend any operational research section who has not yet done so to give consideration to the advantages of machines such as the Vari-typer which is a composing typewriter which gives a variety of changeable type sizes and styles of type with square "justified" margins.

USE OF PHOTOGRAPHS. There are many ways of using suitable photographs to illustrate and add interest to a report, as shown at the end of this paper.

METHODS OF REPRODUCTION. There are now excellent methods for quickly and cheaply reproducing typewritten material, diagrams, photographs, maps, etc. They include very satisfactory systems of enlarging or reducing. A working knowledge of what can be achieved is most helpful in planning the report from the point of view of "communication."


### The Balance Between Science and the Arts in Operational Research Personnel

I hope it has become clear that in my opinion scientific qualifications alone will not carry a man far in operational research. Even if work is of excellent scientific quality, it is of very limited value if it fails to "communicate." I have tried to indicate some of the ways in which the chances of successful "communication" can be improved, and to show that nearly all of them depend on qualities other than science. It depends in the end on the people we employ, on the broadness of their education and experience and on their ability to draw upon the arts as well as upon science. In my view this has a considerable bearing on the selection and training of operational research staffs.

## Conclusions

1. Operational researchers should regard it as their duty to use *every* part of their work to take all permissible steps to influence the making of policy. (They should of course be extremely careful to avoid treading on the toes of those responsible for it.)
2. The process of communication of the results of operational research should start at the beginning of a project. The ease with which it can be set in motion will be affected by all previous work.
3. The principal factors affecting the success with which communication is achieved are:
   a. The character and quality of operational research staff at all levels.
   b. The reputation produced by their personal contacts and by their past work.
   c. The way a particular project has been handled (in order to prepare the way for acceptance).
   d. The way the results are presented.
4. The preparation of a report which "communicates" well is an imaginative and artistic exercise requiring considerable skill and experience. Operational researchers can learn much from authors, journalists, advertisers, schoolmasters and artists.

### USES OF PHOTOGRAPHS IN OPERATIONAL RESEARCH REPORTS

1. A photograph can convey much information in a quick and interesting manner.
2. A photograph can reduce the length of a report and save the time of the reader.
3. A photograph may convince, where a paragraph of text may not.
4. A photograph can suggest things which it may not be possible to mention specifically in the text.
5. Successful operational research as a whole must contain an essential backbone of science but must also contain a considerable measure of the arts. This has an important bearing on the selection and training of operational research staffs.

which may be useful on the communication of results

Beer, Stafford. George Bray Memorial Lecture on the Scope for Operational Research Industry. *J. Inst. Production Engrs* 36, 5 (1957): 298–32.

Bernal, J. D. "Scientific Communication." *The Social Function of Science*, Chap. II (1946). London: Routledge (first published 1939).

Braddock, A. P. *Psychology and Advertising*. London: Butterworths, 1932.

Burt, Cyril. "A Psychological Study of Typography." *Brit. J. Statis. Psychol.* 8 (1955): 29–58.

Cauter, T. and Downham, J. S. *The Communication of Ideas*. London: Chatto and Windus, 1954.

Cherry, Colin. *Human Communication*. London: Chapman and Hall, 1957.

Chisholm, Cecil (ed.). *Communication in Industry*. London: Business Publications, 1955.

Crowther, J. G. "Science in Business." *The Social Relations Science* 523 (1941). London: Macmillan.

Gowers, Ernest. *Plain Words—A Guide to the Use of English*. London: Her Majesty's Stationery Office, 1948.

———. *A.B.C. of Plain Words*. London: Her Majesty's Stationery Office, 1951.

Green, A. T. and Dodd, A. E. "Knowledge—Passing It On and Getting It Used." *Symposium of the Direction of Research Establishment*, Paper 17. London: Her Majesty's Stationery Office, 1957.

Huxley, Aldous. "The Nature of Explanation." *Ends and Means*, 11. London: Chatto and Windus, 1937.

Knapp, Reginald O. *The Presentation of Technical Information*. London: Constable, 1948.

Mansfield, P. J. *The Complete Journalist*. London: Pitman, 1936.

Turner, E. S. *The Shocking History of Advertising*. London: Michael Joseph, 1952.

Warde, Beatrice. "New Light on Typographic Legibility." *Penrose Annu.* 50 (1956): 51–5.

———. *The Crystal Goblet*. London: Sylvan Press, 1955.

Weaver, Lawrence. *Exhibitions and the Arts of Display*. London: Country Life, 1925.

# 5. THE ART OF EXPOSITION

*The Rt. Hon. the Earl of Halsbury*

I once attended a lecture by Sir Lawrence Bragg on the art of lecturing. In introducing his subject he commented: "Anyone who has the nerve to pick this subject for a lecture is asking for trouble." His fears I need hardly say were groundless, for what followed was a model of its kind.

I realize that in talking about the art of exposition I am running a similar risk. My excuse for the attempt is twofold. Firstly, the subject interests me; secondly, it has topical importance for the members of the Operational Research Society, one of whose preoccupations is the presentation of their work in intelligible form to colleagues or employers who may not share their technical and mathematical knowledge.

I know of few pleasures greater than that of watching the growth of understanding in a fellow-mind as the result of instruction and tuition for which one is responsible. In so far as pleasure can be altruistic, I would say that this must rank high among the list of those that are.

There is another pleasure, of course, in arranging one's own knowledge so that it forms a neatly ordered scheme based on minimum assumption and maximum compression so that it is as formally compact as possible. It is primarily egocentric. Other minds at one's low level of sophistication may, of course, enjoy the formalism but that is not the motive for which that formalization was undertaken. It is a selfish pleasure, but, as all work and no play makes Jack a dull boy, why should we forbid it? It may even be useful, albeit inadvertently.

There is a third pleasure to be obtained from writing about the history of a subject that is being taught. On the scale of altruism and egocentricity, it appears to stand intermediate between the extremes.

I will call these three kinds of exposition didactic, logical, and historical, and the first point I want to make is that each may involve a different order so far as the presentation of the subject's component elements is concerned.

Order is something unique. An ordered sequence cannot have two different orders. If, therefore, the didactic order of presentation does not naturally coincide with the logical or historical order, something has to be sacrificed. That something has to be sacrificed is the recurrent theme of this paper.

The first questions that an expositor must therefore ask himself are "Why am I writing this?" and "Whom am I writing it for?"

These questions are extremely important when any kind of technical

Editors' Note: Reprinted with permission from *Operational Research Quarterly*, March/June 1960, pp. 1–15.

exposition is addressed to a non-technical reader, inasmuch as there is a much wider gulf in vocabulary to be bridged than in other situations.

If you will consider the study of classics, literature, history, political economy and, to a large extent, law, you will notice that they are taught very largely in the vocabulary of everyday life. There are, it is true, a few technical terms which occur in each by way of abbreviation or nick-naming, but they are usually avoidable and, if not, can be readily explained. If you have not studied poetry you may not know what a caesura is, but on being told that it is a natural pause occurring in the middle of a line, you will have no difficulty in assimilating the term. If you have not studied history you may not be familiar with the Donation of Constantine but it will be easy for you to follow a simple explanation of what it was—a forgery in terms of which the Papacy claimed to be heir-at-law to the Roman Empire in the West. Even the technical terms of law often carry a suggestion of what they mean: "pleading," "indictment," "interroga-tory," for example.

But the jargon of technology has no such ready connexion with every-day speech. Even an intelligent classicist who could guess correctly at the derivation of words such as "catalyst" or "entropy" would find his knowledge of little avail in using it to deduce the precise sense in which they are used technically, and on encountering nicknames such as Cara-theodory's Principle or the Ergodic Hypothesis, no simple prose explanation could suffice to give him an inkling of what these names stood for.

In attempting any particular piece of exposition, it is therefore essential to ask oneself these questions:

1. Why am I writing this? For my own amusement or to convey information to some third party?
2. To whom, if anyone, is it addressed? What sort of a person do I suppose him to be? What background of general science and mathe-matics may I assume? Am I a specialist reporting to a layman? Or a colleague writing for an equal? Or a junior reporting to a senior?
3. How many words am I allowed for my purpose?
4. What can I hope to say to the person I am writing it for in the number of words allowed? What do I want him to end up with as a result of reading what I am going to write?
5. How am I going to do it?

Before I come to consider these points in detail, I want to dispose briefly of the reasons for which Arts graduates generally enjoy a better reputa-tion than Science graduates as expositors of what they want to convey.

In the first place, they usually have a much easier problem on their hands and can cut their teeth on easy stuff while they gain experience. The scientist only too often has to tackle something intrinsically difficult from the start.

In the second place, Arts graduates get more training in essay writing

*Part IV: Implementation*

than scientists during the formative periods of their careers. They are required to write essays regularly and these essays are subject to criticism, not only for content but for style and manner of presentation, by academic staff who are themselves heirs to a stylistic tradition. Such essays as are written by science students will be judged more for their factual content than their style, and if stylistic failings are pointed out to them it will only rarely be by one who is himself a master of style.

Thirdly, there is practice. Writing is quite hard work. Writing well can be very hard work. To do hard and difficult work well, without prohibitive effort, needs a lot of practice, practice which for the most part scientists don't get for the good reason that they don't, in the literary sense, get called on to write very much.

Ask any distinguished author—the type of man who has twenty or thirty works to his name—what he thinks of his early work. Many such authors would criticize their earlier work as showing faults of inexperience and immaturity. Consider, accordingly, how many scientists ever write twenty to thirty textbooks thereby acquiring the polish that distinguishes the mature author? Probably not one has ever done so in the history of scientific literature. Textbook authors probably produce one work in a career-time. Why then should one suppose that the author's first (and only) work would be, in the technical sense, well written?

With this much preamble let me consider the five questions I have asked above.

(1) *Why am I writing this? For my own amusement or to convey information to some third party?* This question is basic because there is no reason why a man should not write for his own amusement. But unless, when writing for his own amusement, he also writes *well*, there is equally no reason why anyone should bother himself to read it. And if the object of the exercise is to convey information to a third party and no information is conveyed, the exercise fails of its purpose. Much expository work is, in my opinion, bad because the author has never faced up to this issue. His finished effort is cast before his readers almost with the words: "Here's some pearls, you swine!" I have said earlier that didactic exposition is altruistic. Failure to be clear as to why one is expounding something is an essentially egotistic failure.

(2) *To whom, if anyone, is it addressed?* It may, of course, be no more than lecture notes intended to save students the trouble of taking their own. In these circumstances it may serve a useful purpose even if it is unintelligible to anyone not attending a course of the author's lectures. Duplicates of such notes are often sold for general consumption but in my opinion few of them are clear enough to merit general circulation. Aristotle's *Nichomachaean Ethics* has survived across twenty-two centuries by this process and though historians of philosophy may be grateful for it, I doubt if professional philosophers get much satisfaction out of its obscurities. More commonly what issues from the pen of a lecturer,

reader or professor, is a textbook, probably his only work and probably immature in consequence. It is often said of textbooks that they are not really intended to be read save as the accompaniments of a lecture course. Speaking as one who obtained his degree by exclusive reading of textbooks and by total non-attendance at lecture courses, I am not prepared to accept this excuse. Well-written textbooks can be clear as crystal; the reason that reading most of them is torture and that they are incomprehensible without first-aid from a lecturer or director of studies is that they are badly written. The ideal textbook is one that should be crystal clear to any student with the assumed background. So much for a master's writing, to be read, say, by his pupil. What of the reverse process in which a junior is reporting to his senior? To the question "What sort of a person do I suppose him to be?" there can be only one answer in modern times, to wit: "An extremely busy man." It is precisely in these circumstances that an egotistical junior, incapable of writing save for his own pleasure, merits, and probably receives, the undying hatred of his senior for the infliction of yet one more pile of *bumf* to take home at night. In writing for a senior it is well to assume that there was a time when the old man knew twice as much about the subject as oneself, since when he has forgotten half of it; but that it doesn't matter, as he will find his own way back to whatever he needs. He doesn't want a refresher course in the form of an essay. He wants a note of the current situation, of recommendations for action requiring his authority and the reasons for it, together with advance notice, below panic threshold, of anything liable to involve him in difficulties of his junior's making.

It is quite otherwise when tabling monthly reports for the perusal of colleagues. I was once responsible for a laboratory which turned out somewhat massive test results. To prevent my own thoughts falling into confusion and to ensure that my records were periodically straightened out, I wrote a monthly report. I wrote it primarily for myself. Since it had to be legible in future time, manuscript was contraindicated and I had it typed, thereby making copies available for colleagues on a research committee of which I was a member. Everyone took up a copy, but I don't think anyone ever read it; it wasn't intended for that purpose. I of course annexed a page of foolscap drawing attention to any results that mattered. Experimental results that matter sufficiently to require the notice of colleagues do not generally happen with a frequency that requires more than a monthly note.

So much for colleagues. You can treat them more or less as you please because they are in a position to retaliate. All's fair between equals. Blind them with science if you can and scatter triple integrals about your reports, but don't ever try that technique on a layman, especially if he is your senior.

Remember that that is exactly what he expects you to do and will react with exasperation at your first attempt: "What the hell is a Poisson distribution? Why can't this so-and-so write English?" Queen Victoria never liked Mr. Gladstone because he addressed her as if she was a public meeting. There are ways of writing a report which evoke a like hostility in the reader. Face up to the realities of the situation. Is your putative reader a mathematician? The answer must be "yes" or "no." If he is not, do not try and squeeze in a little mathematics with a shoehorn just because *you* are interested in it. This is the egocentric sin: to write for yourself and not for your reader. Your difficulty may be that the subject appears inexplicable without some mathematics and much more interesting with them. Your task is to overcome that difficulty, not to run away from it. If you can't find a way round it, leave it alone and don't write the report. Go to your reader and discuss the difficulty with him. If he's a class of reader, pick a representative sample. If he's your senior, say: "I am due to give an account of my stewardship but it's a horribly technical one. Can you give me some help over what you really want to know?" He'll be delighted to do so, will begin to trust you at once, will happily leave all the technicalities to you, and will tell you what he wants to know which is probably quite simple. Can he, as *your* boss, tell *his* boss that you are earning your keep or are likely to do so within a reasonable period? If you are in operational research you are probably paying for yourself ten times over annually and all you have to do is to quote some results and put in for a rise! A week later he'll be telling *his* boss or his Board, "What I like about my boffins is that they just seem to work for the pleasure of it. If I could only get a few more like young so-and-so, we'd be increasing our dividend twice as often as we do."

Maybe your imagination boggles at the idea of anyone not being a mathematician. If imagination fails you, approach the problem intellectually and ask yourself "Am I an endocrinologist?" (Do you know what ICSH, ACTH and LH are or where the Islets of Langerhans are situated?) Continue, "If then I, being a mathematician, know nothing of endocrinology it is reasonable to suppose that there may be endocrinologists who know nothing of mathematics."

From the standpoint of technique much may be expounded with graphs that would cause alarm and despondency if expressed in analytical form. The National Institute of Industrial Psychology is one of my interests; I am Chairman of its Executive and Research Committee. My colleagues are concerned with policy from the standpoint of controlling the sort of research that is undertaken and ensuring that the results are of interest to industry. They include businessmen, engineers, trades unionists, administrators, representatives of D.S.I.R., and professors concerned with the academic aspects of the subject. Results have as often as not to be reported to them in terms of correlation coefficients and levels of significance, of all of which subjects the lay-members of the Committee are, broadly speaking, ignorant. We have therefore arranged a wall display in the committee room consisting of a number of scatter diagrams each representing some characteristic value of a correlation coefficient between familiar variables. We are accordingly in a position to report results simply by saying "The result looks like *that* [pointing at a scatter diagram] and the connexion between the variables is about the same as that between the price of milk and cheese on the same day." As a result of this simple approach harmony reigns between the technical and non-technical members of the Committee.

A refusal to recognize the limitations of readers accounts for much bad exposition of a semi-popular variety. Frequently some publishing house commissions a work with popular appeal to the educated. The author wants to use the Laplace Transform, say, because it is his pet toy. As a sop to Cerberus he therefore writes an introductory chapter in three parts:

1. A refresher course in algebra
2. Elementary calculus
3. Introduction to the Laplace Transform.

He now feels free to mix his popular exposition with unpopular mathematics and the result is a thoroughly bad book. It will be bad because, in spite of the introductory chapter, it will be incomprehensible to the layman and superficial to the mathematician.

(3) *How many words am I allowed for my purpose?* This must be settled in advance. A textbook may be from 120,000 words upwards. A popular work will be about 60,000 words, the length of a light novel, say. A lecture will permit about 6,000 words and an article in a paper like *The New Scientist* from 1,500 to 2,000. Very occasionally one is asked to rewrite an essay review and given freedom up to 10,000 words, but these essays appear in high-class journals which don't make a profit, so that one is lucky to get £5 for the job! The length of a technical report or paper in the journal of a learned society depends upon the complexity of the subject matter.

(4) *What can I hope to say to the person I am writing for in the number of words allowed?* This is a problem which many expositors fail to solve. One can usually say *something* in a sentence, e.g., "Biochemists are those who attempt to describe biological functioning in chemical terms." A second and a third sentence will not really enable one to say much more. To go significantly further one must have *substantially* more latitude. On going further, however, one meets a fundamental difficulty. Is the reader supposed to be a chemist or not? If not, then one must face the impossibility of introducing him to the whole of chemistry in part of a paper in order to render the whole intelligible with reference to only a part of chemistry.

There must be a limit *somewhere* at which biochemistry transcends the understanding of the non-chemically minded. Between the limit and another set by the possession of a degree in chemistry there is a sort of

*Part IV: Implementation*

dead-zone in which nothing can be done for the layman. Outside these limits what one can say depends on the number of words allowed for saying it. One cannot hope to say in 1,500 words what would require 15,000. Something has to be sacrificed but the exact nature of the sacrifice has to be thought out.

The spoken word conveys less than the written word, for in a spoken lecture the audience cannot pause to rehear something they have not taken in as a reader can pause to reread an obscure paragraph. In communicating engineering terms there must be more redundancy in a lecture than in a written essay. In a discursive didactically homogeneous lecture such as the present one, this difficulty is not so acute.

One point well made will be of more value than two points veiled in obscurity or doubt. If from this lecture tonight you take away the thought that expounding your results is as technically difficult as getting them and requires as much preparation and forethought, I shall have made the one point I seek to.

(5) *How am I to say it?* Here I can only offer a piece of negative advice. Do not suppose that your first thoughts on the matter will necessarily prove adequate. They may in special circumstances, but the odds are against it, so be prepared to have to rewrite what you have written again and again until it conforms to some ideal of perfection in your own mind. The reason that I cannot say more is that I have no fixed pattern to which I work. Sometimes I have brooded over a subject for years, waiting for an opportunity to go on record. When the opportunity comes, I may already have the subject worked out in my mind and can commit it to paper spontaneously in a form which needs little subsequent revision. On most occasions I have to write and rewrite to get it as I like it. *In extremis* I write a first draft in order to have something to bite on. It is usually a slapdash, bull-at-a-gate-affair, egocentric, diffuse, overlong and with some essential facts blank or filled in with guess-work. At this stage I have, so to speak, got the subject out of my system and can approach it dispassionately. Having done so I can start to try and identify the reader. This and considerations of length settle what I am going to omit and what I am going to emphasize, and I can go to draft 2 which represents the solid basis of what I am going to write. At this stage a lot of fact checking is done as a result of which my own thinking begins to evolve and the presentation begins to rearrange itself in my mind. Consequently, new paragraphs get inserted with pins in the course of the revision, old paragraphs get rewritten and scissors and paste get to work, cutting the whole thing up and rejoining it so that the presentation follows my latest ideas. The resulting mess could be called draft 3, and a terrible mess it often is at this stage. Draft 4 then emerges from draft 3 stylistically homogenized and rewritten in longhand for retyping. At this point I try and get finality over two matters of style and form originally specified by Aristotle:

1. The thing must have a backbone. It must be about something in particular, not everything in general.
2. It must have a beginning, a middle and an end.

Draft 4 may then get "tried out on the dog," sometimes a member of my family enlisted for the purpose. They are all non-technical and if the verdict is "incomprehensible," then I must begin again because what one non-technical person finds incomprehensible another will find the same. I do not wish you to suppose that everything I write needs this treatment. A broad spectrum of birth-pangs lies between the extremes of spontaneity and agony represented by the foregoing examples. Very often the document is not an essay but a committee report in which paragraphs from different hands are inserted. In this case I always try and ensure that the mass at stage 3 is rewritten in longhand and homogenized by a single author who can be relied on to write good English.

Notwithstanding all of which care and trouble, I have of course my failures like everyone else.

I want now to turn to two illustrations, one of bad and one of good exposition.

For bad exposition I will quote generally from my examination of some essays submitted in a competition intended to foster improvement in the presentation and exposition of technical matter by technical writers. The terms of reference included the following:

1. *Intention.* The essays were to be readily understood by
   a. Other scientists
   b. Directors of industrial firms
   c. Others interested in the advance of science and technology.
2. *Requirement.*
   a. About 3,000 words
   b. The essay should disclose
      (1) The scientific background
      (2) The experimental results
      (3) The potential application of the project or process in industry.
3. *Assessment.* The essay was judged on
   a. Technical content
   b. Presentation
   c. Style.

I found very little evidence that the great majority of the candidates had taken the slightest trouble to read their terms of reference, let alone to think about them. Many made no attempt to confine themselves to 3,000 words. A number merely submitted departmental research reports by permission of their employers, apparently unaware that the whole character of these reports was out of keeping with the objects for which the competition was instituted. There was little evidence that any of them had been revised so as to comply with requirements of presentation and style.

Now let me turn to the first part of the above terms. It presents a problem inasmuch as three *different* classes of readers are presupposed:

1. *Other scientists.* This *must* mean scientists working in *other fields*; for an article written to be read by other scientists in the same field would merely be a technical paper.
2. *Directors of industry.* There is no reason to suppose that a director of industry has any scientific background at all. He may be a salesman, a lawyer or an accountant. Alternatively, if he is in the scientific instrument industry he may know quite a lot about it.
3. *Others interested in the advance of science and technology.* This does not state what the interest is supposed to be nor whether it is material or intellectual.

Now, it has to be remembered that the essays were commissioned by judges in a competition, not by editors in a journal. Nothing prevented any candidate from making a note to the effect that he was exploiting the latitude given by the incompatible backgrounds of the supposititious readers so as to select *one* of them as his target. Only one candidate made any attempt to do so, however. Many others made a vague compromise between the requirements of (1), (2) and (3) and produced something both dull by criterion (1) and incomprehensible by criterion (2). The majority, however, seemed to have no particular reader in mind; they just wrote what came into their heads. The result was, to my way of thinking, very disappointing. It only indicated that most of the candidates hadn't a clue as to what was expected of them.

I now come to a more cheerful topic illustrating good exposition and for this purpose I have chosen what I regard as a modern masterpiece in textbook form: *The Structure of Physical Chemistry* by Sir Cyril Hinshelwood. Remembering that the author is not only President of the Royal Society but literate in seven languages, one would of course expect something good, but the excellence one discovers is not merely literary; it is expository excellence. The author makes you feel that he wants you to love the subject as he does, and ends up by making you do so. Anyone who really knew this book would know all he needed and he could learn it without attending a single lecture for it is all lucid from the first word to the last.

I want you to note the title: *The* Structure *of Physical Chemistry*. It gives you a foretaste of what you will get by reading it. You will in fact acquire inside your head the intellectual structure in terms of which physical chemists do their thinking. *The structure*: neither emasculated by formalism nor cluttered with obscuring detail. Let us turn to the introduction where the author tells us what he is going to do and why he is writing the book. In his own words:

> Physical chemistry is a difficult and diversified subject. The difficulty can, of course, be overcome by a suitable intensity of application and the diversity dealt with in some measure, by judicious specialization. This is very well as far as it goes, but leaves something to be desired, because there is, it is to be hoped, still room for a liberal occupation with wide studies, and this in a manner which goes beyond the polite interest of the dilettante. In the light of a good long spell of University teaching, however, I have the impression that this aspect of the matter is in some danger of neglect. I thought, therefore, I would like to write a book of moderate compass which, in no way competing with more formal works, should lay emphasis on the structure and continuity of the whole subject and try to show the relation of its various parts to one another. Certain themes or, one might almost say, leitmotifs, run through physical chemistry, and these would be used to unify the composition.
>
> The treatment would be neither historical, nor formally deductive, but at each stage I would try to indicate the route by which an inquiring mind might most simply and naturally proceed in its attempt to understand that part of the nature of things included in physical chemistry. This approach I have ventured to designate humanistic. The proper study of mankind, no doubt, is man, but one of the greatest activities of man is to find things out.
>
> Apart from the question of seeing the subject as a whole, there is that of seeing it with a sober judgement. It seems to me specially important in modern physical chemistry to be clear and honest about fundamentals. This is not so easy as it sounds. Some of the current working notions are expressed in words which easily become invested with a more literally descriptive character than they deserve, and many young chemists—this is my impression at least—are led to think they understand things which in fact they do not. Something simple and direct seems to be conveyed by words such as "resonance" and "activity", which is not legitimately conveyed at all. By certain descriptions, which it is easy to give, one is reminded of Alice: "Somehow it seems to fill my head with ideas—only I don't exactly know what they are." Many of the mathematical equations which serve important technical purposes in the modern forms of theoretical chemistry are of a highly abstract kind, but they have acquired a dangerous seductiveness in that they clothe themselves rather readily in metaphors. Occasionally it is salutary to regard this metaphorical apparel with the eyes of the child who surveyed the emperor's new clothes. I have done my best here and there to help the uninitiated reader keep in mind just what the content of theories amounts to.

The author, you see, has faced up to the problem I put to you earlier. His mind is quite clear on three points:

1. Why he is writing the book
2. The sort of book it is going to be
3. The class of readers whom it is intended to help.

The egocentric note is held in complete abeyance. Students are in danger of failing to see the wood for the trees. The book is to help them perceive their subject as a whole. It is not an egocentric expression of the author's personality as writer but an altruistic expression of sympathy with the personality of the reader.

The chapters that follow embody a most skillful blend of logical and didactic orders. The subject not only unrolls in an order which makes it easy to learn, but each chapter follows logically on its predecessor as well. The order alone is a masterpiece of stage management.

It is organized into parts, sub-divided into chapters. Each part commences with a short summary in beautifully clear prose of what that part is going to be about and of the relation that it bears to its predecessors. I would dearly like to quote from many of these summaries, but I must refrain from reasons of space and time and confine myself to two extracts which, however, I will quote *in extenso*.

Part I is entitled "The World as a Molecular Chaos," and Part II is entitled "Control of the Chaos by the Quantum Laws." When I first read the title of Part II, I remember my pleasure at the chosen phrase—"Control of the Chaos by the Quantum Laws." As a professional chemist I was, of course, familiar with all that Hinshelwood wrote of and my reading had included a more rather than a less than average amount of quantum theory, but I had never seen the connexion in just that way before. That single phrase seemed to illuminate what I already knew, so that I saw it in a new light and the quality of my understanding was irreversibly altered. With this much preamble I now come to the two synopses.

*Part I*

Some of the ancient philosophers conceived the world to be made up of primordial particles in random motion, but their theories were not very fruitful since they lacked the necessary empirical basis. The formation of this was a long, complex, and far from obvious process.

Quantitative relations between the masses, and in certain cases the volumes, of substances which combine chemically establish the atomic theory as a scientific doctrine, and rather subtle coherence arguments reveal the distinction between atoms and molecules. Developments in physics lead to the recognition of heat as the invisible motion of the molecules themselves, and the kinetic picture of matter emerges.

Even in the first primitive version, this picture gives a satisfying representation of nature in many of its broad aspects. Molecules are envisaged as microscopic masses following the laws which Newtonian mechanics prescribe for macroscopic bodies. They are believed to be in chaotic motion and also to exert forces upon one another at small distances. Their motions tend to scatter them through all space: the forces to agglomerate them into condensed phases. The conflict between these two tendencies governs the existence of material systems in their various states, determines the range of stability of gases, liquids, and solids, and regulates the extent to which various possible combinations of atoms into molecules occur.

Reasonable estimates can be made of the absolute sizes, masses, speeds, and modes of motion of molecules, and coherent explanations can be given of many of the physical properties of matter in its different forms.

At this level of interpretation nothing is yet postulated about the forces, except that they manifest themselves in the measurable energy changes which accompany almost every kind of physical and chemical transformation. It is necessary, therefore, to describe the state of a chaotic system of particles primarily in terms of its energy. Such a description is provided in statistical theory.

In the world of molecular chaos various energy states are regarded as so many boxes occupied by molecules at random, and everything tends to that condition which may be realized in the largest number of ways. This idea leads to the definition of entropy, a function which measures the probability of a molecular assemblage, and to the laws of thermodynamics, which prescribe the conditions of equilibrium and the direction of possible changes in all such processes as expansion and contraction, melting and evaporation, and in actual chemical transformations. These laws themselves are closely related to empirical observations about heat-changes which can be used to provide an independent basis for them.

Given only an empirical knowledge of the energy changes accompanying atomic and molecular regroupings, the dynamical and statistical laws (or the equivalent thermodynamical principles) predict the relations of solids, liquids and gases for single substances and for mixtures, and also the dependence of chemical equilibrium upon concentration and temperature.

But the representation so made is limited in two ways. First, the forces remain unknown. The energy changes are measurable by experiment, but their nature remains unexplained. Secondly, the actual prescription of the condition of molecular chaos proves on closer inspection to present certain subtle problems which cannot be solved at this stage. If molecules are assigned to states according to the laws of probability, then what constitutes a state? In the first instance, equal ranges of momentum can be satisfactorily regarded as defining a series of states. But while this idea leads to valuable laws regarding changes in entropy, and the dependence of all kinds of equilibrium upon variables such as concentration and temperature, it leaves quite unsolved the question of the absolute position of chemical and physical equilibria.

Scientific explanations seek to describe the unknown in terms of the known. The first attempt to such an explanation of the material forms and relations of the world works in terms of particles which are themselves small-scale models of grosser objects. It goes a long way, but reaches a boundary beyond which it cannot pass.

*Part II*

As a result of a long series of intricate discoveries a solution is found to the problem of knowing where, in the absolute sense, this equilibrium lies between the different states of aggregation of matter and between the various configurations of atoms concerned in chemical transformations.

The first stage is the emergence of the quantum theory, according to which the energy of atomic or molecular systems varies discontinuously. The laws governing the various discrete series of possible energy states are discoverable from the study of such phenomena as specific heats and radiation. They evolve through different forms and are at length crystallized in rules whereby the energies are defined in terms of the permissible solutions of a semi-empirical differential equation, known as the wave equation.

The foundation of this equation is the discovery that on the scale of electronic or atomic phenomena particles obey dynamical laws which are neither precisely those followed by macroscopic masses nor yet those followed by light waves, but are of a special kind.

The new rules impart to the theory an abstract basis. Atoms and molecules can no longer be regarded as small-scale versions of ordinary objects. Furthermore, we have to conclude that there is no physical sense in treating different permutations of individual atoms or molecules within a given energy state as theoretically distinguishable systems.

Given these apparent sacrifices of the primitive simplicity, energy states become, in compensation, like so many exactly defined boxes, the allocation of molecules to which can be treated by the laws of probability. Absolute equilibria are now seen to be governed by the interplay of two major factors: on the one hand, the tendency of atoms and molecules to assume a condition of minimal potential energy, and on the other hand, their tendency to fill impartially all energetically equivalent states.

With the equilibrium of solid and vapour, for example, the potential energy factor favours condensation of all the molecules to solid. But in the vapour the range of possible energy levels is much greater and molecules populate states according, as it were, to the housing conditions, quantum levels representing in effect accommodation. Expressed in another way, the atoms and molecules escape from the restraints imposed by the forces acting upon them in so far as they achieve fuller self-realization in conditions where more modes of motion and more quantum levels offer them opportunity. The quantum theory having given exact formulations of the accommodation ranges, these statements can be translated into precise terms which lead to a quantitative treatment of all types of equilibrium.

At this stage the nature of the forces and of the interaction energies still remains unknown.

For those of you who are professional mathematicians rather than chemists or physicists I would recommend a study of Forsyth's *Theory of Function of a Complex Variable* as an object lesson in exposition.

It is longer than any work that a modern publisher would be prepared to support, the present costs of paper and typesetting being what they are. It remains a great work in my opinion because the author leads one on continuously throughout the course of an exciting adventure and never ceases to hold one's hand on the way. By contrast, modern formalized and compressed treatments of the same subject are about as intellectually stimulating as a breakfast of wet blotting paper.

What is the relevance of this to operational research? I think it is very relevant because operational research has to be explained and expounded to those who will benefit from it in order that they may employ it and do so. If operational research workers do not expound their work to actual or potential employers, it is quite certain that no one else will do so. And if they expound it badly or obscurely so that their techniques are undervalued and their skills lie fallow, it is the nation that will be the loser.

The exposition of operational research is attended by certain intrinsic difficulties. Nothing issues from it in the form of hardware which can be pointed to as "the result." Results show up in statistics of performance, rarely unmixed with, and often inseparable from, results derived by other methods. The merit of the operational researcher's work may be assessable only by accountants, themselves unable to follow his methods. By contrast colleagues in the engineering and physical sciences who may be employed alongside him and who are qualified to follow his line of thought may have no access to information which would confirm the success of his activities.

Many technical workers suffer from some of these difficulties; they are enhanced for operational research workers inasmuch as their technique is essentially mathematical and mathematics is the most forbidding and least popular of all subjects outside the ranks of its practitioners. I know many soldiers, sailors, tinkers and tailors who are quite respectable amateur engineers. I cannot recall one amateur mathematician.

If in these circumstances operational research workers expound their results so as to fall into any of the pitfalls of which I have spoken, the result can only be unfortunate.

May I at this stage say a few words about the problem of reporting to a *Board*, not a managerial Board responsible for local operations but the sort of non-executive Board that has overall responsibility to shareholders. You may only be called on to address such a Board once in a lifetime, but on that one occasion it is incumbent on you to be a credit to your profession. You will probably have at most a quarter of an hour. Don't make the mistakes of either trying to teach your audience about operational research in that time, or of condescending to them because they don't know what it is already. One member may be a solicitor, another a chartered accountant, a third a merchant banker, a fourth a sales director from another industry, and so on. You must assume that they have only two features in common. The first is ignorance of operational research. The second is a highly developed shrewdness in judging of men and affairs. They will be quick to assess your capacity for seeing your own subject in perspective, for distinguishing the wood from the trees. In these circumstances be simple and non-technical, and don't get into an argument about technicalities. If you are on a sticky wicket the chairman or the technical director will probably come to your rescue if you give them a chance. If what they say isn't up to your own standard of rigour, let well alone and shut up! You may know more of operational research than they do, but they know more about their colleagues than you do.

Now to some more specific problems.

I note that some difficulty has attended the definition of what operational research *is*. I was myself embroiled in similar difficulties over the definition of automation a few years ago. It was distressing to find that people will embark on definitions without any previous instruction in philosophy or formal logic, where definition is itself the subject of discussion. It is because expositors are floundering about in unfamiliar territory that they get into these difficulties. There is no excuse for them.

A definition may be "denotational" as in a dictionary. In this sense one may say that a dog is a quadruped that wags its tail and barks. If you know the meaning of "quadruped," "wag," "tail" and "bark," you then know what a dog is. Alternatively, a definition may be "ostensive," as when one shows an object to a child and names it so that the child may come to associate the object with its name. In this sense one points at a dog and says "dog." Every vocabulary must contain *some* names ostensively defined, and the object of the exercise is merely to enable people to use words correctly—that is, in a similar sense to that in which other people use them. From this point of view it is not necessary to say more of the words "operational research" than that "their meaning will become clear to anyone who reads what follows." This is to employ the ostensive approach. The game of reducing a vocabulary to the minimum number of ostensive elements is one we can leave to lexicographers.

In expounding work to laymen we must, I think, use the method of the catalogue so that the reader has before him a long list of problems which, though they may appear physically diverse, are nevertheless structurally similar and therefore describable by a single mathematical formula. We want the layman to recognize a queue under its diverse manifestation so that by thinking of service times and waiting periods he can call us in to help him with problems that have occurred to him as problems, not as Acts of God, or the Queen's Enemies.

Distributions—Poissonian, binomial and normal—require to be explained by examples from occurrences and by graphs for the purpose of illustrating properties. There is no reason why the layman should not learn to recognize a distribution that is Poissonian. It is as unnecessary for him to know about its mathematical description as it is for a spin-bowler to know the mathematics of gravitation and aerodynamics. Above all, this illustration must be in concrete terms and *copious*. An abstract presentation coupled to a solitary instance will achieve nothing.

Results need to be presented graphically and the graphs must be described in clear prose stating what they represent. Not even the simplest terms such as maximum and minimum should be hurried over. They may present unexpected difficulties to some layman and deserve a paragraph at their first occurrence and a sentence on subsequent occurrences. And, of course, graphs must be clearly labelled in practical units so that they come alive for the reader.

Finally, results must be quoted wherever possible in monetary terms. We must blow our trumpet a bit louder whenever we save something. These are perhaps rather vulgar considerations to be put forward in a presidential address to a learned society, but they spring from one simple proposition that has inspired the present work. The object of exposition is the transfer of information and understanding from the expositor to his readers or audience. If, in fact, nothing is conveyed, then the exercise has failed in its purpose. The most common reason for failure is attempting too much because the problem has not been seen as such and its associated difficulties correspondingly underestimated. Egotism is usually at the heart thereof.

# C. Organizational and Behavioral Factors

## 6. FACTORS RELATED TO THE IMPLEMENTATION OF OPERATIONS RESEARCH SOLUTIONS [1]

### *Lars Lonnstedt*

The use of mathematical models for problem solving in business has led to the development of a new type of specialist—the operations researcher. Operationally defined, operations research (OR) consists of a class of mathematical/statistical research techniques which have come to be utilized for solving problems likely to arise within organizations. Included

[1]This study constitutes part of a larger, international study under the leadership of Professor Michael Radnor, Graduate School of Business, Northwestern University.

Editors' Note: Reprinted with permission from *Interfaces*, February 1975, pp. 23-30, published by The Institute of Management Sciences.

among OR techniques are linear, non-linear, dynamic and heuristic programming, stock queuing and game theories, simulation and network planning. Some large companies have their own operations research divisions; others call in OR consultants when they are needed. In either situation problems can arise. These may be organizational problems, or problems arising from decision makers' (users') lack of familiarity with OR methods for problem solving. The following investigation attempts to shed some light on these questions.

## Research Design

SAMPLE. The study sample was composed of 107 OR projects proposed for implementation prior to the summer of 1970 in twelve companies listed on the Stockholm Stock Exchange. These 12 firms had their own OR divisions.[2] Of the 107 proposed OR projects, 29 were reported as not implemented by the user. The projects were generated by 25 separate OR groups.

DATA COLLECTION. Personal interviews were conducted with the chief of the operations research activity within the firm and with the 46 operations researchers who had been responsible for the different projects. Also, a list of the OR projects was compiled. In addition, the OR users were identified and given a questionnaire, concerning characteristics of the problem and the solution process. Telephone interviews were then held with those persons who had been the operations researchers' contacts on the user side. Since the same user could be connected with more than one project, the number of interviews was approximately 80.

NONRESPONSES AND THE POSSIBILITY OF GENERALIZATION. There were missing responses to some questions. A possible reason for such was uncertainty on the part of the respondents, particularly since many years had passed since the implementation of some of the projects. It will be clear from the presentation how these nonresponses modified the conclusion of this study.

Since neither the firms nor the projects were selected by random sampling, there is no statistical basis for generalizing beyond the particular cases under examination. The fact that all of the firms were large and located in Sweden makes it difficult to generalize to firms in other countries or to Swedish firms of different sizes. Therefore, there is reason to believe that some of the relationships found within the firms studied would not apply to the same extent in other samples. Nevertheless, certain

[2]The study by Nicander and Silvander, 1969, indicated those Swedish companies using OR and which of those had their own OR divisions.

*Part IV: Implementation*

relationships emerged from the research that were so strong that there is reason to believe that they could have general applicability.

## Collaboration Between Users and Operations Researcher and Proposal Implementation

One method for encouraging people to abandon an old and well-known way of doing things in favor of a new way is to engage them in carrying out the change (Bennis, 1966, Katz and Kahn, 1966 and Leavitt, 1965). This participation is intended to give the individuals involved in the change the chance to influence its shape and future application. There should, however, be a mutual exchange of experiences and a mutual adjustment. The one sponsoring a change should be in a position to explain the aim of the change and the reason for it. The same could be said about the introduction of OR procedures (see Radnor, Rubenstein and Tansik, 1970).

The user and the operations researcher should, consequently, collaborate in problem solving. In order to investigate the occurrence of such collaboration, the users in this study were asked if they participated in defining problems. Collaboration is probably also influenced by the identity of the project initiator. Since, according to the above, changes should be founded upon mutual cooperation, difficulties may arise if the operations researcher defines a problem which, in the users' opinion, does not exist.

THE USERS' PARTICIPATION IN PROBLEM DEFINITION. Users were asked if they had collaborated with the operations researchers in defining problems. As Figure 1 shows, the number of non-implemented proposals is greater when users did not participate in problem definition. (Chi-square = 19.1, $p < .001$.)

Missing responses accounted for 15 proposals. Of these, four were not

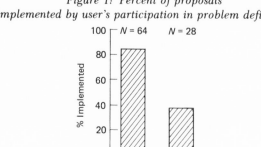

*Figure 1: Percent of proposals
implemented by user's participation in problem definition*

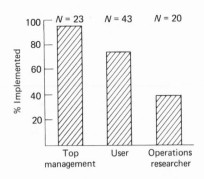

*Figure 2: Percent of proposals*
*implemented by status of project initiator*

implemented. One might conclude that the number of nonresponses does not affect what kind of relationship exists between non-participation in problem definition and proposal implementation. The respondent's memory can however be unreliable for such matters as participation in problem definition. Also, the data do not show what is cause and what is effect. A user finding an implemented problem solution to be very good, may later "recall" that he participated in defining the problem, whether or not this was actually the case.

INITIATOR OF PROJECT. All but one of those projects initiated by top management were implemented. Seventy-five percent of the projects initiated by the user were implemented. However, when the user regarded the operations researcher as project initiator, more than one-half of the projects were not implemented (Figure 2). (Chi-square = 16.7, $p$ = .001.)

In 21 cases no information was obtained as to the initiator's identity. Of those, five were cases of non-implementation. A large number of non-responses was due to the user's inability to decide whether project initiative came from top management or from the operations researcher. In spite of these nonresponses the findings indicate that there is a positive relationship between the identity of the project initiator and the implementation of projects. This confirms the findings of Collcutts (1965) and Heiman (1964).

When the question of the identity of the project initiator was put to the operations researchers, findings were similar, although from their perspective, the effect of the identity of the project initiator on project implementation was not as pronounced (Chi-square = 5.9, $p$ < .05). This is to be expected since the answers were an expression of the questioned persons' perceptions. The answers may also be a result of retrospective adjustment of the operations researchers' perceptions, and reflect an attitude of optimism toward proposals, regardless of the identity of the initiator. In addition, if the initiator of the project and participation of

*Part IV: Implementation*

user in problem definition are cross tabulated interrelations between them appear.

## Characteristics of the Problem and Proposal Implementation

Economic considerations and mathematical difficulties in the construction of models may require the operations researcher to make certain adjustments in his proposals and methods. In some cases such adjustments will limit the proposals to such an extent that they will be rejected by the user. One adjustment, made primarily for economic reasons, is limiting the scope of the problem to be solved. This can be done through eliminating variables or treating some aspects of a problem as given. On other occasions the scope of a problem may be limited by the researcher's inability to quantify variables or the unavailability of relevant data. Data which is not readily available can be obtained through research, but this requires additional time and money. Such limiting factors lead one to expect a connection between limitation of the problem, quantifiability of the variables and availability of the data on the one hand, and the implementation of related OR proposals on the other. In addition, one might expect an interrelation to exist between limitation, quantifiability and availability of the data.

LIMITING THE SCOPE OF THE PROBLEM. The operations researchers were asked if they had to limit the scope of the problem in constructing their models. Responses were categorized according to whether (A) the whole problem, (B) part of the problem, or (C) a small part of the problem was considered in model construction. An analysis of the responses reveals that proposals from models using a "small part of the problem" remained non-implemented to a much greater extent than the proposals from the two less limited models (Figure 3). (Chi-square $= 52.5$, $p = .0001$.)

The number of nonresponses (two) does not change the outcome to any

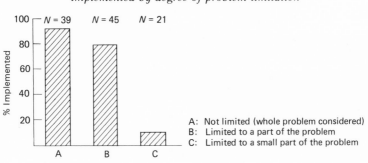

*Figure 3: Percent of proposals
implemented by degree of problem limitation*

A: Not limited (whole problem considered)
B: Limited to a part of the problem
C: Limited to a small part of the problem

significant extent. The conclusion is, therefore, that a relationship exists between problem limitation and implementation of the proposals studied. This is consistent with the conclusions of other researchers (see Ackoff, 1968).

QUANTIFIABILITY OF VARIABLES. The following three groupings indicate the extent to which the variables were quantifiable: (A) all variables of the problem quantifiable, (B) the most important variables quantifiable and (C) the most important variables non-quantifiable. As can be seen from Figure 4, the percent of non-implemented proposals is much greater for groups A and B than for group C. (Chi-square = 24.4, $p < .0001$.) There were only two nonresponses.

DATA AVAILABILITY. Data availability has also been divided into three groupings: A) data is already available, B) data must be collected and C) data is partially unobtainable. According to the operations researchers, availability and proposed implementation accompany one another (Figure 5). (Chi-square = 33.0, $p < .0001$.)

Figure 4: Percent of proposals
implemented by quantifiability of variables

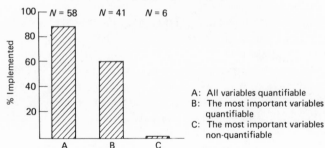

A: All variables quantifiable
B: The most important variables quantifiable
C: The most important variables non-quantifiable

Figure 5: Percent of proposals
implemented by degree of data availability

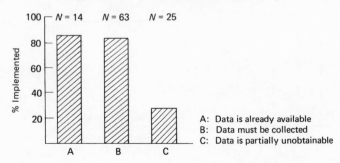

A: Data is already available
B: Data must be collected
C: Data is partially unobtainable

The nonresponses (five) were not significant enough in number to challenge the results. The conclusion is, therefore, that there exists a positive relationship between data availability and the implementation of proposals. This finding is consistent with the conclusions drawn by Slocombe (1968) and Vatter (1966). In addition, a set of cross tabulations shows an interrelationship between problem limitation, quantifiability of variables and data availability.

## Proposal Value and Cost Related to Proposal Implementation

The value of an innovation is of particular interest to the user. Does the innovation constitute an improvement? This question is especially important to an OR user. He should be expected to compare the cost of OR with the possible revenue gains from using it. Cost implies in this instance the user's expenditure. Will the user be charged for the operations researcher's services? It was expected that both a proposal's value and its cost would be related to implementation.

VALUE OF THE PROPOSAL. The user was asked about the value of the proposal as a basis for decision making. The replies were distributed according to the following alternatives: A) the proposal has value or B) the proposal lacks or has insignificant value. The replies received clearly indicate that as the number of implemented proposals increased the greater their perceived value (Figure 6). (Chi-square = 34.1, $p < .0001$.)

The conclusion is, consequently, that there exists a strong positive relationship between the value of the proposal and its implementation. These results are comparable to Heiman's (1964). Nonresponses (15) were relatively numerous, so these results should be taken with caution.

*Figure 6: Percent of proposals implemented by user's perception of project values*

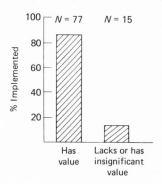

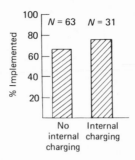

*Figure 7: Percent of proposals*
*implemented by use of internal charging*

COST OF USING OPERATION RESEARCH. The users were also asked if they had to pay for the work performed by the operations researchers (internal charging). In 31 (33%) of the projects this was the case. Figure 7 shows that the number of proposals implemented was slightly larger for this group than for the group where no internal charging occurred. (Chi-square = .085, $p < .4$.) It must, however, be stated that low significance level of the chi-square and the number of missing responses (13) do not permit one to draw conclusions regarding the relationship between the user's expenditure and the implementation of proposals.

## Summary and Conclusions

In the twelve firms studied there exists a positive relationship between the user's participation in defining the problem and the implementation of OR proposals. The identity of the project initiator also appears to influence implementation. It is not, however, solely the relationship between user and operations researcher that determines the success of the project. Problem characteristics may also have an influence. The findings indicate that there exists a relationship between problem limitation, the quantifiability of variables and the availability of the data on one hand, and the implementation of the proposals on the other. A relationship between the perceived value of an OR proposal and its implementation was also demonstrated. Data relating the cost of the solution (measured as the occurrence of internal charging) and the implementation was too deficient to permit any conclusions. A summary of the above findings appear in Table 1.

Other factors exist which may influence proposal implementation. Some of these are: (1) the length of time OR activity has existed in the organization; (2) the amount of money spent by the organization on OR; (3) the particular OR techniques being used and (4) the identity (top management or other) of the initiator of original activity in the firm.

| Variable group | Variable | Chi square | Signifi-cance ($P =$) | Influence of nonresponses on conclusion | Relationship with proposal implemen-tation |
|---|---|---|---|---|---|
| Collabor-ation | User's participa-tion | 19.1 | < .001 | May influence (15) | Positive significant (somewhat ques-tionable) |
| | Initiator of project | 16.7 | < .001 | May influence (21) | Positive significant (highly question-able) |
| Character-istic of problem | Problem limitation | 52.5 | < .0001 | No influence (2) | Positive significant |
| | Quantifi-ability of variables | 24.4 | < .0001 | No influence (2) | Positive significant |
| | Availabil-ity of data | 33.0 | < .0001 | No influence (5) | Positive significant |
| Proposal value and cost | Value of resultant solution | 34.1 | < .0001 | May influence (15) | Positive significant (somewhat ques-tionable) |
| | Internal charging | 0.85 | < .4 | May influence (13) | Positive non-significant (somewhat ques-tionable) |

When these factors were controlled, only one (the length of time OR activity has existed in the firm) significantly reduced the strength of the original relationships. If OR activity has existed for some years and when the user has previously participated in some OR project, the impact of the original variables is reduced. The other factors had no such influence.

What has been learned about the management of OR projects? One may conclude that it is fruitful to conceive of OR implementation as a continuous process. This process starts by generating a project to solve some existing problem. Regardless of who initiates the project, the oper-ations researcher should consider himself to be a consultant. With the operations researcher in the role of consultant, the user should feel more interested and involved in the OR project. It is important at the outset that the user define the problem, also outlining his goals and resource limitations. Because of his previous experience the operations researcher may be able to help in this phase. To clarify the problem variables and existing relationships among them research is necessary. This is one of the operations researchers tasks. The user is, naturally, a valuable source of information here and should, consequently, participate in the work and take the opportunity to evaluate the results. Obtaining data may be difficult; hence the user's participation in the research may be a great help. The operations researcher is responsible for the construction of the mathematical model, its solution and verification, as this is his special field. Because the user bases his decisions on the solution, it is important that the operations researcher keep him informed of the progress of the project. This should be done in order to enable the user to influence the course of the work and to judge the quality of the proposed solution. The user and the operations researcher should therefore discuss the assumptions on which the solution is based, the limitations imposed, the factors to be considered constants, which variable relationships are to be considered as linear, etc. Such interactions between operations researcher and user should be considered important steps in arriving at a solution.

If the user decides to tackle the problem in accordance with the operations researcher's proposal, it is important that they continue to cooperate. The operations researcher may offer clarifications and explanations while the execution is being planned. It then rests with the user, possibly with assistance, to see to it that the plan is followed and the execution conforms to the intent of the proposal. The process of implementation ends with the establishment of a new routine.[3]

#### REFERENCES

Ackoff, R. L. *Scientific Method: Optimizing Applied Research Decisions.* New York: John Wiley & Sons, 1968.

Bennis, W. G. *Changing Organizations.* New York, 1966.

Churchman, C. W. and Schainblatt, A. H. "The Researcher and the Manager: A Dialectic of Implementation." *Management Science*, Vol. 11, No. 4 (Feb. 1965).

Collcutts, R. H. "The First Twenty Years Operational Research." The British Iron and Steel Research Association (BISRA), Operational Research Department, 1965.

Heiman, D. R. "A Procedure for Predicting the Potential Success or Failure of an OR/MS Activity." Unpublished Master thesis, Northwestern University, May 1964.

Huysman, J. *The Implementation of Operations Research.* New York: John Wiley & Sons, 1970.

[3]Further discussions on the implementation of operations research can be found in Huysman (1970) and Churchman and Schainblatt (1965).

Katz, D. and Kahn, R. L. *The Social Psychology of Organizations.* New York, 1966.

Leavitt, H. J. "Applied Organizational Change in Industry: Structural, Technological and Humanistic Approaches." In *Handbook of Organizations*, edited by J. G. March. Chicago, 1965.

Nicander, U. and Silvander, L-B. "Kartlaggning av operationsanalysens utbredning i svenska borsnoterade foretag (Survey of the Spread of Operations Research in Enterprises Quoted on the Stock Market)." The Department of Business Administration, Stockholm University, 1969.

Radnor, M.; Rubenstein, A. H., and Tansik, D. A. "Implementation in Operations Research and Research and Development in Government and Business Organizations." *Operations Research*, Vol. 18, No. 6 (Nov./Dec. 1970).

Rubenstein, A. H.; Radnor, M.; Baker, N. R.; Heiman, D. R. and McColly, J. B. "Some Organizational Factors Related to the Effectiveness of Management Science Groups in Industry." *Management Science*, Vol. 13, No. 8 (April 1967).

Schumacher, C. and Smith, B. A. "A Sample Survey of Industrial Operations Research Activities." *Operations Research*, Vol. 13, No. 6 (Nov./Dec. 1965).

Slocombe, D. M. "Investigations of Some Operations Research Groups." Imperial College, London University, 1968.

Vatter, W. "The Use of Operations Research in American Companies." *Accounting Review*, Vol. 42, No. 4 (Oct. 1967).

# 7. THE POLITICS OF MANAGEMENT SCIENCE

*Martin K. Starr*

---

The use of psychological attributes to explain consumer behavior has proved helpful. Perhaps it should influence the study of managers and their associates. Thus, implementation problems can be examined in terms of the interacting life styles of managers and management scientists. This viewpoint provides some interesting perspectives. Not facetiously, we might learn something about carrying a project through to completion by studying various categories of attitudes. In such terms, we could attempt to relate and match the mind of the management scientist (called the model builder) with that of the manager. Many appealing possibilities are found in the literature. For example, if the manager and the model builder differ in any of the following terms, what significance would this have?

Subjective data-maker or an objective data-taker

Gradual improver (Coué) or a major mover

Normative or descriptive problem resolver

Editors' Note: Reprinted with permission from *Interfaces*, June 1971, pp. 31–37, published by The Institute of Management Sciences.

An exact or approximate solution seeker

Classical or heuristic model builder

Total systems conceptualizer or practical subsystem user

An analyzer or synthesizer of situations

Topical specializer or hierarchical generalizer[1]

Thesis-maker or antithesis debater

Leveler or sharpener[2]

Politician or nonpolitician

As we peruse such a list of potential differences in life styles, a question keeps arising, "Match the model builder and manager for what purpose?"

To make the manager more satisfied?

To make the model builder happier?

To make the system work better?

The management scientist is loyal to his manager, so the first of these three alternatives looks right. Purely personally, the second is compelling. Professionally, it is the third one to which the model builder's credo is tuned. Realistically, the first goal is usually the one that the model builder pursues, often at some expense to the second (personal) objective. Since professionalism requires that the system's benefit be the central issue, the third objective is often assumed to be satisfied by achievement of the first. To explain how this arrangement of attitudes can be viewed as consistent requires consideration of political factors.

### The Apolitical Brain

The brain is an instrument for thinking; the mind a set of cognitive relations. The mind is politically oriented; the brain is used in attempting to achieve political objectives set by the mind. We speak of changing one's mind, not one's brain. No one knows enough about minds, intellect or mentality, character, attitudes or thinking abilities to do more than conjecture about how such relationships work.

Why speculate about such matters when there are hard facts to be transmitted about queuing theory, semi-Markov processes, and the general assignment problem? Perhaps the best answer is that the payoffs for these conjectures are unknown, whereas the payoffs for the next queuing variant are disappointingly marginal. Various astute observers have noted that

---

[1]More appropriate to present-day discussions, we might contrast a specialist in generalizing or a generalist in specializing.

[2]Concepts obtained from staff psychologists of the Menninger Foundation, Topeka, Kansas.

*Part IV: Implementation*

an improvement in creative mentality of some very small amount would be multiplied into astounding gains in "real" GNP.[3] But the model builder's mind is not evaluated in terms of creativity or political savvy—only as a brain. This is the manager's point of view and most model builders think the manager is quite right.

There are factors of logic, consistency and processing speed, memory and file characteristics, and other machine-brain characteristics to deal with. The factor of courage[4]—that is, courage to maintain an honest position (i.e., a "fair" coin, a reliable machine)—is treated as a critical behavioral element of the implementation problem. Curiosity and veracity are additional, related behavioral elements. Veracity, we note, requires knowing the truth and then telling it "as it is."

Kenneth Boulding explains that veracity and curiosity are peculiar properties of the "scientific subculture."[5] He makes these choice points, "Science developed a value system which . . . put a high value on curiosity, a human trait that we may have inherited from the apes but which is severely discouraged in most folk cultures. Curiosity is supposed to have killed the cat—I don't believe I ever found out how; children in most rural or working class cultures around the world are admonished sharply against it. The second value of the scientific subculture is the high value which is put on veracity, that is, not telling lies. Not telling lies is not quite the same thing as knowing the truth, but it is the prerequisite of the development of a culture devoted to the production of truth. If curiosity has traditionally been discouraged in lower-class cultures, veracity has been discouraged in upper-class cultures, where telling lies and getting away with it has been almost the essence of social intercourse . . . the better socialized you are, however, the more your reality testing capacity is impaired. You are tuned in to accept what people around you accept, whether that is true or not. Even science itself, of course, is not exempt from the dangers of socialization and it is not even inconceivable that scientific subculture could destroy its own capacity for reality testing."

The model builder has been educated to accept the assumption that it is evident when truth is present or is not. Each management scientist, brought up on the principle of parsimony, reacts to the expectation of "truth" with a 0, 1 programmed brain. However, the manager is prepared to test "truth" in a different reality than the model builder. His is a political context which has the paradoxical property of being able to convert

[3]Not only as GNP is presently measured, but even more so when it will be modified to reflect all contributions to national welfare.

[4]Consider Asch's studies which showed that when a rigged group agreed on an untruthful judgment concerning a perceived length, the "free individual" not in on the plot would often agree with the group's evaluation. S. E. Asch, "Effects of Group Pressure Upon the Modification and Distortion of Judgments," in Eleanor E. Maccoby et al., eds., Readings in Social Psychology, 3rd ed., Holt, Rinehart & Winston, 1958, pp. 174–183.

[5]Kenneth E. Boulding, "The Specialist with a Universal Mind," Management Science, Vol. 14, No. 12, August 1968, pp. B647–B653.

subsystem's truths to system's falsehoods. The relationship is consistent because the model builder uses his brain whereas the manager uses his mind.

## The Political Mind

Because the implementation problem has not been solved, it seems necessary to reconsider the role of the model builder. A significant contrast can be drawn between the mentalities of the management scientist as the model builder and the manager as the model user. Individuals pursuing these different roles of builder and user have disparate histories of experience, life objectives, and tastes. By tradition, the model builder is expected to remain apolitical. But, how realistic is this position?

Consider the following problem. A group of managers are deciding which factors to include in a major management study. The managers disagree. Some want short-term tactical considerations, others believe that major strategic, long-term issues should be involved. They turn to their management science consultant who is recognized by everyone to be on the spot. While there are issues to be settled, the process of settlement (that leads indifferent onlookers to a courtroom) becomes interesting in its own right. Should the consultant[6] say what he really happens to think? Or should he note who is saying what and try to reach a politically sensible (implementable) decision? Do the consultant's professional ethics permit him political evaluation?

No one has ever specified appropriate consultant's reaction under the circumstances. Any simple picture of interpersonal relations will not do. In the realms of politics and science, there are unanswered questions about the relationships of managers and model builders. In coupling the model builder's functions with those of one manager, the connections that must be made are between science and politics. Finding an appropriate interface between science and politics is equivalent to designing an effective communication system between the manager and the model builder (as shown in the figure below).

Worse luck, in many situations as in our example, the model builder must be able to relate his scientific accomplishments to the political considerations of many managers, e.g., both the short-term advocates and the long-term advocates, the production-oriented and the market-oriented, etc. The astute model builder recognizes that he may be in the position of the pollster whose published "truths" will change the vote. What should be done is not the issue if it does not match what can be done. A political enigma exists. Can it be cleared up by discussion?

---

[6]In the sense of industrial anthropology, all model building advice is consultation. Clearly this includes staff management scientists.

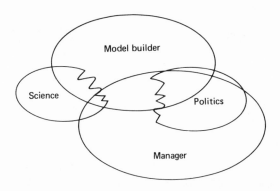

**Dimensions for Discussion**

An approach to matching the model builder's "truth" and the manager's politics has been suggested. Churchman and Schainblatt discuss communication between managers and scientists.[7]

"Our examination of what operations researchers and social scientists have had to say about the relationship between manager and scientist has yielded four rather distinct ideas. We call these four concepts the *separate-function position*, the *communication position*, the *persuasion position*, and the *mutual understanding position*." These categories can be represented as follows:

|  | Model builder understands manager | Model builder does not understand manager |
|---|---|---|
| Manager understands model builder | *Mutual understanding* | *Communication* of what is "right". Facts + explanation |
| Manager does not understand model builder | Model builder *persuades* manager because he understands his personality. | Statement of what is right—take it or leave it. *Separate function* |

These categories cannot be faulted. In fact, they are fine, but they do not explain the political reasons that support any one of the four types instead of any other. They do not yield insight concerning how to move a relation from one cell to another. Entirely neglected is the model builder's problem when he is dealing with many managers. What is missing is the political environment of the problem. If the model builder's mentality is not a political one and his solution does not include political considera-

[7]C. West Churchman and A. H. Schainblatt, "The Researcher and the Manager: A Dialectic of Implementation," *Management Science*, Vol. 11, No. 4, February 1965, pp. B69–B87.

tions, then the model builder doesn't understand the managerial context of his problem. But, if the political frame is available to be used by the model builder . . . can he be trusted by the manager? In other words, can any entry in the column, "Model builder understands the manager" be permitted to exist?

### Who Pleases Whom

Obviously, both managers and model builders perceive the political environments. But they react differently to them because they have fundamentally different roles and objectives. Above all, the manager does not care to "please" his model builders, but the model builders do want to "please" their managers. Respect, which is seldom lacking in either direction, is not the same as pleasing. Let us examine this question of roles a little more fully.

Eric Berne developed a psychiatric communication model[8] which subdivided the individual into three parts (reminding one of the Freudian triad). We can obtain various interaction patterns, for example:

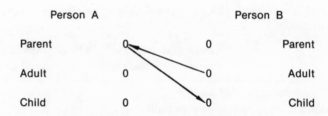

*Potentials for 2-persons interacting.*
*(One example is illustrated)*

Berne hypothesized that human relations are represented by different *sequences* of who speaks how to whom—noting particularly which part of each individual speaks to which part of the other. For example, if A, acting as a parent, speaks to B as though he were a child, but is answered by B as though he were an adult, then a game (usually fraught with hostility) ensues.

The same line of reasoning can be applied to the model builder and the manager. Mutual understanding in these terms cannot occur if each manager knows all about politics, but the model builder does not. The only role that makes sense for the management scientist is that of a political scientist who includes managerial attitudes in reaching his solution. To

[8]Eric Berne, *Games People Play*, Grove Press, Inc., New York, 1964.

achieve implementation, compromise seems essential. The model builder must be able to explain the existing bases for honest negotiations within the organization.

It may therefore be suggested that two changes in relations would help. First, management should encourage model builders to maintain a keen awareness of politics. Second, model builders should respect the importance of political error as well as scientific error.

## Political Reality

At the present time, the model builder is motivated to "please" his managers, but managers are not symmetrically motivated. Believing this, it is unlikely that an aware manager would care to be persuaded by a model builder who appears to be a politician. The only political role that the manager is likely to accept as symbiotic is that of the political scientist.

The political science view carries the seeds for honest implementation. The alternatives are to be either political or apolitical, and neither will do. Management will isolate the findings of an apolitical model builder and reinterpret them as needed. Political views will be discarded as naive. The manager looks for scientific analysis *that reflects political realities*.

A new dimension for management science appears. Management cannot disregard the advice of an uncorrupted political scientist whose base of operations is the organization and whose unambiguous objective is to make the system work better. Under most circumstances management will ultimately seek out such advice. Compromise becomes part of the acceptable scientific solution.

Let us return to our "on the spot" consultant, reporting to many managers involved in personal political competitions. This model builder explains to every manager what the political realities are and how his recommendations are likely to affect each of the various participants. As a political scientist he notes that managerial preference exists for Type I errors which constitute rejection of good alternatives because such errors are usually impossible to detect. As a political scientist he recommends that the system should learn from errors rather than condemning and penalizing individual managers.

## Thing-making

As Erich Fromm points out in a superb guest editorial for *Management Science*[9] many managers are bureaucrats. Fromm's definition is that bureau-

---

[9]Erich Fromm, "Thoughts on Bureaucracy," *Management Science*, Vol. 16, No. 12, August 1970, pp. B699–B705.

cracy is "treating people as things." There are far greater "thing-making" forces operating in the world than one immediately perceives. Thing-making is an error-reducing technique. It superimposes *arbitrary* social standards for judging human behavior. Such standards, although of arbitrary character, are political means for achieving conformity.

If the model builder's professionalism does not seem to allow him to be scientifically political in his professional judgment, then the bureaucratic manager perceives the model builder as an additional "thing" to cope with. What kind of a "thing"? The astounding but most logical answer is a "thing-maker." Not every manager, but many managers, view their management science consultants as being even better at "thing-making" than their personnel departments and consumer complaint departments. The manager appreciates apolitical model building attitudes that "in the name of truth" apply the central limit theorem to create 2.8 people per household and that can honestly find one number to represent thousands of "mean" aspirations.

## Uncertainty

Ultimately, the mind of the model builder is at issue because the model builder cannot identify with a thing-making role. The reason for the discrepancy is not politics but the uncertainty that surrounds every complex problem. The model builder knows that as his awareness increases his certitude recedes. Arbitrary forces begin to play predominate roles. He calls them arbitrary because they are political. The model builder (as presently cultured and trained) may prefer to be considered an instrument (a brain) rather than a political intellect (a mind). But if this is so, then a wall has been erected blocking, not surrounding, management science. Undoubtedly, some of us, on principle, will choose to batter the wall down. Hopefully, others will decide to walk or run around its end. There is obviously no blanket description but there is much evidence that management scientists (as a subset of all scientists) lean heavily in this direction, of being able to include political forces in their evaluation of all relevant systems factors.

# 8. PROGRAMMING COUNTERPRODUCTIVE METHODS TO INSURE THE RAPID TERMINATION OF OPERATIONS RESEARCH/MANAGEMENT SCIENCE DEPARTMENTS

*Russell W. Fenske*

---

This article deals with a very important new phase of management strategy: the development of a program to insure the rapid and effective demise of operations research or management science functions in any organization. While this problem is a subproblem of the general case of terminating any bothersome department in any organization, there are unique characteristics in this instance which can be exploited to expedite the terminal phases of the liquidation.

While many articles published on OR/MS are extremely theoretical in nature, this plan is practical and will most certainly kill off an OR/MS department. Although no one firm has been able to implement all of these techniques simultaneously, each has been used effectively many times to provide the necessary "coup de grace."

Since the one person in an organization who can most effectively plan its termination is the individual responsible for that department, this strategy is discussed from the point of view of the OR/MS manager. While it is well understood that considerable assistance can be obtained from other department heads, an efficient program can only be implemented with the full marshalling of the resources of the OR/MS manager.

## I. Establish OR as the Prima Donna of the Organization

It is very important to make sure that everyone in the organization understands how important OR is. There are many status symbols in an organization and each of these should be utilized. Certainly, selection and embellishment of titles should be done carefully. Length of titles, as well as the use of the terms "Chief," "Senior," "Corporate," "Division," "Assistant to the President," etc., should be considered. Every effort should be utilized to insure that the largest and best offices are obtained for the whole staff. A particularly effective strategy is to install an OR analyst in an office significantly better than one of the top administrators and then make sure that the administrator becomes aware of the situation. Another status symbol has to do with the level in the organization to which the OR/MS

Editors' Note: Reprinted with permission from *Interfaces*, November 1972, pp. 30–32, published by The Institute of Management Sciences.

manager reports. The ideal position involves reporting to the top administrative officer with a not too heavily veiled implication that this function is really more important than others at the same level but is constrained by the fact that there are no higher levels.

A second method of indicating importance is to develop a "mystique" of OR/MS. This involves continuously injecting technical jargon into all conversations without ever bothering to translate. The use of "stochastic," "queue input," and "successive iterations" are preferable to uncertainty, waiting line arrivals, and additional trials. An extremely significant expansion of the language effect can be made if all OR staff personnel "look down" on those who do not know the so-called buzz words. Ideally the non-OR person should be made to feel like a traveler in a foreign country with a strange language who is excluded from conversations because of a lack of comprehension.

A third way of indicating importance is the use of the very reliable tools of "red tape" and bureaucracy. All contacts with OR personnel and programs should be enmeshed in as many different forms, approvals, justifications, reports, and memos as possible. Make sure it is understood that these activities are to insure that the very valuable resources of this staff are not dissipated without appropriate justification and deliberation.

Finally, concentrate on applying sophisticated standard models and ignore problems that are less "elegant" regardless of their importance to the organization. Although the following words cannot be used, it should be made clear to everyone that "simple tools are for simple minds."

## II. Insure that Most Managers Will Not Use the OR Services

The use of red tape and bureaucracy discussed above not only clarifies the importance of the function but also can be used to frustrate any manager who really wishes to utilize the services. If the initial exploration of a project can be sufficiently delayed and tied up in detail, the manager may give up before he can even discuss the problem with you.

Another method to deter managers is to assign priorities on the basis of the degree of technical challenge in a problem rather than the needs of the organization. Obviously, a problem involving the layout of compartments in a desk drawer involving a new integer programming algorithm is much more challenging than a stock status and replenishment system.

## III. Create a Maximum of Personnel Problems

The best way to create people problems is to ignore the people. This involves concentrating entirely on techniques, specifically the mathematics, computer programs and physical implications of the problem and ignoring the human factor entirely. If this cannot be done, the next best step is to treat people like other inanimate factors of a project without considering behavioral effects.

A second approach is to insure that all the line managers are so upset over your activities and empire that they will find themselves in competition to see who does the best job of "cutting you up" in meetings, interoffice communications, and at organizational social functions.

An important way to create antagonism in the organization is to make the top managers feel that the continued existence of your department jeopardizes their jobs. They must be made to feel that all traditional management functions can be done better by algorithms, computers, OR/MS analysts, and decision theory application. If they cannot be made to feel that they are fully expendable, they should at least be made to feel that they are obsolete as managers and will soon be replaced by bright, young "quantitative types."

## IV. Maximize the Internal Inefficiencies of the OR Operation

The best way to interfere with the operations of any organization is to tamper with the internal communication and information system. This would involve contradictory, late, and incorrect communications. However, an even better way is to never allow a system of information exchange to develop among the members of the OR/MS department. In this way communications between staff members can be kept to an absolute minimum. This can be effected by scattered offices, unclear responsibilities, reprimands for "excessive visiting," limiting any information transmission to vertical paths in the organization, and discouragement of either formal or informal coordination meetings.

## V. Minimize the Success of Any Project Undertaken

A positive means of jeopardizing the success of a project is to make sure the line operating personnel are only involved in the implementation phase. Afterwards, it is too late for them to meddle with their messy details that destroy the "beauty" of the techniques.

Since all projects involve data of some kind, the quality of these data can be used to sink a project. If the data are already available from some other department, one should always accept their validity without ever auditing in any way the accuracy, methods of collection, and previous computations. If the data are gathered by the OR/MS staff, then one must make sure that they do not waste their time on extraneous items such as verification, error checking, etc.

Another significant factor concerning allocation of effort has to do with the concentration of techniques. A good rule of thumb to remember is to utilize a 95%–5% split on effort devoted to techniques versus implementation.

A third fact of allocation of effort involves priorities. In any firm a search will turn up some extremely complex projects which may take years or, ideally, forever to complete and which can absorb extraordinary amounts of human and financial resources. These are the projects to seek out and assign the highest priorities. An added benefit can be obtained if the benefits of any of these projects would be negligible or at least minimal in comparison to the resources required.

A final way to affect a project is to forget it once it has been installed. There are almost no problems that will remain static forever. As assumed conditions change, discrepancies will begin to accumulate and soon both parameters and relationships will be inappropriate for the problem.

## VI. To the Future

As in most areas of scientific endeavor, the quest for knowledge must not stagnate but must continuously push forward the frontiers through research. The author is continuing to explore this very important new area of management and would request readers to advise him of any new and creative strategies that they may have observed.

# Part V:  Conclusion

# 1. THE WIT AND WISDOM OF
# R. E. D. WOOLSEY

*Walter B. Newsom, Thad B. Green*
*and Sang M. Lee*

---

Gene Woolsey is a practitioner and a scholar in the area of decision sciences. He is the principal scientist in The Institute for Operations Research, and professor at the Colorado School of Mines. He has acted as a consultant to a variety of organizations including the Sandia Corporation and the Information Systems Division of General Electric Company. He has held positions in Control Data Corporation and Sandia Corporation. He has written research reports in addition to many articles and columns which prick the conscience of decision scientists. Although he has been actively involved in the use of mathematical/integer/geometric programming, his basic interest is the study of methods to solve real world problems [1].

His credentials are outstanding. However, he has maintained a perspective about the use of decision sciences. At the same time he has a wit that appears in his written words. One of his rules is: *He who checks not his optimum solution against his constraints is indeed dumb* [3]. There is much to be learned from the above rule. He has expressed wisdom for all decision scientists, but he has expressed this wisdom in a way that both has meaning to the decision scientist and also has some wit.

Since he has great enthusiasm for the use of decision sciences in real world problems and since he has had such great experience in the application of decision science techniques in the real world, he has two main concerns that decision scientists should be made aware of: (1) training the decision scientist, and (2) assisting the decision scientist in moving through the decision science process.

His concern about the training of the decision scientist can best be demonstrated by quoting from his letter to the editor of *Operations Research* [2]:

> For some years now it has been my privilege to participate in operations-research and management-science conferences in the role of comic relief; that is, my subject matter has been real-world applications. In the past, the academic power structure of the profession has condescended to allow a certain number of us to appear at these meetings so long as we keep our place and don't take ourselves too seriously, it being well understood that it is much more important to design yet another algorithm (that converges in

Editors' Note: Article prepared especially for this book.

a finite number of steps) than actually to solve a real problem. When one attends our meetings, he often gets the uneasy feeling that the National Science Foundation is really a patron of the arts rather than the sciences.

Why has this situation come about? Why do so many of us on the firing line sit still for professional journals that are unreadable and conferences that have little relation to how operations research and management science are actually used in the world at large?

The first thing that comes to mind is simply that we front-line troops are more concerned with getting the job done, understood, and implemented—this is what we are paid for, and we get virtually no brownie points for publishing our results. Further, profit-making concerns have the quaint notion that, if they know how to do something better, it might be considered a competitive advantage. In short, if you really sell your approach to your company, the chances are good that they will never let it out the door unless it is rewritten so as to be of no use to anyone—of course, candor compels me to admit that this at once makes it publishable in the journals of our profession. The OR worker that gets a project actually implemented in a government agency often finds that the heavy hand of security or politics assures him that his success will never be seen again, unless cleverly disguised as an article for *Operations Research*. Further, as some of us work rather than teach, we simply do not have the free time to participate in a society that does not appear to be result oriented.

We must realize, however, that the academic member of our profession does not have a choice as to participation. He is required to do so. The publication of papers in the journals and participation in his professional society are the totems he must satisfy in order to ensure his orderly progress toward a Professorship. Since the decisions as to his participation and/or publication are determined by his fellow academics, there is no question that he will write and present whatever the current fashion dictates.

Recently, I addressed a group of young professors of OR/MS. After my usual polemic, I was asked: "Given that it is necessary to continue to write the required trash in order to advance, how can we tell it like it is without committing professional suicide?" I answered that it depends on what peer group one wants to satisfy. I pointed out that, if one gains a reputation as a practitioner who works on a money-back guarantee, he can have the respect of the people with problems to solve, plus the solace of commercial solvency. These two things will tend to attract students with similar goals, thus increasing his worth to his institution. Eventually his students will go forth. Being result oriented, they will accomplish results and become distinguished alumni, perhaps even successful enough to come back and endow a chair for his eminent old age.

I was then asked: "Well, that's all very well for you, but how do we get the necessary experience to be able to get away with it?" I suggested that, before proposing to teach operations research or management science, he actually *do some*. If I understood his question correctly, he wanted to know where to find work.

The most obvious place to find work is in his university. Universities today seem to have many problems in common: parking, registration, classroom scheduling, the capital-budgeting problems of expansion, and others.

I then asked if he had ever approached his institution's administration with a proposal to do a study on any one of these subjects. He said he had not—nor had any other professor in the room. I then asked them to comment on an administration's possible reaction to a proposal by a professor to do a free study of one of his institution's problems. It was generally agreed that "anyone crazy enough to propose such a thing would be welcomed with open arms." It has always struck me as rather strange that a School of Business Administration is not expected to show a reasonable profit on its operation. If we can once get over the point of view that education is, by its very nature, a nonprofit enterprise, some very exciting possibilities will emerge. Consider what a recommendation it would be for a faculty member to be part of such an operation. A Business School that supports, say, the departments of classics, art, and drama, and is expected to supply management and financial advice to the university will be rather easy to justify.

With the wealth of portfolio models in management science, isn't it natural to consider testing them on a portion of the university's investment? I have been asking this question of university administrators and management scientists for some years now. I had expected that the administrators might be reluctant, but was unprepared for the usual reaction of the management scientists. As the possibility of a real test approached certainty, the faculty member's assurance diminished rapidly—such phrases appeared as "Well, it really *is* a conceptual tool, and I'd like to work on it a while longer before we actually put in *data.*"

This now leads us to the air of condescension and noblesse oblige of the "pure" OR/MS scientist to his "less able" brothers who do applications. After some years of bitter experience in OR/MS, I can only conclude that you win a few and you lose a few. *The only way to be sure that you never strike out is simply to make sure you never come to bat.* Therefore, I find it amusing when prizes are given in our profession for methods that are satisfying on aesthetic grounds, but which, for reasons immediately obvious to the practitioner, are ludicrous in practice. One example that immediately comes to mind is a model of an alkylation process that appeared in a recent book on mathematical programming. In this model, effects of hydrofluoric and sulfuric acid alkylation systems were indiscriminately mixed. For example, the yield relationships are based on HF units and acid consumption on $H_2SO_4$. The acid dilution factor is also based on $H_2SO_4$ units, but reactor temperature and acid strength are based on HF. I have now seen this paper referred to six times in the literature as a shining example for all to follow.

Let me make a suggestion to those who propose to "do" OR/MS in an area that they know nothing about. SHUT UP AND LISTEN to what is going on *now* from the man who is doing it *now*. After you understand perfectly what is going on from *his* point of view, you may *try* to improve it. As an example of the lack of communication between "them" and "us," I recall the following question from a staff member of a government think tank that was being forced, on short notice, to survive without service money: "Do you mean to tell us that, in order to *do* OR/MS in chemical engineering, we have to know something about *chemical engineering?*" It must be remembered that this man had been supported by the Federal Government for some five years for just doing his thing, without any reference to applications whatever. He just assumed that it was going to go on forever. This often leads to such statements as: "It must be useful—they paid for it, didn't they?"

I have no quarrel with the "pure" OR/MS scientist, so long as he does not pretend to be what he is not: a practitioner. There is no question that, if the theologians of our profession don't do their work, we parish priests cannot do ours. But what is happening in our profession seems to be that our theology is approaching "the peace of God"—that is, it passeth all understanding. If we don't understand what is being handed down to us, we are certainly going to be unable to pass useful interpretations on to the user. The basic hypocrisy of an integer programming theoretician accepting an invitation to a conference where some real logistics problems will be presented to obtain advice from the assembled experts is still something that infuriates me. I remember asking the gentleman in question how many real problems he had ever (1) attempted, or (2) solved. On receiving his answer, I asked if he didn't perhaps feel that he was accepting the invitation under false pretense. He did not, because he was an accepted expert in the field.

So long as we have experts that have never actually implemented a solution, I submit that our profession has a problem. To put the point even more strongly, I feel that no one should be allowed to teach OR/MS unless he can present some years of experience on the firing line. I recall interviewing a young man with an M.S. in OR/MS while I was at the Sandia Corporation. He was a graduate of a respected university, and one of the demigods of our profession was his thesis professor. He was the perfect personification of a man with a bag of cures scouring the world for the right disease. Upon being presented with a few of the problems we were then confronted with, he saïd: "See here, Woolsey, I'm a problem definer, not some grotty problem solver." I then pointed out that we had enough problem definers already— we called them *management*; and if he were a good problem solver, in course of time he might get to be one of *them*, but not at Sandia. I suggested that he go back to school and get his Ph.D., as he would certainly do the least harm that way.

This leads at once to the question: Is it ethical for a professor or school to graduate a person for whom there is no demand? One eminent man of our profession has suggested that he is not running a trade school, and that his theoretically trained graduates just need some exposure to real-world situations to master them without any particular difficulty. I think that, if what he asserts is true, it shows that any man is able to triumph over his education. I believe, simply, that it is not right to graduate someone who has never even been exposed to a *real* OR/MS problem. Further, I believe that, to teach in our profession without at least some experience, even of failure, is a crime—one whose usual title is fraud.

He then follows this criticism with some very direct suggestions as to what can be done to improve the educational process:

First off, let us dispose at once of the notion that OR/MS is a stand-alone discipline that can be offered as an undergraduate major. This type of program tends to generate people who believe that they can optimize anything, in spite of the fact that they don't know any real-world discipline well enough to do it at all. The horrible example, referred to earlier, of a young management scientist attempting to optimize a process that he had no experience with is, unfortunately, typical of this kind of graduate.

When these graduates go on to Master's and Doctor's degrees, they are almost ruined for any useful work. They have little or no inclination to master some grotty discipline well enough to even *do* it, much less optimize. Up until lately, however, there were always enough think tanks, theoretical OR/MS departments, and industrial OR/MS groups to absorb these parasites. Now that times are hard, the worker bees are nosing the drones out of the hive. The "nonessential" OR/MS departments in large corporations disappear in the proverbial puff of smoke.

Let us require that, in order to get a graduate degree in OR/MS, the applicant present work experience in the field to which he wishes to return after graduation. If he has no work experience, a degree in that field will admit him (conditionally) to the program. The reason for this is the simple fact that a degree in a field no more makes a person competent in it than being in a garage makes me a car. The student will be expected to minor in his chosen field for his graduate degree and his thesis or dissertation topics must be some application of OR/MS to this field.

In the course of his graduate work, each course will require a term paper applying the given field to a real-world problem found by the student. This requirement will be somewhat eased for the student because of the working arrangements for generating real problems with local industries and governments. The student's professor shall be expected to supply real problem situations for the education of the students in effective communication. For example, the homework for students shall often be of the type where the student has to write a one-page quick and dirty to solve some specific problem such as (for example) a sequencing rule for minimizing set-up, tear-down time on a Sundstrand lathe. The homework will then be collected and taken to a shop foreman with exactly this problem, who will be asked to separate the papers into three piles:

First Pile: Anything he *cannot read* (understand).
Second Pile: Anything he *can read* (understand), and from this, the third pile.
Third Pile: Anything he might actually *use*.

Upon these papers being returned to me, I have assigned grades as follows:

First Pile: F
Second Pile: C
Third Pile: A.

From my experience I have found that only a few assignments like this will show a truly amazing growth of understanding (and humility) on the part of the students.

When the professor does local consulting, his graduate students should expect to come along, shut up, and watch what he does. The post mortem with the student can be an eye-opener for both concerned. The student often is upset that the customer is so "stupid." The professor then has the golden opportunity to explain the difference between stupidity and ignorance. Ignorance may be overcome with education offered with patience and humor in the absence of condescension; but stupidity, on the other hand, is invincible. The fastest way I know to turn ignorance into stupidity is to patronize the customer.

The student often tends to believe himself superior to the customer because he finds that the customer is totally unaware of, say, the integer-programming formulation of capital-budgeting problems. The professor may gently remind the student that the customer in question has been choosing projects for twenty years and has never made less than 20 per cent on the company's investment in every one of them! It is very easy to look down on a skilled man, such as a master machinist, until the student is made to understand that (1) the machinist has spent as long learning his trade as the student has his (or more), (2) the machinist's work is right or it isn't, and (3) if the student is fortunate, he will make as much money in five years as the machinist does right now. The main point here is that both sides are ignorant—they are just ignorant about different things. The student, in turn, has some contributions to make to the professor. Very often, the student is not as sold on the professor's particular algorithmic bag as is the professor, and he will see approaches that might be more easily implemented in the given situation than will the professor's own.

Lastly, work-study programs are absolutely necessary for the proper development of future practitioners. If the professor makes it known that he wants his students to work in a real-world situation where the student can see applications of what he has been taught, industries and local government will beat a path to his door.

Woolsey then turns to the area of application of decision science techniques in real world settings. He makes some of the same points that have been made by other authors in this book. However, he uses a number of interesting examples, rules or axioms to make his points. He reflects on the past of scientific management and the future of management science in his column in *Interfaces* in May 1976 [14]. He cites Frederick Taylor's four principles of management:

First. The development of a true science.

Second. The scientific selection of the workman.

Third. His scientific education and development.

Fourth. Intimate friendly cooperation between management and the men.

He then applies these principles to the profession of decision sciences. He suggests that the first two principles are still working reasonably well. He suggests that the third principle is not being achieved too well. As noted earlier, he has been critical of the education and development of decision scientists. However, he is very critical when it comes to the fourth principle:

We are now left with the fourth principle, that of friendly cooperation between management and the men. It is easy to understand that those OR/ MS groups that last, *have* established the last principle as the sine qua non of survival. In my opinion, the businessmen of Frederick Taylor's time took over his first three principles with enthusiasm. Using these first three principles, management can insure that they will have spectacular increases in productivity rather quickly. It should be self-evident that advanced time-and-motion study results, in the hands of the typical theory-x manager of 1890 could have a fantastic effect on productivity. Taylor's last principle, that of workman-manager friendly *cooperation* was swept under the rug and forgotten. In Taylor's book, he repeatedly points out that no strikes or other labor difficulties *ever* took place where all of his principles were accepted by *each and every* level of management. On this basis, Taylor forecasted a great new day of management-worker amity.

He summarizes the problems that decision scientists face today. "Finally, let's realize that *cooperation* is the final, most difficult optimization problem of all" [p. 4]. In order to achieve this cooperation, the decision scientist would be well advised to follow Woolsey's rules. He may appear to be quite pessimistic about the application of these rules by decision scientists since he has several articles addressed to St. Jude [1, 3]. St. Jude is the patron saint of desperate causes. In these two articles he presents some interesting examples which he then tries to summarize by his rules:

> *If the cost of collecting the data for a model is greater than the amount you can save by solving it, you* shouldn't *do that.* [3] *Run as many different lengths at one time as possible until the time to do the internal dynamic programming starts to make expensive increases in time.* [1]

He has developed an axiom of consulting which every decision scientist should remember:

> *If I make the decision, and I am proven right, you will never remember. If I make the decision, and I am proven wrong, you will never* forget! [1]

He then suggests that there are really only two rules that the decision scientist should remember and apply and he will be successful. "The first rule of OR is that you must formulate the problem in the jargon used by the manager, *not yours*. The second rule is that managers by and large could care less about the sophistication of your method, they want to solve the problem with data *they* put in, and be able to read off the answer when it comes out, in *their terms* [1].

Although his appeals to St. Jude which were cited earlier do indeed imply pessimism, he is basically an optimist. This optimism can best be demonstrated by presenting his article which appeared in *Health Services Research* in its entirety [5].

Although the methodology of operations research has been around for some time now, its documented successes in the health care field are few. A recent study by David and Ruth Stimson showed that real acceptance of operations research in hospitals is sadly lacking, and a careful review of the literature indicates that there are salient reasons for this unfortunate state of affairs. Many of the journal articles that appear address themselves to potential applications rather than to successful (or unsuccessful) case studies. All too often the articles are written on a level of mathematical jargon that can be appreciated only by the author's colleagues. The average hospital administrator is made to feel that he *should* be able to understand these articles, but he doesn't have the time, as he is busy just keeping the hospital afloat from day to day.

For these reasons and others, such as the *veni, vidi, vici* style of reporting so often used, health administrators are to be forgiven if they feel that OR is not for them. We would like to suggest to such administrators that OR *can* be of use to them, provided they think small rather than big. They may be comforted to know that

Operations research is a *tool* that aids in but does not replace good old experienced decision making.

Operations research does *not* have to be expensive in terms of time or money.

Good operations research should look, feel, and taste like common sense in that it should be easy to understand and use.

Many operations research studies do *not* need a digital computer.

Operations research is often more useful in "fine-tuning" the day-to-day operations of health services than for major planning.

These arcane trade secrets may be illustrated by a brief case history, a study carried out at a large Denver hospital in December 1970. The problem was to assign night nursing personnel to floors in such a way as to maximize total patient benefit. A certain minimum number of personnel were always supposed to be available on each floor, but there were usually more people reporting for work than this minimum number. The question was where to put the additional people.

The investigator's approach rested on quantifying the nursing supervisor's intuitive method of personnel scheduling, because the values of the prospective user must be incorporated in any system if it is to be accepted, and in any case the response of a capable, experienced individual often comes closer to reality than a so-called "objective" evaluation.

The supervisor was asked to list all potential assignments to the various floors above and beyond the minimum required and then to rank them in order of decreasing utility in terms of patient benefit. The assignment ranked as most important was arbitrarily given a numerical score of 100, and the other assignments were scored in relation to that one (e.g., an assignment half as important as the most important one was given a value of 50, an assignment one-third as important was scored at 33 and so on). Once these utility ratings (we call them "utles") had been determined, they were checked for internal consistency by several methods and differences were reconciled. It may be noted in passing that the insights such a rating scheme can provide are often as important to potential users as the final solution.

Had only one personnel type been used, or had assignment ratings for each type been the same, the problem would have been solved at this point. One would merely assign personnel to floors in order of decreasing utility until all extra personnel had assignments. The actual problem was more complex, however, because any of three personnel types—RNs, LPNs, and aides—could be assigned to any floor, and the utle value would be different for each type. To see how such a situation complicates the decision-making process, consider four assignments: Assignment A has utility ratings of 100, 80, and 30 for RHs, LPNs, and aides, respectively; for Assignment B, the ratings are 90, 60, and 40; for Assignment C, 50, 50, and 30; and for Assignment D, 80, 20, and 15. A naive approach would be to make the assignments that have the largest individual utles; thus if two RNs and one LPN were available, one might assign the RNs to A and B, and the LPN to C, for a total utility of $100 + 90 + 50 = 240$. On closer inspection, however, we see that assigning the LPN to A and the RNs to B and D yields a total utility of $80 + 90 + 80 = 250$, making this a better set of assignments. Note that to make this better assignment one needed to consider tradeoffs, or what an economist would call the "opportunity cost" associated with each assignment.

In the simplified example above, the optimal solution could be determined by inspection. In the actual case, the number of potential assignments made it necessary to resort to a systematic method, and the investigators used a mathematical solution procedure known as the "out-of-kilter algorithm."

It might be supposed that the project was now completed. But as often happens in real-life OR investigations, last-minute inspection brought to light a new and hitherto unsuspected problem. The original problem as posed was based on the assumption that the required minimum level of staffing would always be provided; should the number not be reached, overtime help would be used. Let us say, for example, that 100 RNs were required. Since no RN is on duty every night, more than 100 are needed to provide the minimum level each night. But how many more than 100 are needed? Without seeking the optimal answer, the number required can easily be estimated as follows: Since each nurse works 5 days out of 7, or 5/7 of a week, 7/5 persons will be needed to man one position for an entire week; furthermore, each nurse works only about 48 weeks of the year (because of sick leave, vacations, and holidays), so that additionally 52/48 persons will be needed to fill one position for a year. The estimated minimum staff level for RNs would thus be 100 x (7/5) x (52/48), or 152, in order to have 100 RNs on duty nightly, *if* it were actually possible to schedule a fraction of a nurse. Since in real life only whole nurses can be scheduled, the solution will involve some amount of overstaffing, such as having 104 nurses on duty at once, so the 152 figure is undoubtedly somewhat low. In the actual case the number of nursing personnel employed was found to be below even the low rough estimate. Thus in trying to get an answer to the question "How can we best allocate our additional help?" a more pressing question was uncovered, namely, "How many personnel are needed just to meet the bare requirements?"

No earth-shattering significance can be claimed for the study described, nor even any particular originality. But the outlay of time and money required was negligible and normal staff operations were not disrupted. The problem tackled was one the customer wanted solved (and not a broader one that the investigators might have found more interesting). The solution was found by modeling and quantifying the supervisor's own feelings about desirable and acceptable scheduling. And the result was a solution that was *used*.

All this is not to say that costly, time-consuming, and sophisticated methodologies have no place. But too often the sophisticated method will deliver the optimal answer long after the need has passed. We have learned to our pain that often an overlooked simple-minded approach will get a good answer quickly. From these premises we can at once derive two rules:

*Rule I: Until you have exhausted the set of simple-minded answers, do not proceed to sophisticated answers.*

*Rule II: The optimum solution delivered after you need it is worthless. Settle for a Quick & Dirty answer now.*

One problem that has doomed many a promising system is simply that the ultimate user was never consulted as to his or her feelings about the system. One system cited in the Stimsons' book never got off the ground because the proposers wanted to replace doctor-to-nurse communication with doctor-to-teletype-to-nurse communication. Apparently it never occurred to anyone that nurses might not *like* being told what to do by a teletype rather than a doctor. Rotational scheduling systems are another area where a mathematically optimal system should never be implemented without giving considerable thought to the system's effect on the emotional well-being of the people affected by it. And a little common sense will tell the systems designer or the administrator that the new computerized forms better look mighty like the old uncomputerized forms. If they don't, we predict that the new system will fail or will operate badly for some time for the following reasons: (1) the new forms will be ignored, or (2) the new forms will be filled in wrong. From the above we derive the following rule:

*Rule III: If the ultimate user doesn't understand the system, he will resist it.*

A continuing thread in many operations research case studies in health care and elsewhere is that somehow the cost of doing the study is never considered to be a real cost. This often comes about because the study "comes out of somebody else's budget" in large industrial organizations or the government. The user may satisfy his short-term goals only to sink the firm as a whole. A beautiful example of this was a company in Canada that proposed a five-year capital budgeting model to do its corporate planning. One of the authors of this article was contacted for suggestions. On close questioning the operations research analyst admitted that the costs of collecting the data for the model had not really been looked into because "the bean counters [accountants] do all that stuff" (translation: "It doesn't come out of our budget"). Some elementary computations done over the phone showed that the cost of collecting the data for the model could make a noticeable dent in the gross national product of Canada. A few weeks later a letter was received from the company stating that the model was being "reevaluated in the light of data collection costs." The rule that can be derived here is as follows:

*Rule IV: If the costs of building a system are greater than the amount it will save you, don't do it.*

The above case now leads us to an area that will separate the sheep from the goats when dealing with consultants and/or computer salesmen. Whenever a new system is being considered, unless the potential savings can be *shown* to be in excess of potential costs, it should not be done. Now this is just, in a sense, a restatement of Rule IV above. A closer look, however, will reveal some rather interesting facts about how organizations operate. It should be self-evident that the consultant who proposes a "better" computer has an ax to grind. The first thing to do when there is a proposal to "upgrade" present operating procedures is to find out how much the present system costs. Every reader of this article has probably heard horror stories about a hospital that put in an elaborate data-processing system to replace its "out moded" tab shop and then found out that it was paying twice as much to do the same thing. The administrator's greatest friend in these situations is his friendly local bean-counting department. Just make it a rule that whenever a "better" system is proposed the proposer must first convince the accountants. If you have the time, you can get much innocent amusement from watching the consultant/salesman square off with your accountants. One local hospital administrator has made it a rule that all such proposals be routed automatically through his accountants, with the result that he hasn't seen a consultant in years. From the above we can formulate the following rule:

*Rule V: If you don't know how much the present system costs, any fool can plainly see that you have no basis for comparison.*

The final rule cautions against the pitfall that should be obvious to the user of OR but usually isn't; it is the tendency to hit the problem with the biggest and best method at hand, no matter what. A prime example of this is the common problem in hospitals of how many of various types of high-cost inventory items should be stocked. Most of the inventory models in the OR literature will calculate the optimal number of items to have on hand to minimize cost, but we have yet to see an inventory system in a hospital or elsewhere that first asks the question, "Should we stock the damn thing at all?" We will send free to anyone who asks a fill-in-the-blank Quick & Dirty to determine whether it is more cost-effective to stock a high-cost inventory item or to order it as needed. It is written in English on one 8 1/2 x 11 sheet of paper with an example, and it is within the capability of most hospital clerks (and consultants). This now leads us to the last and greatest commandment, and all the others are like unto it:

Rule VI: *DON'T DO WITH MORE WHEN YOU CAN DO WITH LESS.*

R. E. D. Woolsey and David A. Gulley

We the editors of this book, sincerely hope that you will be successful decision scientists. Your success will not only be a function of your decision science expertise, but also of your expertise as a behavioral scientist. To paraphrase Woolsey's rule:

*He who checks not his optimum solution against his people is indeed dumb.* [3]

### REFERENCES

1. Woolsey, R. E. D. "A Candle to Saint Jude, or Four Real World Applications of Integer Programming." *Interfaces*, Vol. 2, No. 2, February 1972, pp. 20-27.
2. ———. Letter to the Editor, "Operations Research and Management Science Today, or, Does an Education in Checkers Really Prepare One for a Life of Chess." *Operations Research*, Vol. 20, No. 3, May-June 1972, pp. 729-737.
3. ———. "A Novena to St. Jude, or Four Edifying Case Studies in Mathematical Programming." *Interfaces*, Vol. 4, No. 1, November 1973, pp. 32-39.
4. Woolsey, Gene. The Fifth Column, "Reflections on the Past of Scientific Management and the Future of Management Science." *Interfaces*, Vol. 6, No. 3, May 1976, pp. 3-4.
5. Woolsey, R. E. D., and David Gulley. Reprinted with permission from "You Can *Too* Use Operations Research." *Health Services Research*, Vol. 8, No. 2, Summer 1973, pp. 97-101. Copyright 1973 by the Hospital Research and Educational Trust, 840 North Lake Shore Drive, Chicago, Il. 60611.